This notebook was created by: ______________________

S0-BCA-651

Eagle's Wings

Considering God's Creation

A creative biblical approach
to natural science

Mortimer and Smith

Hello!

First and foremost:

***"Praise God from whom all blessings flow,
Praise Him all creatures here below."***

—the Doxology

Then, we want to say "Thank you" to our families and friends who helped us get this book ready for you to enjoy!

"Believe it or not, we were once children," we say to our own children, "and this is the way we wish we had been taught!" We hope that this book will inspire your creativity and your interest in the world around you. We also hope that it will fill you with a wonder and love for the God who created it all.

Have fun!

Mrs. Mortimer & Mrs. Smith

Revised 1996, 1998, 1999, 2001, 2002

ISBN: 1-931292-13-2 (Student Book)
ISBN: 1-931292-12-4 (2 Volume Set)

Please visit our website for other product information: **www.EaglesWingsEd.com**

TABLE OF CONTENTS

Bold-faced numbers indicate ***Considering God's Creation* Teacher's Manual** page number.
Italic numbers indicate *notebook* page number, located in the student notebook.
Please note: Pages that are to be cut out of the notebook will be blank on the back.

CREATION

THE UNIVERSE: STARS, SUN and PLANETS

THE EARTH

NON-LIVING THINGS: ROCKS and MINERALS

WEATHER

THE PLANT KINGDOM

THE ANIMAL KINGDOM

And God Was Pleased

And God Was Pleased!

On the **first** day of creation,
God made the dark and light,
And He called it day and night.
And God was pleased.

On the **second** day of creation,
God made the water and the air,
And this was the atmosphere.
And God was pleased.

On the **third** day of creation,
God made the land and sea,
And every plant, flower,
grass and tree.
And God was pleased.

On the **fourth** day of creation,
God made the stars, the moon, the sun,
Thus the seasons were begun.
And God was pleased.

On the **fifth** day of creation,
God made the birds and fish,
And any sea creature you could wish.
And God was pleased.

On the **sixth** day of creation,
God made animals fill the land,
Then He formed man with His hand.
And God was pleased.

On the **seventh** day of creation,
God looked at what He'd done,
And rested to enjoy each one.
And God was pleased.

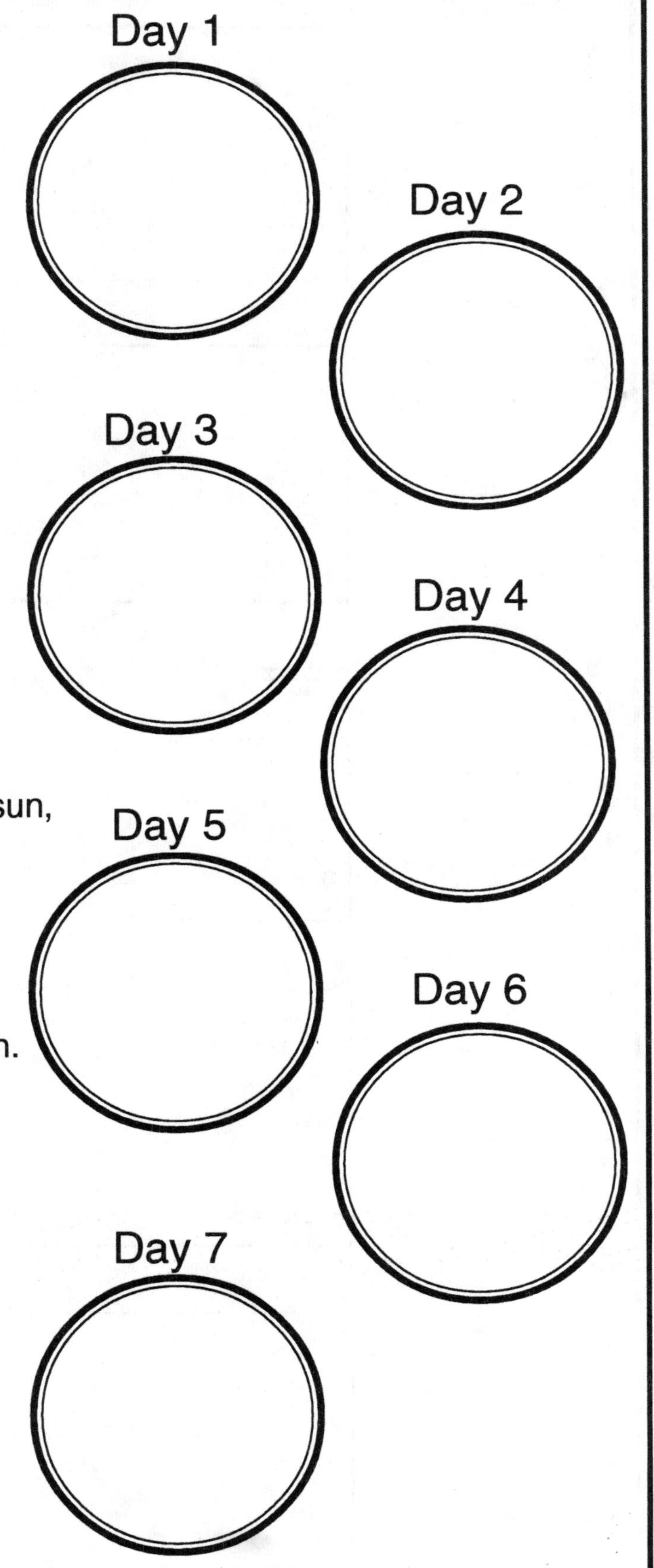
Day 1
Day 2
Day 3
Day 4
Day 5
Day 6
Day 7

Sing along with the words of this song. Then draw a picture to represent each day of creation.

Not by Chance

1st Drawing:
A. ______
B. ______
C. ______
D. ______
E. ______
F. ______
G. ______
H. ______
I. ______
J. ______

2nd Drawing:
A. ______
B. ______
C. ______
D. ______
E. ______
F. ______
G. ______
H. ______
I. ______
J. ______

3rd Drawing:
A. ______
B. ______
C. ______
D. ______
E. ______
F. ______
G. ______
H. ______
I. ______
J. ______

 Cut out and discuss each of the ten major stages of creation on "Not by Chance" (page 2). Then close your eyes and pick up the slips in random order. Record the results and repeat two more times. Finally, glue the slips in correct order on this page.

Not by Chance (page 2)

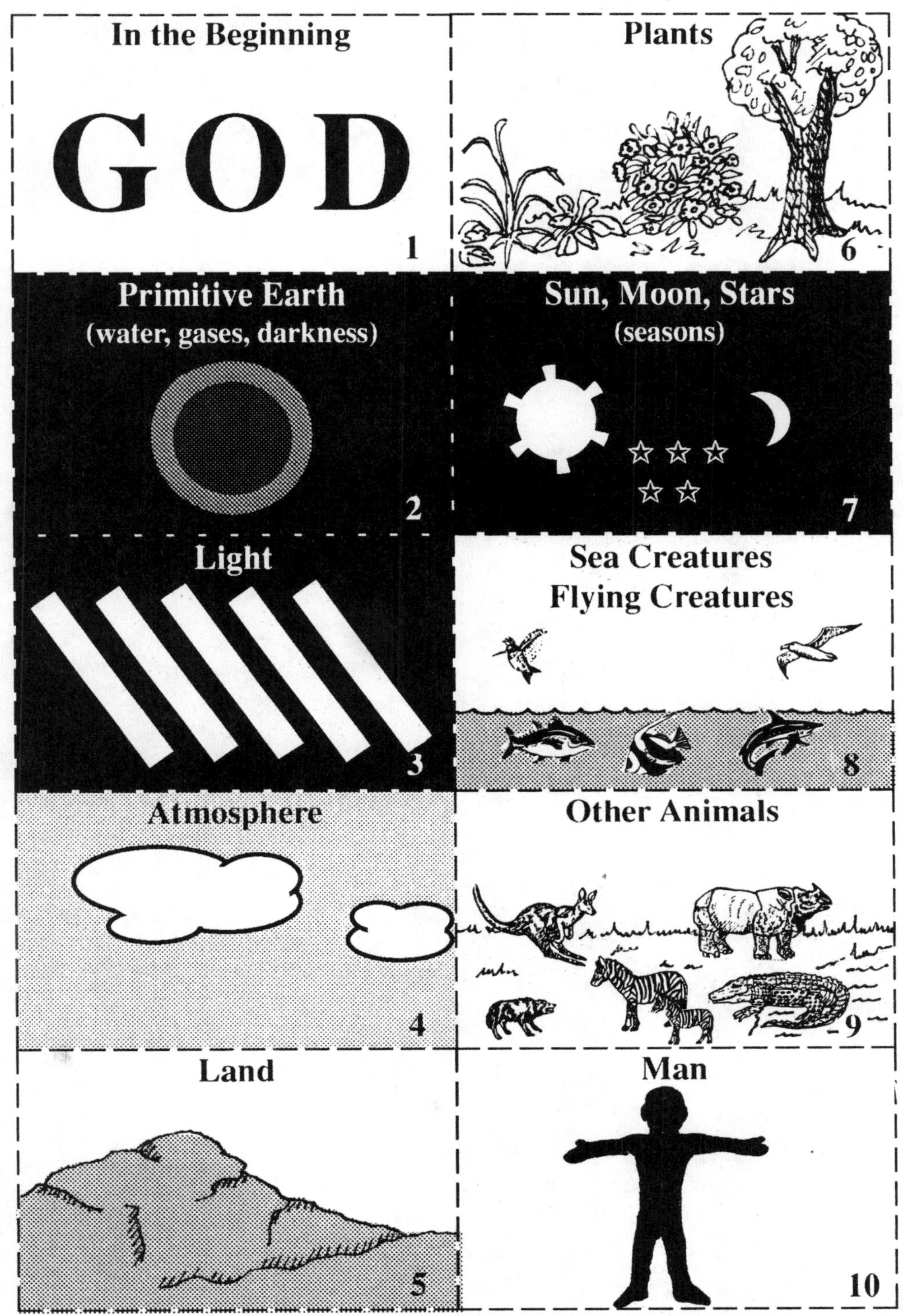
In the Beginning
GOD
1
Plants
6
Primitive Earth
(water, gases, darkness)
2
Sun, Moon, Stars
(seasons)
7
Light
3
Sea Creatures
Flying Creatures
8
Atmosphere
4
Other Animals
9
Land
5
Man
10

Considering God's Universe

glue 1
glue 2
glue 3
glue 4
glue 5
glue 6
glue 7
glue 8
glue 9
glue 10
tree
me

In God's immense Universe, among the innumerable galaxies, is our galaxy, the 1)______________________________. In the Milky Way Galaxy, with all its billions of stars, is our star and its planets, called the 2)__________________________. Out of the nine planets in our Solar System, only one, the 3)_________________, can support life. On Earth, with all its oceans and lands, is a continent called 4)___________________. There in North America is a country called 5)_________________. In the United States, one of its fifty states is 6)_______________. Through Colorado is a ridge of tall, rugged mountains known as the 7)____. In the Rocky Mountains is a tall mountain called 8)__________________. On Pike's Peak is a 9)__________________ with lots of trees. In that forest is a particular pine 10)___________. Sitting under the shade of that tree is 11)_________. And I am considering, pondering and contemplating God's immense Universe.

Cut and carefully glue or tape the pages from "Considering God's Universe" (page 2). Begin gluing in reverse order, (10, 9, etc.), making sure each page can open freely. Then fill in the blanks to the story, using the word from the corresponding page number.

Scientist Detective

Scientist: ______________________ Born: ______ Died: ______

BC —|—|—|—|—|—|—|—|—|—|—|—|— AD

200 0 200 400 600 800 1000 1200 1400 1600 1800 2000

Background:

Nationality: ______________________

Parents: ______________________

Influence was: ❐ helpful ❐ injuring

Example: ______________________

Portrait

Schooling: ______________________

Family:

Spouse: ______________________

Number of children: ______________________

Turning point experience that got him/her into field of work:

____

Religion: ❐ There is a personal God. ❐ There is no God.

❐ There are many gods. ❐ Science is 'god'. ❐ Man is 'god'.

Did religion affect work: ❐ a lot? ❐ a little? ❐ none at all?

Example: ______________________

Field of contribution:

astronomy botany zoology psychology geology medicine physics ______

Major contributions: ❐ Invention ❐ Theory ❐ Discovery

Best known for: ______________________

Far-reaching results: ______________________

Considering God's Universe (page 2)

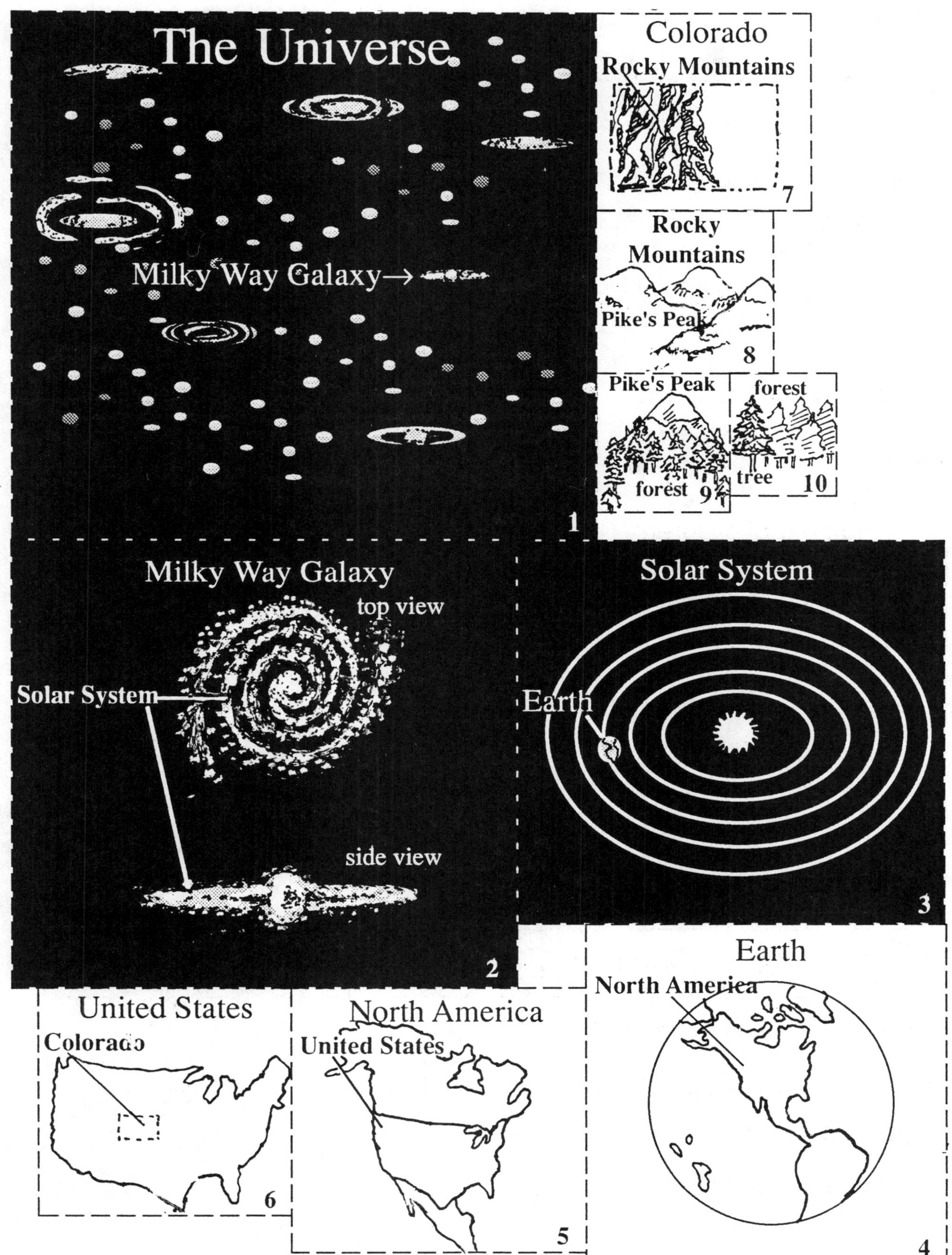

The Universe
Milky Way Galaxy→
1
Colorado
Rocky Mountains
7
Rocky Mountains
Pike's Peak
8
Pike's Peak
forest
9
forest
tree
10
Milky Way Galaxy
top view
Solar System
side view
2
Solar System
Earth
3
Earth
North America
4
North America
United States
5
United States
Colorado
6

Star Slides

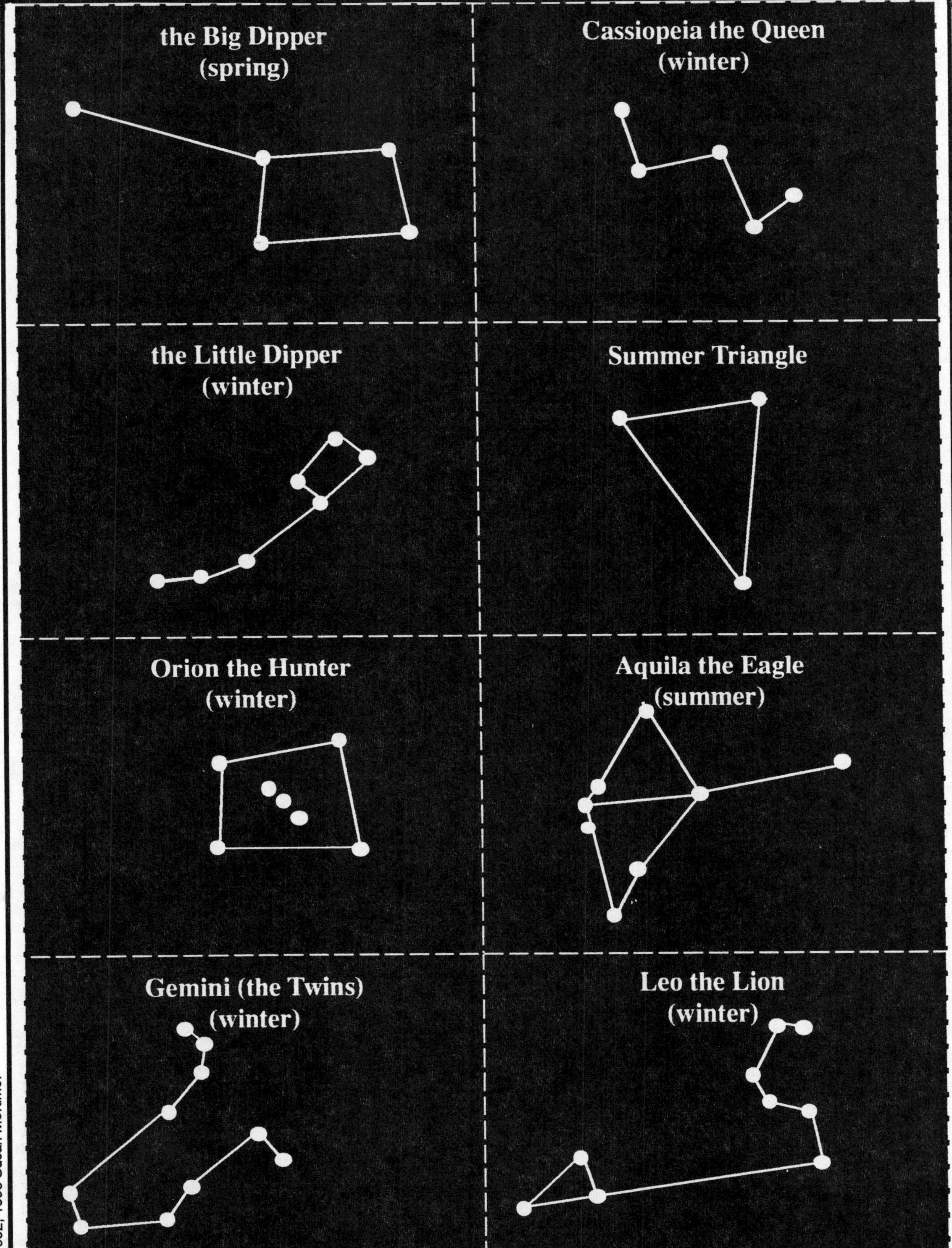
the Big Dipper
(spring)
Cassiopeia the Queen
(winter)
the Little Dipper
(winter)
Summer Triangle
Orion the Hunter
(winter)
Aquila the Eagle
(summer)
Gemini (the Twins)
(winter)
Leo the Lion
(winter)

Cut and glue onto heavy paper. Punch holes with pencil. Tape "slide" over 2"x 3" opening in a box. Cut a hole for a flashlight in the opposite end and "project" on wall in dark room. Direct the light to reach above the "slide" and do not point directly at it. Make other 'slides' of your own.

Glue "The Planets" (page 2) here.

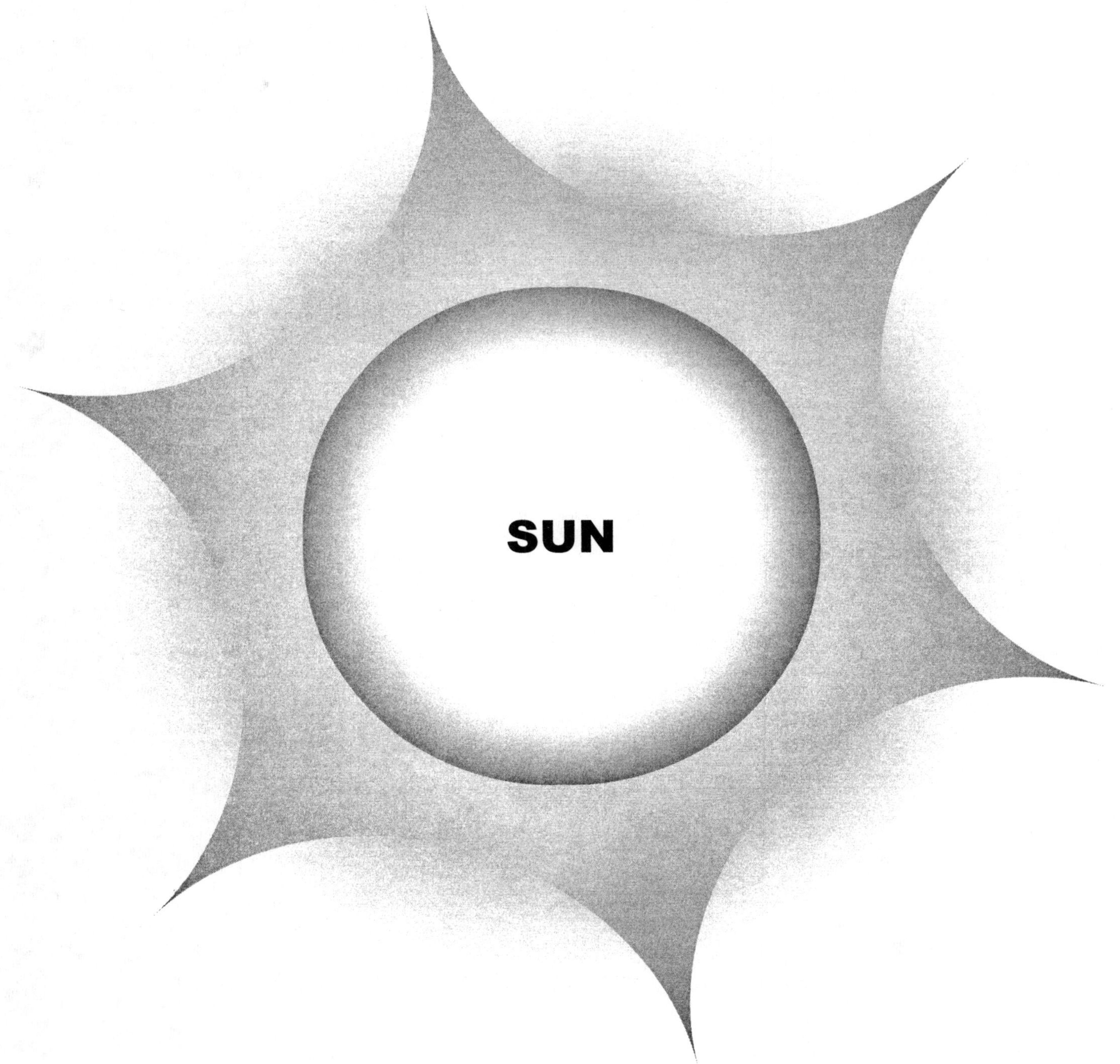
SUN

The Planets

The planets, starting from the sun, are Mercury and Venus,
The Earth, then Mars and Jupiter, and Saturn and Uranus.
The next in line is Neptune, and Pluto after that.
The Lord our God fixed them in space,
And He keeps them all in place.

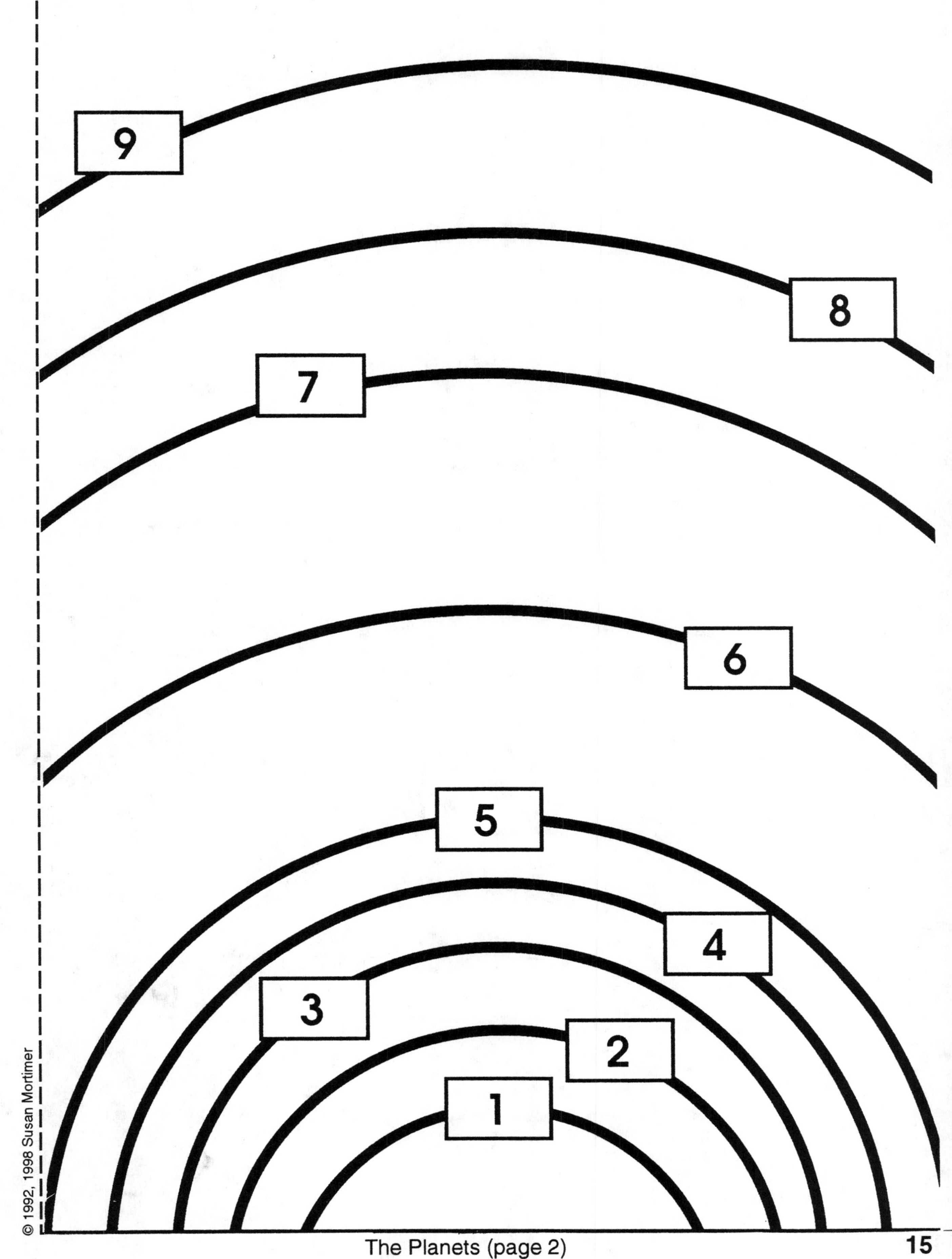
9
8
7
6
5
4
3
2
1

The Planets (page 3)

Color the planets. Cut out on the dotted lines. Tape a 4 inch piece of string at center top, behind planet name. Fold on solid line and glue insides of circles together. Tape top of string over the correct number on Planets (p. 2).

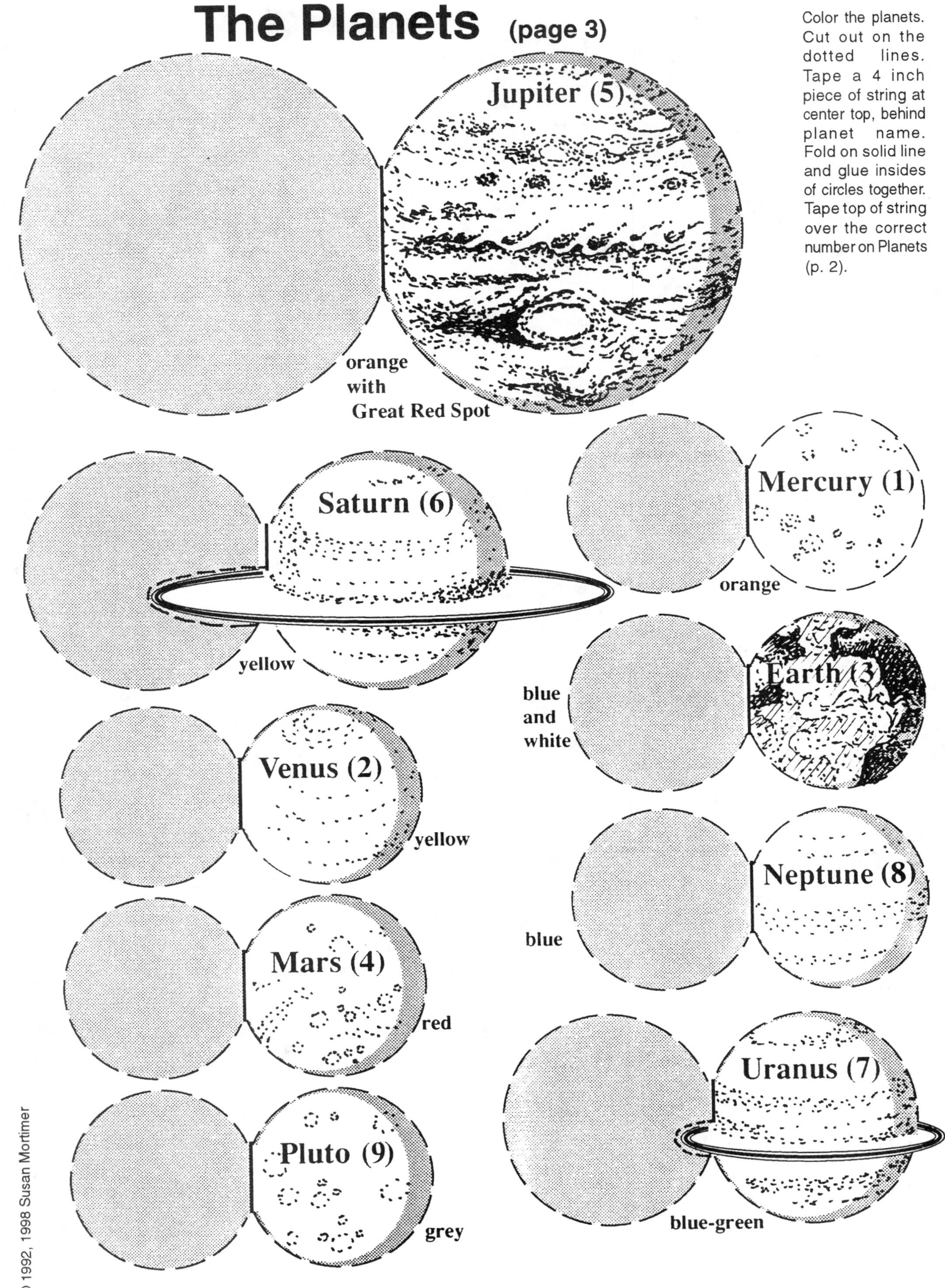

Jupiter (5)
orange
with
Great Red Spot
Mercury (1)
orange
Saturn (6)
yellow
Earth (3)
blue
and
white
Venus (2)
yellow
Neptune (8)
blue
Mars (4)
red
Uranus (7)
blue-green
Pluto (9)
grey

Solar System Detective

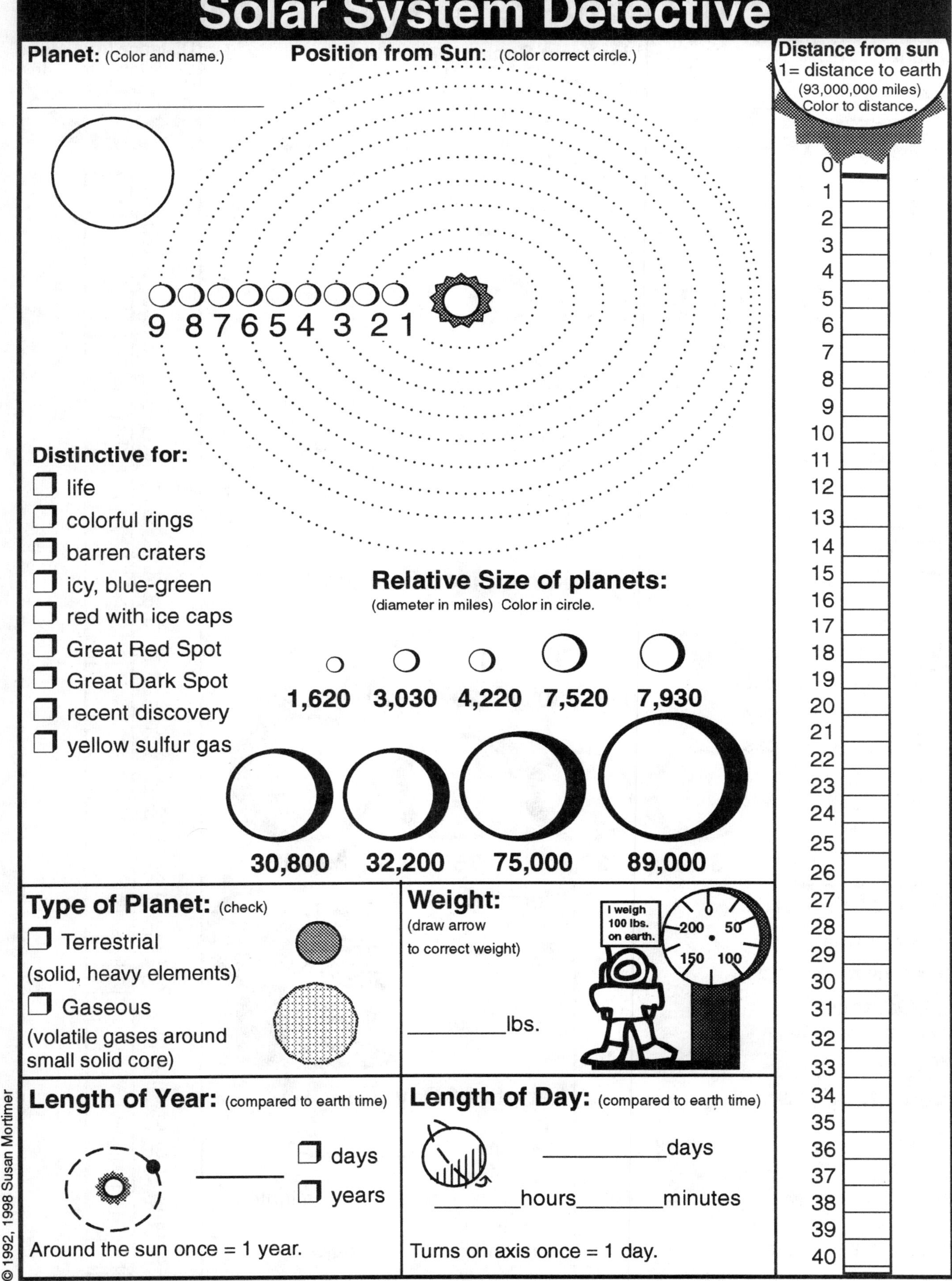

Planet: (Color and name.)
Position from Sun: (Color correct circle.)
9 8 7 6 5 4 3 2 1
Distance from sun
1= distance to earth
(93,000,000 miles)
Color to distance.
0
1
2
3
4
5
6
7
8
9
10
11
12
13
14
15
16
17
18
19
20
21
22
23
24
25
26
27
28
29
30
31
32
33
34
35
36
37
38
39
40
Distinctive for:
life
colorful rings
barren craters
icy, blue-green
red with ice caps
Great Red Spot
Great Dark Spot
recent discovery
yellow sulfur gas
Relative Size of planets:
(diameter in miles) Color in circle.
1,620
3,030
4,220
7,520
7,930
30,800
32,200
75,000
89,000
Type of Planet: (check)
Terrestrial
(solid, heavy elements)
Gaseous
(volatile gases around small solid core)
Weight:
(draw arrow to correct weight)
I weigh 100 lbs. on earth.
0
50
100
150
200
_______lbs.
Length of Year: (compared to earth time)
days
years
Around the sun once = 1 year.
Length of Day: (compared to earth time)
__________days
_______hours_______minutes
Turns on axis once = 1 day.

Complete this notebook page for each planet, as the teacher reads about it.

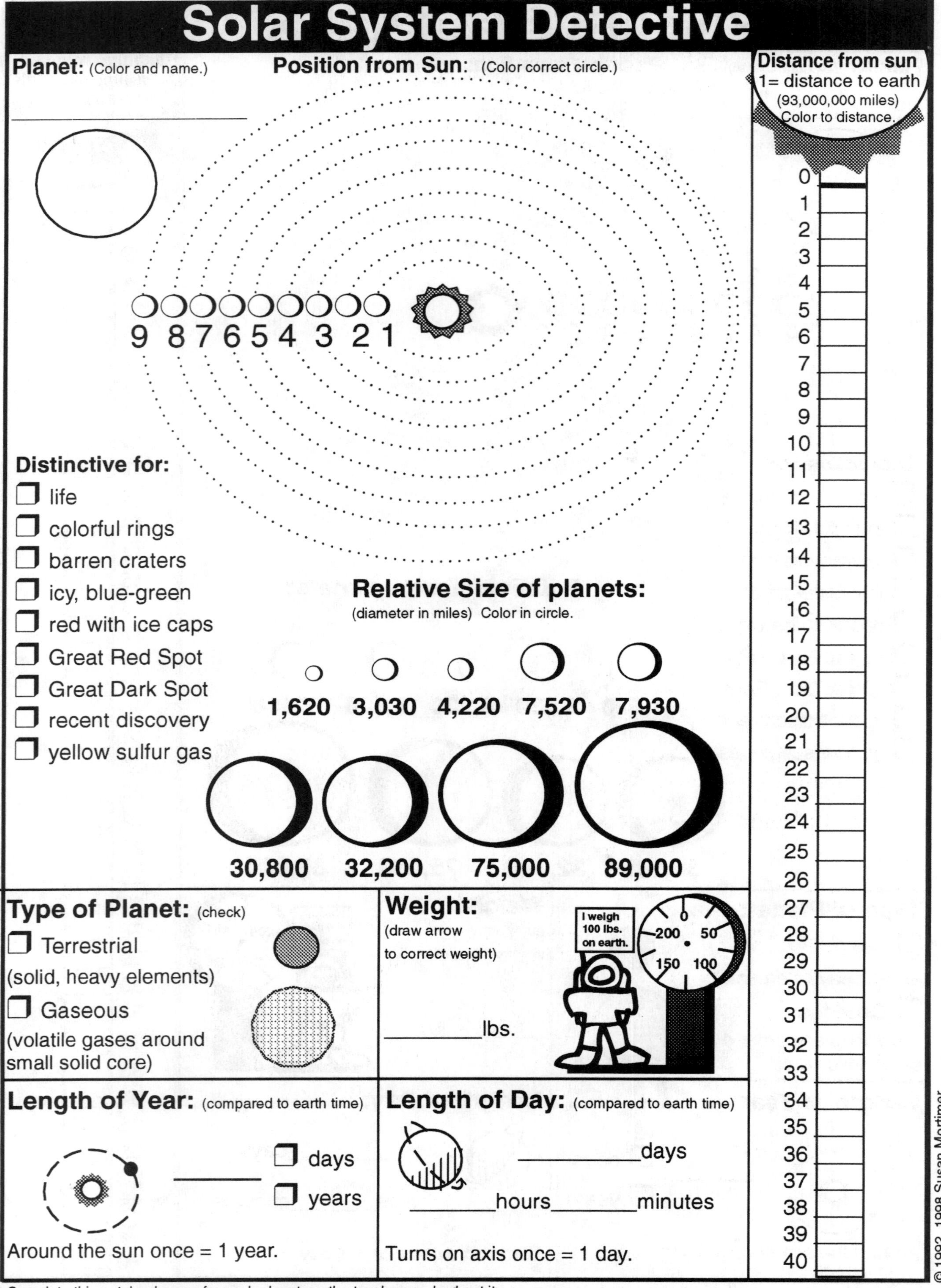
Solar System Detective
Planet: (Color and name.)
Position from Sun: (Color correct circle.)
9 8 7 6 5 4 3 2 1
Distance from sun
1= distance to earth
(93,000,000 miles)
Color to distance.
0
1
2
3
4
5
6
7
8
9
10
11
12
13
14
15
16
17
18
19
20
21
22
23
24
25
26
27
28
29
30
31
32
33
34
35
36
37
38
39
40
Distinctive for:
life
colorful rings
barren craters
icy, blue-green
red with ice caps
Great Red Spot
Great Dark Spot
recent discovery
yellow sulfur gas
Relative Size of planets:
(diameter in miles) Color in circle.
1,620
3,030
4,220
7,520
7,930
30,800
32,200
75,000
89,000
Type of Planet: (check)
Terrestrial
(solid, heavy elements)
Gaseous
(volatile gases around small solid core)
Weight:
(draw arrow to correct weight)
lbs.
I weigh 100 lbs. on earth.
0
50
100
150
200
Length of Year: (compared to earth time)
days
years
Around the sun once = 1 year.
Length of Day: (compared to earth time)
days
hours
minutes
Turns on axis once = 1 day.

 Complete this notebook page for each planet, as the teacher reads about it.

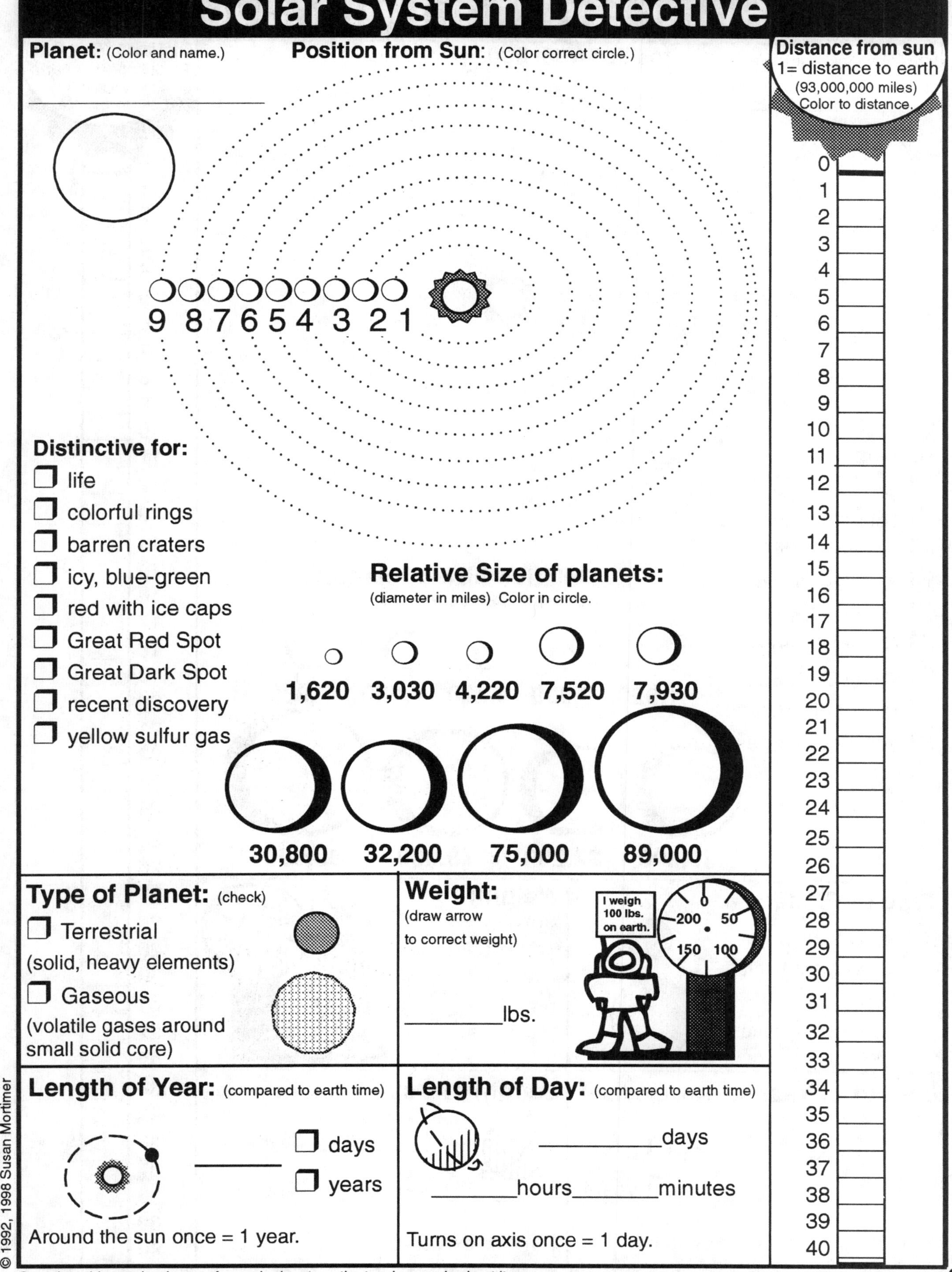
Solar System Detective
Planet: (Color and name.)
Position from Sun: (Color correct circle.)
9 8 7 6 5 4 3 2 1
Distance from sun
1= distance to earth
(93,000,000 miles)
Color to distance.
0 1 2 3 4 5 6 7 8 9 10 11 12 13 14 15 16 17 18 19 20 21 22 23 24 25 26 27 28 29 30 31 32 33 34 35 36 37 38 39 40
Distinctive for:
life
colorful rings
barren craters
icy, blue-green
red with ice caps
Great Red Spot
Great Dark Spot
recent discovery
yellow sulfur gas
Relative Size of planets:
(diameter in miles) Color in circle.
1,620 3,030 4,220 7,520 7,930
30,800 32,200 75,000 89,000
Type of Planet: (check)
Terrestrial
(solid, heavy elements)
Gaseous
(volatile gases around small solid core)
Weight:
(draw arrow to correct weight)
I weigh 100 lbs. on earth.
0 50 100 150 200
lbs.
Length of Year: (compared to earth time)
days
years
Around the sun once = 1 year.
Length of Day: (compared to earth time)
days
hours minutes
Turns on axis once = 1 day.

Complete this notebook page for each planet, as the teacher reads about it.

Solar System Detective

Planet: (Color and name.)

Position from Sun: (Color correct circle.)

9 8 7 6 5 4 3 2 1

Distance from sun
1= distance to earth
(93,000,000 miles)
Color to distance.

0 1 2 3 4 5 6 7 8 9 10 11 12 13 14 15 16 17 18 19 20 21 22 23 24 25 26 27 28 29 30 31 32 33 34 35 36 37 38 39 40

Distinctive for:

- ❒ life
- ❒ colorful rings
- ❒ barren craters
- ❒ icy, blue-green
- ❒ red with ice caps
- ❒ Great Red Spot
- ❒ Great Dark Spot
- ❒ recent discovery
- ❒ yellow sulfur gas

Relative Size of planets:
(diameter in miles) Color in circle.

1,620 3,030 4,220 7,520 7,930

30,800 32,200 75,000 89,000

Type of Planet: (check)

❒ Terrestrial
(solid, heavy elements)

❒ Gaseous
(volatile gases around small solid core)

Weight:
(draw arrow to correct weight)

I weigh 100 lbs. on earth.

0 50 100 150 200

__________lbs.

Length of Year: (compared to earth time)

__________ ❒ days ❒ years

Around the sun once = 1 year.

Length of Day: (compared to earth time)

___________days

________hours________minutes

Turns on axis once = 1 day.

 Complete this notebook page for each planet, as the teacher reads about it.

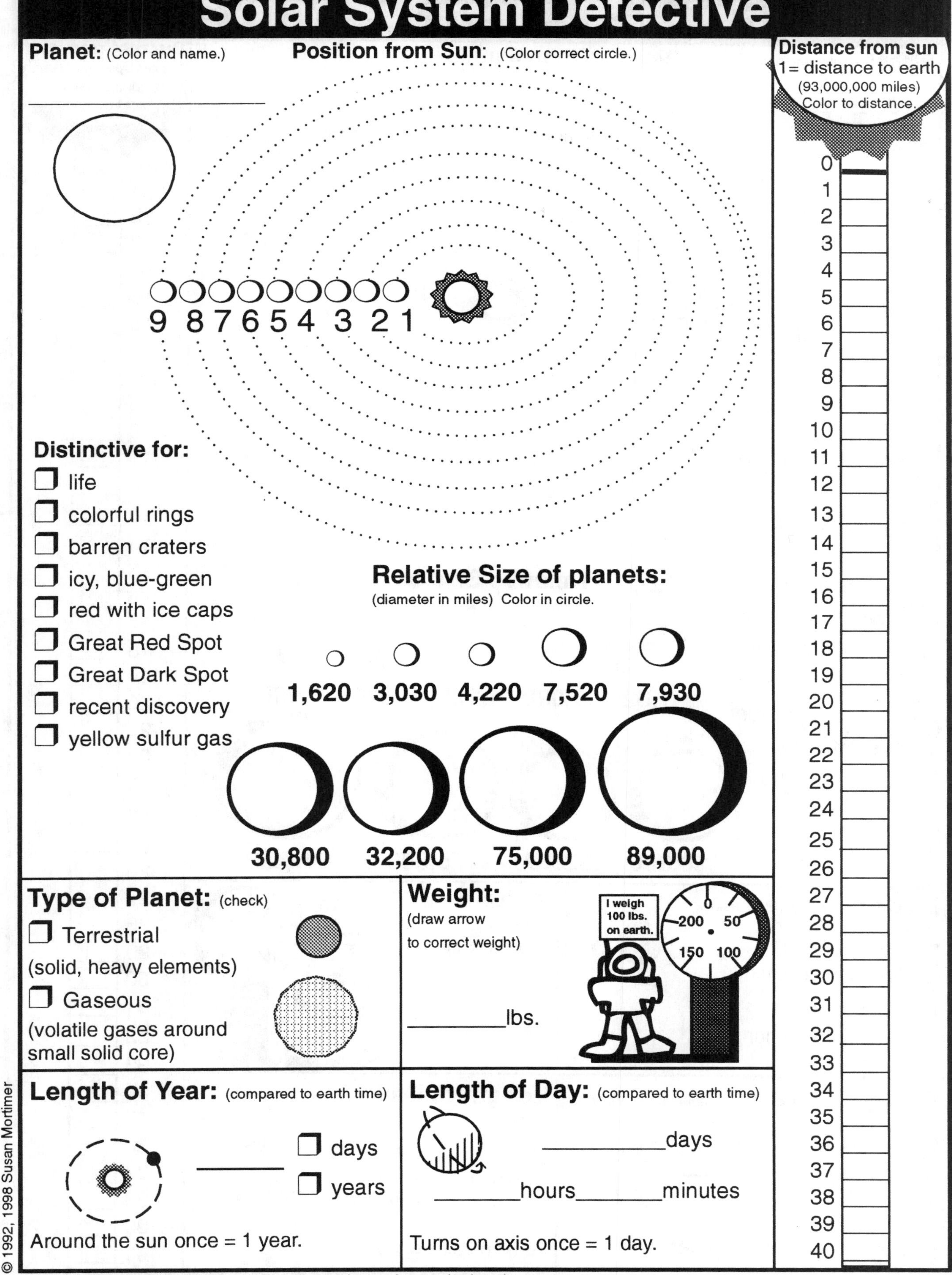

Solar System Detective

Planet: (Color and name.)

Position from Sun: (Color correct circle.)

9 8 7 6 5 4 3 2 1

Distance from sun
1= distance to earth
(93,000,000 miles)
Color to distance.

0 1 2 3 4 5 6 7 8 9 10 11 12 13 14 15 16 17 18 19 20 21 22 23 24 25 26 27 28 29 30 31 32 33 34 35 36 37 38 39 40

Distinctive for:

- ❐ life
- ❐ colorful rings
- ❐ barren craters
- ❐ icy, blue-green
- ❐ red with ice caps
- ❐ Great Red Spot
- ❐ Great Dark Spot
- ❐ recent discovery
- ❐ yellow sulfur gas

Relative Size of planets:
(diameter in miles) Color in circle.

1,620 3,030 4,220 7,520 7,930

30,800 32,200 75,000 89,000

Type of Planet: (check)

❐ Terrestrial
(solid, heavy elements)

❐ Gaseous
(volatile gases around small solid core)

Weight:
(draw arrow to correct weight)

________lbs.

I weigh 100 lbs. on earth.
0
50
100
150
200

Length of Year: (compared to earth time)

________ ❐ days ❐ years

Around the sun once = 1 year.

Length of Day: (compared to earth time)

__________days

________hours________minutes

Turns on axis once = 1 day.

Complete this notebook page for each planet, as the teacher reads about it.

Solar System Detective

Planet: (Color and name.)

____

Position from Sun: (Color correct circle.)

9 8 7 6 5 4 3 2 1

Distance from sun
1= distance to earth
(93,000,000 miles)
Color to distance.

0 1 2 3 4 5 6 7 8 9 10 11 12 13 14 15 16 17 18 19 20 21 22 23 24 25 26 27 28 29 30 31 32 33 34 35 36 37 38 39 40

Distinctive for:

- ❒ life
- ❒ colorful rings
- ❒ barren craters
- ❒ icy, blue-green
- ❒ red with ice caps
- ❒ Great Red Spot
- ❒ Great Dark Spot
- ❒ recent discovery
- ❒ yellow sulfur gas

Relative Size of planets:
(diameter in miles) Color in circle.

1,620 3,030 4,220 7,520 7,930

30,800 32,200 75,000 89,000

Type of Planet: (check)

❒ Terrestrial
(solid, heavy elements)

❒ Gaseous
(volatile gases around small solid core)

Weight:
(draw arrow to correct weight)

I weigh 100 lbs. on earth.

0 50 100 150 200

__________lbs.

Length of Year: (compared to earth time)

__________ ❒ days ❒ years

Around the sun once = 1 year.

Length of Day: (compared to earth time)

__________days

__________hours__________minutes

Turns on axis once = 1 day.

 Complete this notebook page for each planet, as the teacher reads about it.

Solar System Detective

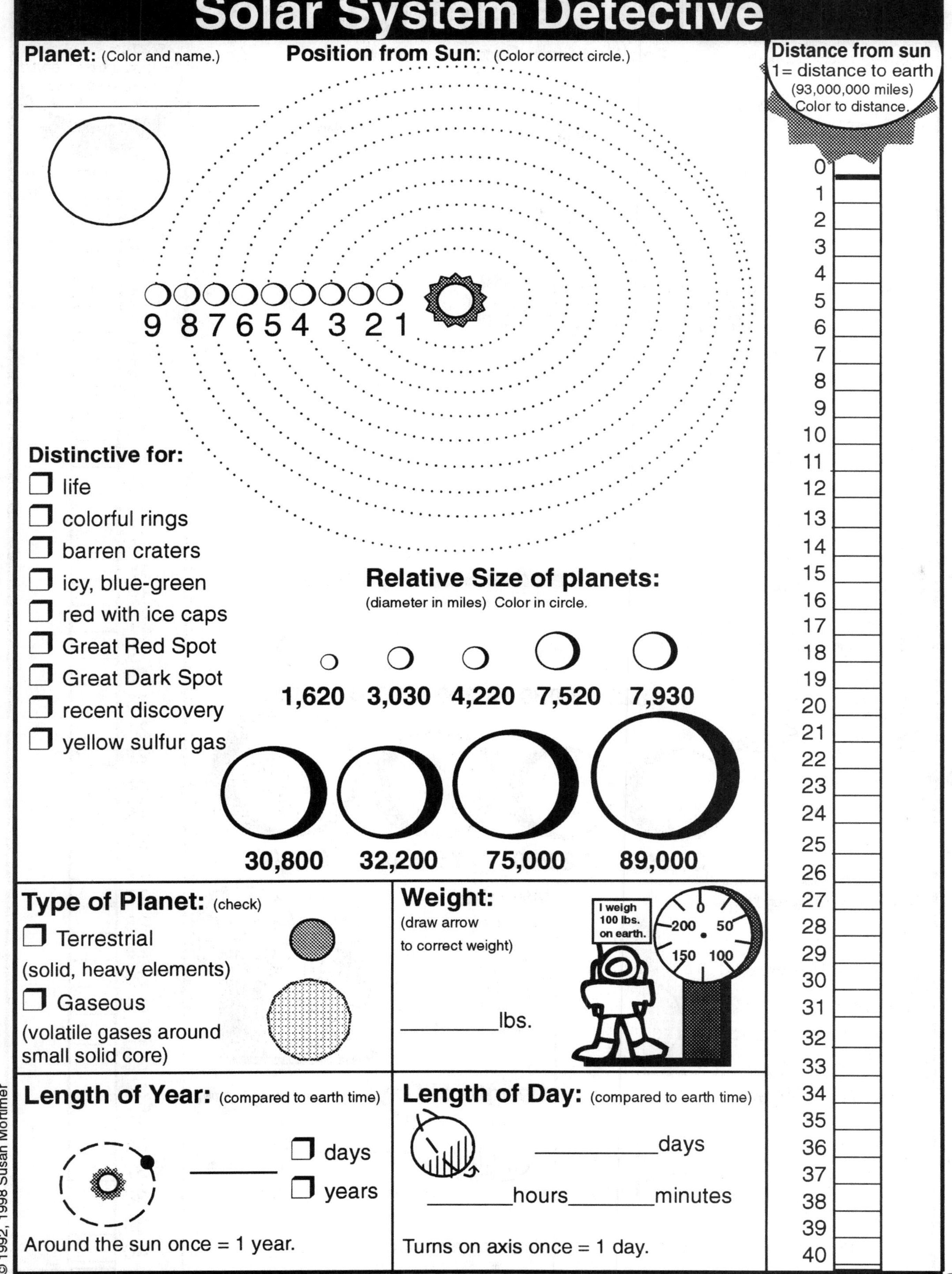

Planet: (Color and name.)
Position from Sun: (Color correct circle.)
9 8 7 6 5 4 3 2 1
Distance from sun
1= distance to earth
(93,000,000 miles)
Color to distance.
0
1
2
3
4
5
6
7
8
9
10
11
12
13
14
15
16
17
18
19
20
21
22
23
24
25
26
27
28
29
30
31
32
33
34
35
36
37
38
39
40
Distinctive for:
life
colorful rings
barren craters
icy, blue-green
red with ice caps
Great Red Spot
Great Dark Spot
recent discovery
yellow sulfur gas
Relative Size of planets:
(diameter in miles) Color in circle.
1,620
3,030
4,220
7,520
7,930
30,800
32,200
75,000
89,000
Type of Planet: (check)
Terrestrial
(solid, heavy elements)
Gaseous
(volatile gases around small solid core)
Weight:
(draw arrow to correct weight)
_______lbs.
I weigh 100 lbs. on earth.
0
50
100
150
200
Length of Year: (compared to earth time)
days
years
Around the sun once = 1 year.
Length of Day: (compared to earth time)
_________days
_______hours_______minutes
Turns on axis once = 1 day.

Complete this notebook page for each planet, as the teacher reads about it.

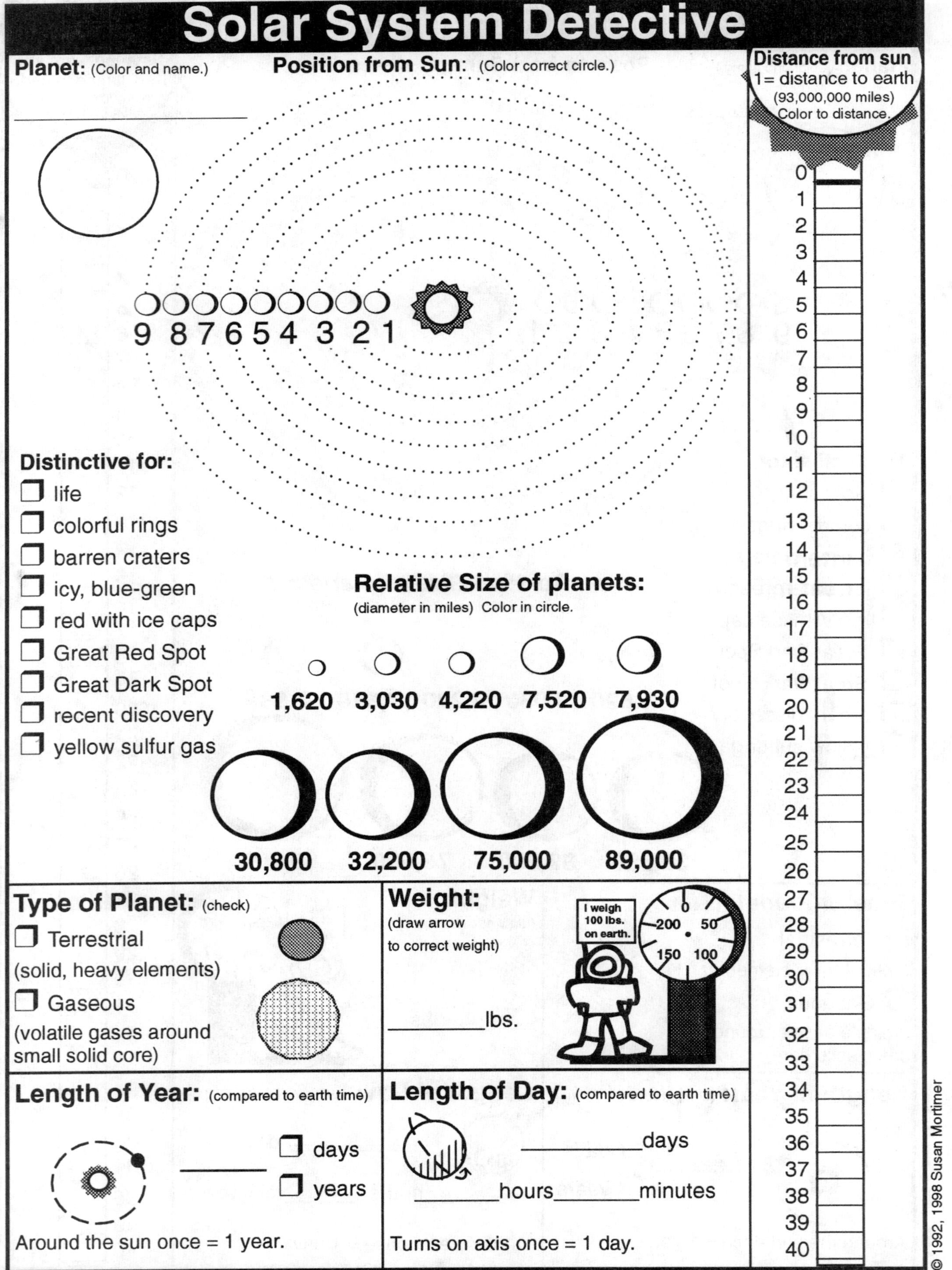

Solar System Detective
Planet: (Color and name.)
Position from Sun: (Color correct circle.)
9 8 7 6 5 4 3 2 1
Distinctive for:
life
colorful rings
barren craters
icy, blue-green
red with ice caps
Great Red Spot
Great Dark Spot
recent discovery
yellow sulfur gas
Relative Size of planets:
(diameter in miles) Color in circle.
1,620
3,030
4,220
7,520
7,930
30,800
32,200
75,000
89,000
Distance from sun
1= distance to earth
(93,000,000 miles)
Color to distance.
0
1
2
3
4
5
6
7
8
9
10
11
12
13
14
15
16
17
18
19
20
21
22
23
24
25
26
27
28
29
30
31
32
33
34
35
36
37
38
39
40
Type of Planet: (check)
Terrestrial
(solid, heavy elements)
Gaseous
(volatile gases around small solid core)
Weight:
(draw arrow to correct weight)
I weigh 100 lbs. on earth.
0
50
100
150
200
lbs.
Length of Year: (compared to earth time)
days
years
Around the sun once = 1 year.
Length of Day: (compared to earth time)
days
hours
minutes
Turns on axis once = 1 day.

 Complete this notebook page for each planet, as the teacher reads about it.

The Rock Cycle

g l u e

Extrusive rocks cool more rapidly on the surface. Obsidian is a black transparent glass, while pumice, though chemically the same, has gas bubbles trapped in it. It is light with a rough sponge-like appearance.

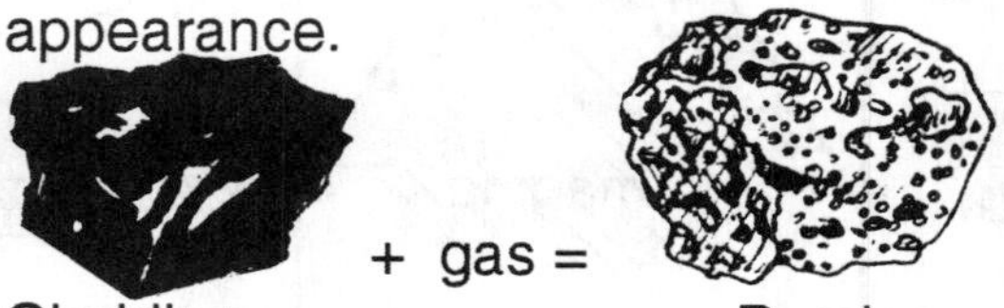

+ gas =

Obsidian (coat with or clear fingernail polish.)

Pumice

3a

Erosion: Water and wind break down rocks.

Intensive heat melts rocks.

g l u e

Fossil Examples

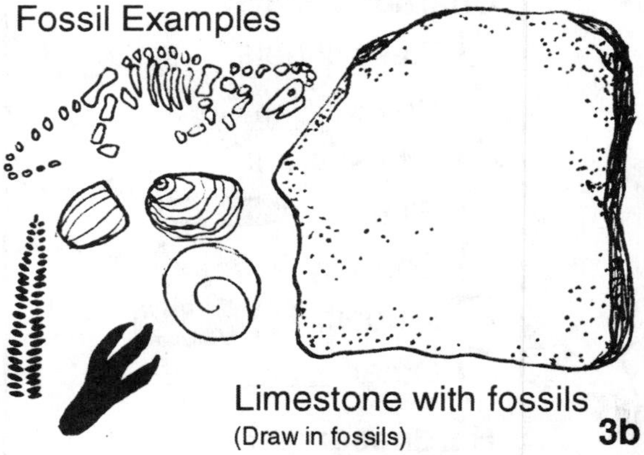

Limestone with fossils
(Draw in fossils)

3b

Heat and pressure change rocks.

Erosion: Water and wind break down rocks.

g l u e

Graphite, used for pencil lead, turns into diamond under intense heat and pressure.

+ heat & pressure =

Graphite
(color with pencil)

Diamond
(coat with clear fingernail polish)

3c

Rock Detective

Name of rock or mineral:

Colors:

Streak color:
(color of scratch mark on sidewalk)

Texture:
- ❒ Fine 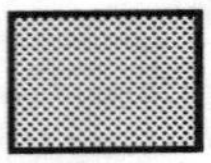
- ❒ Medium 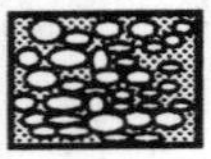
- ❒ Coarse

Weight:
- ❒ Extra light 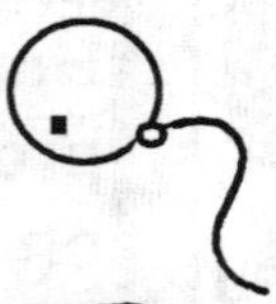
- ❒ Average 
- ❒ Extra heavy

Shine or luster:
- ❒ No shine (earthy)
- ❒ Metallic
- ❒ Non-metallic
  - ❒ Brilliant
  - ❒ Dull
  - ❒ Greasy
  - ❒ Glassy
  - ❒ Pearly
  - ❒ Silky

Three Types of Rocks (color matching type)

Igneous from volcanos	Sedimentary settling in water	Metamorphic pressure and heat
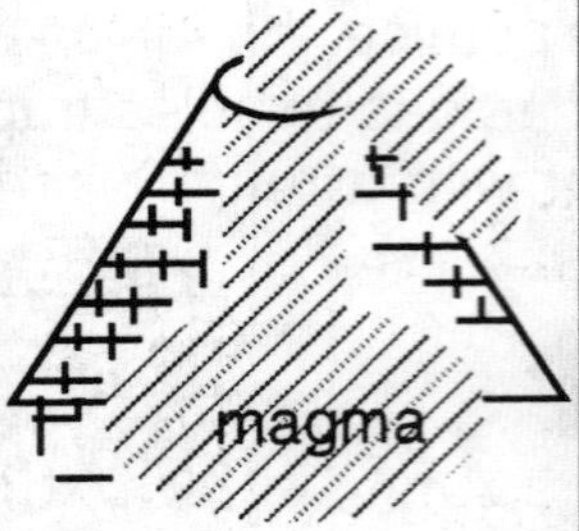 magma	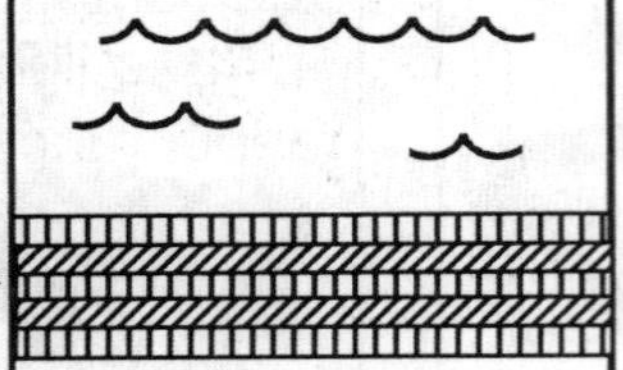	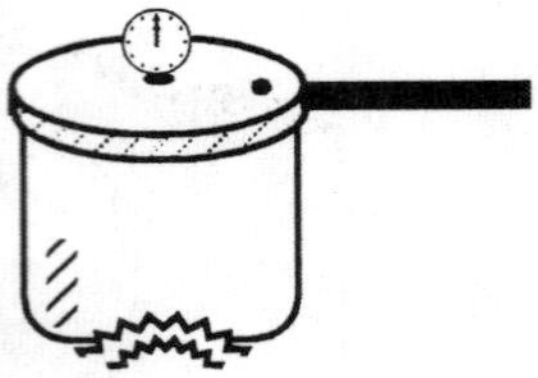
Extrusive type forms if magma (melted rock) cools above ground; intrusive if it cools below ground. **Can be solid or crystalline.**	Made from clay, mud, sand, silt or gravel. Forms in water. **Only type of rock to contain fossils. Usually in layered formation.**	Formed when igneous or sedimentary rock are heated under pressure. **Has characteristic bands and splits easily into sheets.**

Characteristics:
- ❒ Flaky sheets
- ❒ Holes
- ❒ Transparant
- ❒ Flat
- ❒ Crumbly
- ❒ Smooth
- ❒ Other________

Hardness:

1. Talc
2. Gypsum

❒ 2.5 Fingernail

3. Calcite

❒ 3.5 Penny

4. Fluorite
5. Apatite

❒ 5.5 Steel nail

6. Orthoclase

❒ 6.5 Steel file

7. Quartz
8. Topaz
9. Corundum
10. Diamond

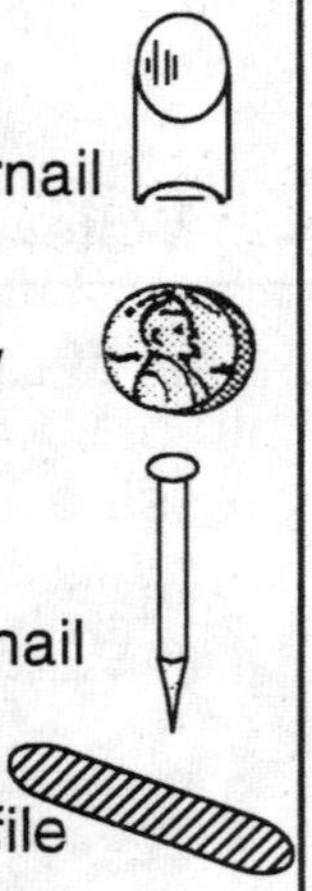

Cleavage: (Direction rock would split or break.)
- ❒ None
- ❒ 1 plane
- ❒ 2 planes
- ❒ 3 planes
- ❒ other

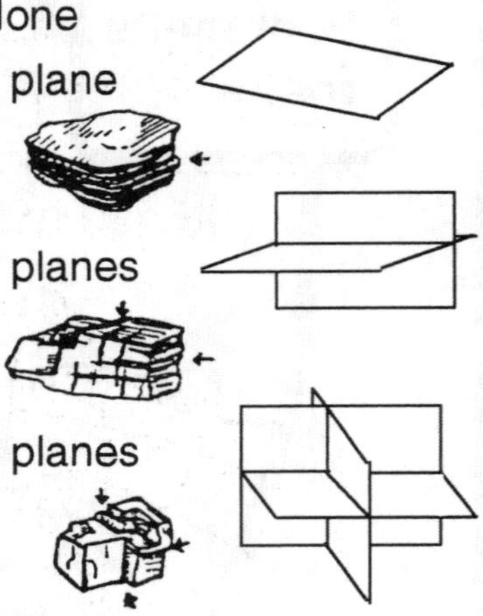

Shapes of crystals:
(Color matching shape)

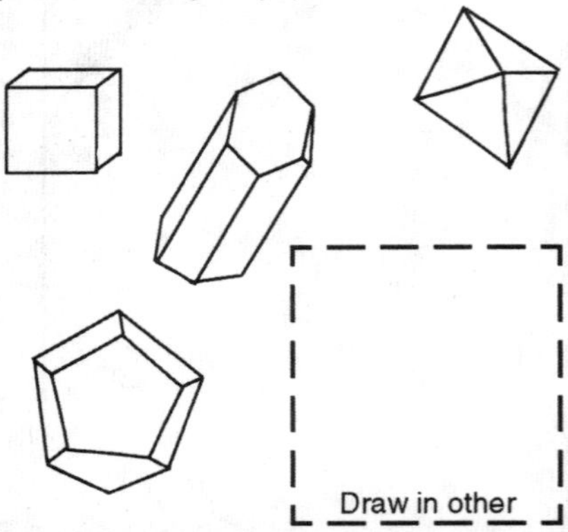

Draw in other

The Rock Cycle (page 2)

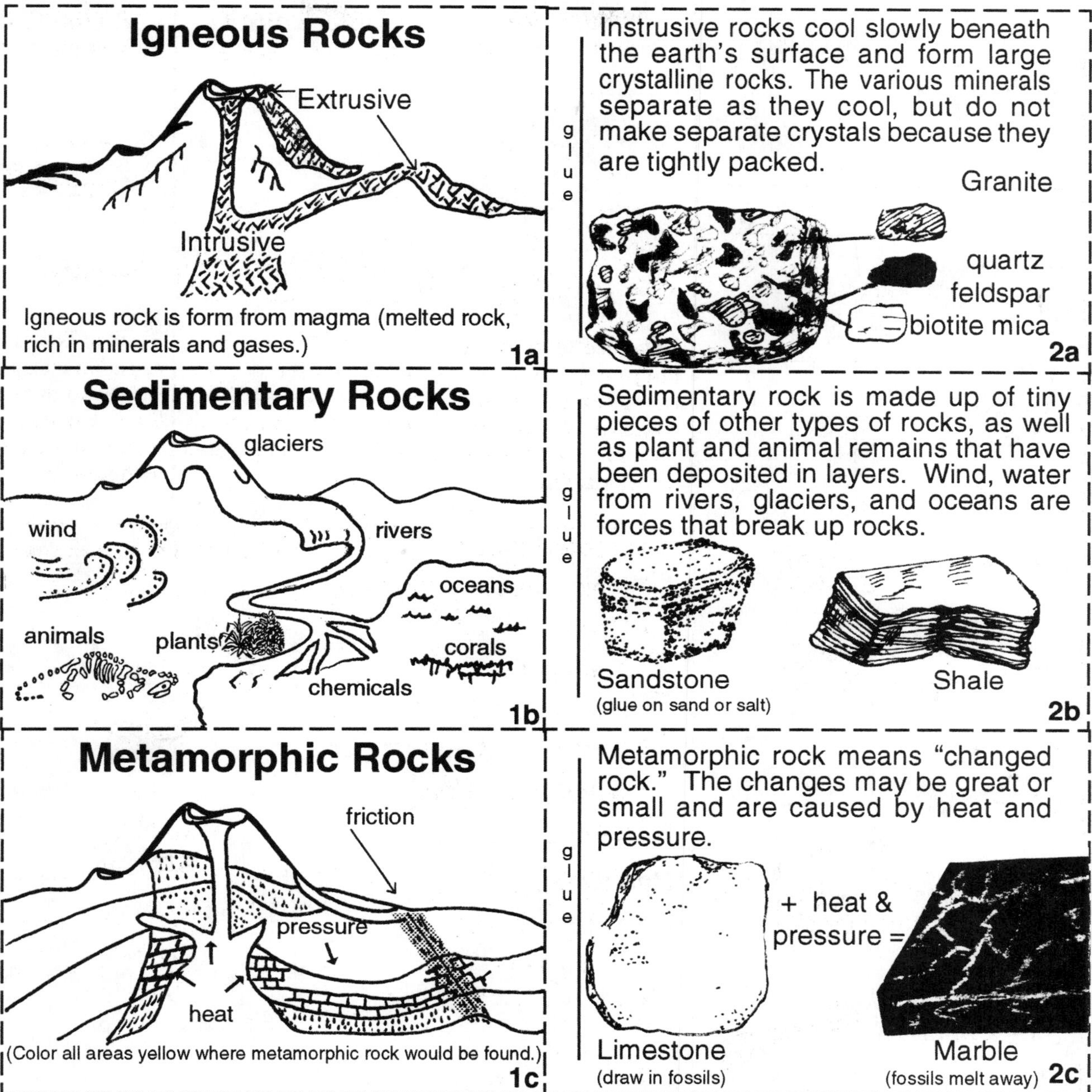

Igneous Rocks
Extrusive
Intrusive
Igneous rock is form from magma (melted rock, rich in minerals and gases.)
1a
Instrusive rocks cool slowly beneath the earth's surface and form large crystalline rocks. The various minerals separate as they cool, but do not make separate crystals because they are tightly packed.
glue
Granite
quartz
feldspar
biotite mica
2a
Sedimentary Rocks
glaciers
wind
rivers
oceans
animals
plants
corals
chemicals
1b
Sedimentary rock is made up of tiny pieces of other types of rocks, as well as plant and animal remains that have been deposited in layers. Wind, water from rivers, glaciers, and oceans are forces that break up rocks.
glue
Sandstone
(glue on sand or salt)
Shale
2b
Metamorphic Rocks
friction
pressure
heat
(Color all areas yellow where metamorphic rock would be found.)
1c
Metamorphic rock means "changed rock." The changes may be great or small and are caused by heat and pressure.
glue
+ heat & pressure =
Limestone
(draw in fossils)
Marble
(fossils melt away)
2c

Follow directions given for each page. Allow time to dry. Then cut out each page and glue (in reverse order) on "Rock Cycle" page.

Rock Detective

Name of rock or mineral: ______________________

Colors: ______________________

____

____

Streak color: (color of scratch mark on sidewalk)

____

Texture:

❐ Fine

❐ Medium

❐ Coarse

Weight:

❐ Extra light

❐ Average

❐ Extra heavy

Shine or luster:

❐ No shine (earthy)

❐ Metallic

❐ Non-metallic

- ❐ Brilliant
- ❐ Dull
- ❐ Greasy
- ❐ Glassy
- ❐ Pearly
- ❐ Silky

Three Types of Rocks (color matching type)

Igneous	Sedimentary	Metamorphic
from volcanos	settling in water	pressure and heat
magma		
Extrusive type forms if magma (melted rock) cools above ground; intrusive if it cools below ground. **Can be solid or crystalline.**	Made from clay, mud, sand, silt or gravel. Forms in water. **Only type of rock to contain fossils. Usually in layered formation.**	Formed when igneous or sedimentary rock are heated under pressure. **Has characteristic bands and splits easily into sheets.**

Characteristics:

❐ Flaky sheets

❐ Holes

❐ Transparant

❐ Flat

❐ Crumbly

❐ Smooth

❐ Other______________

Hardness:

1. Talc
2. Gypsum

❐ 2.5 Fingernail

3. Calcite

❐ 3.5 Penny

4. Fluorite
5. Apatite

❐ 5.5 Steel nail

6. Orthoclase

❐ 6.5 Steel file

7. Quartz
8. Topaz
9. Corundum
10. Diamond

Cleavage: (Direction rock would split or break.)

❐ None

❐ 1 plane

❐ 2 planes

❐ 3 planes

❐ other

Shapes of crystals:

(Color matching shape)

Draw in other

Rock Detective

Name of rock or mineral: ____________________

Colors: ____________________

Streak color:
(color of scratch mark on sidewalk) ____________________

Texture:
- ❐ Fine
- ❐ Medium
- ❐ Coarse

Weight:
- ❐ Extra light
- ❐ Average
- ❐ Extra heavy

Shine or luster:
- ❐ No shine (earthy)
- ❐ Metallic
- ❐ Non-metallic
  - ❐ Brilliant
  - ❐ Dull
  - ❐ Greasy
  - ❐ Glassy
  - ❐ Pearly
  - ❐ Silky

Three Types of Rocks (color matching type)

Igneous from volcanos	**Sedimentary** settling in water	**Metamorphic** pressure and heat
magma		
Extrusive type forms if magma (melted rock) cools above ground; intrusive if it cools below ground. **Can be solid or crystalline.**	Made from clay, mud, sand, silt or gravel. Forms in water. **Only type of rock to contain fossils. Usually in layered formation.**	Formed when igneous or sedimentary rock are heated under pressure. **Has characteristic bands and splits easily into sheets.**

Characteristics:
- ❐ Flaky sheets
- ❐ Holes
- ❐ Transparant
- ❐ Flat
- ❐ Crumbly
- ❐ Smooth
- ❐ Other__________

Hardness:

1. Talc
2. Gypsum

❐ 2.5 Fingernail

3. Calcite

❐ 3.5 Penny

4. Fluorite
5. Apatite

❐ 5.5 Steel nail

6. Orthoclase

❐ 6.5 Steel file

7. Quartz
8. Topaz
9. Corundum
10. Diamond

Cleavage: (Direction rock would split or break.)
- ❐ None
- ❐ 1 plane
- ❐ 2 planes
- ❐ 3 planes
- ❐ other

Shapes of crystals:
(Color matching shape)

Draw in other

Rock Detective

Name of rock or mineral:

Colors:

Streak color:
(color of scratch mark on sidewalk)

Texture:
- ❒ Fine
- ❒ Medium
- ❒ Coarse

Weight:
- ❒ Extra light
- ❒ Average
- ❒ Extra heavy

Shine or luster:
- ❒ No shine (earthy)
- ❒ Metallic
- ❒ Non-metallic
  - ❒ Brilliant
  - ❒ Dull
  - ❒ Greasy
  - ❒ Glassy
  - ❒ Pearly
  - ❒ Silky

Three Types of Rocks (color matching type)

Igneous	Sedimentary	Metamorphic
from volcanos	settling in water	pressure and heat
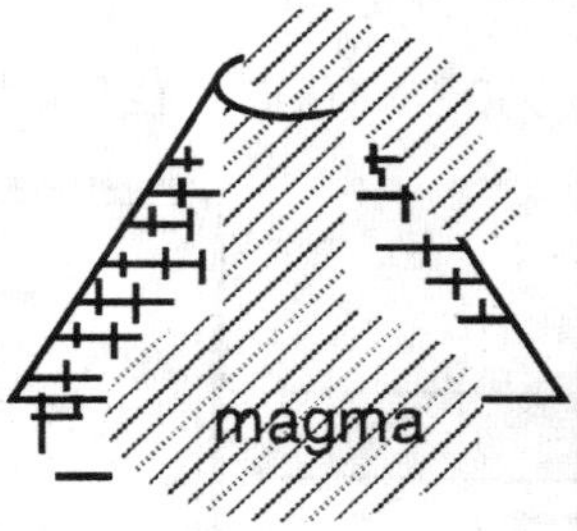 magma	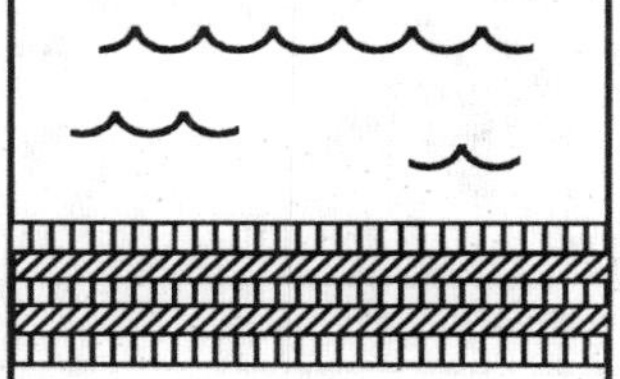	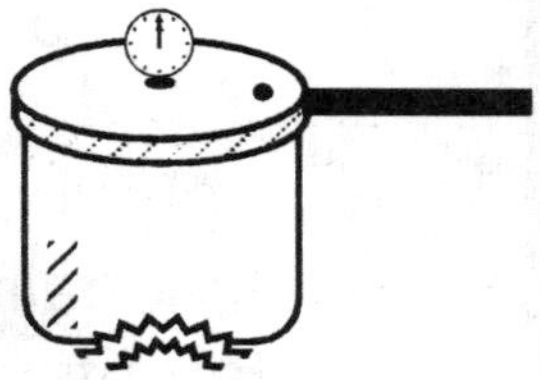
Extrusive type forms if magma (melted rock) cools above ground; intrusive if it cools below ground. **Can be solid or crystalline.**	Made from clay, mud, sand, silt or gravel. Forms in water. **Only type of rock to contain fossils. Usually in layered formation.**	Formed when igneous or sedimentary rock are heated under pressure. **Has characteristic bands and splits easily into sheets.**

Characteristics:
- ❒ Flaky sheets
- ❒ Holes
- ❒ Transparant
- ❒ Flat
- ❒ Crumbly
- ❒ Smooth
- ❒ Other__________

Hardness:

1. Talc
2. Gypsum

❒ 2.5 Fingernail

3. Calcite

❒ 3.5 Penny

4. Fluorite
5. Apatite

❒ 5.5 Steel nail

6. Orthoclase

❒ 6.5 Steel file

7. Quartz
8. Topaz
9. Corundum
10. Diamond

Cleavage: (Direction rock would split or break.)
- ❒ None
- ❒ 1 plane 
- ❒ 2 planes 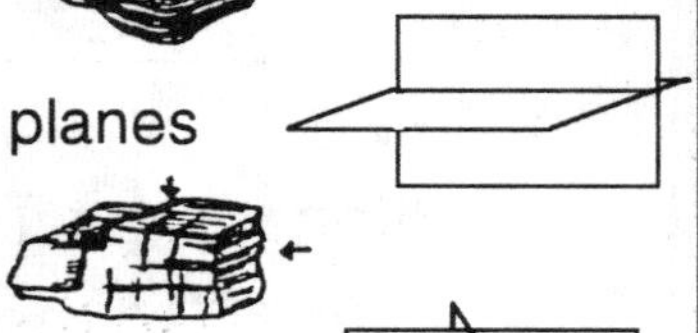
- ❒ 3 planes 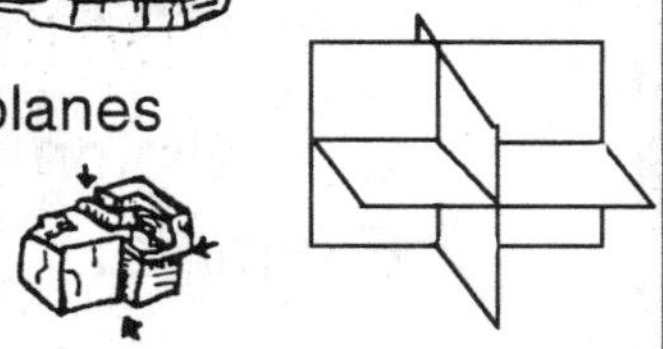
- ❒ other

Shapes of crystals:
(Color matching shape)

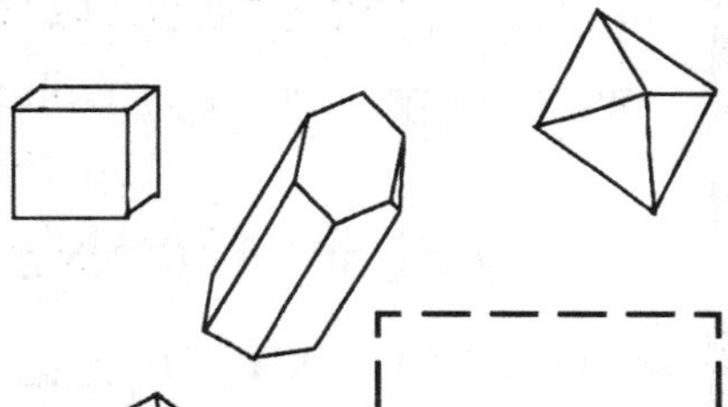

Draw in other

Scientist Detective

Scientist: ______________________ Born: _______ Died: _______

BC —|—|—|—|—|—|—|—|—|—|—|—|— AD

200 0 200 400 600 800 1000 1200 1400 1600 1800 2000

Portrait

Background:

Nationality: ______________________

Parents: ______________________

Influence was: ❑ helpful ❑ injuring

Example: ______________________

Schooling: ______________________

Family:

Spouse: ______________________

Number of children: ______________________

Turning point experience that got him/her into field of work:

____

Religion: ❑ There is a personal God. ❑ There is no God.

❑ There are many gods. ❑ Science is 'god'. ❑ Man is 'god'.

Did religion affect work: ❑ a lot? ❑ a little? ❑ none at all?

Example: ______________________

Field of contribution:

astronomy | botany | zoology | psychology | geology | medicine | physics | __________

Major contributions: ❑ Invention ❑ Theory ❑ Discovery

Best known for: ______________________

Far-reaching results: ______________________

Weather Recipe

Weather = Sun + Air + Water + Rotation & Revolution + Land

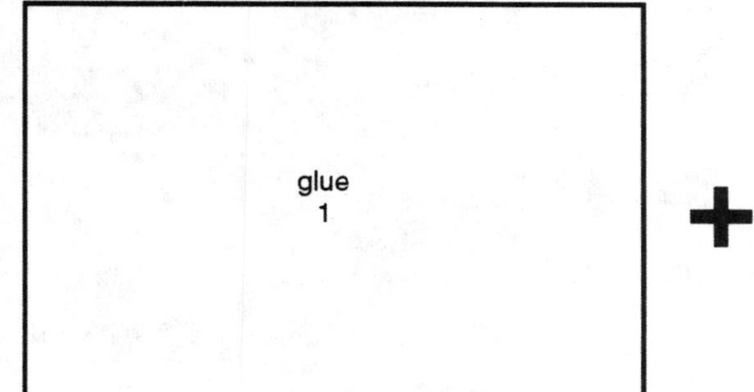
glue
1

Weather =

Sun

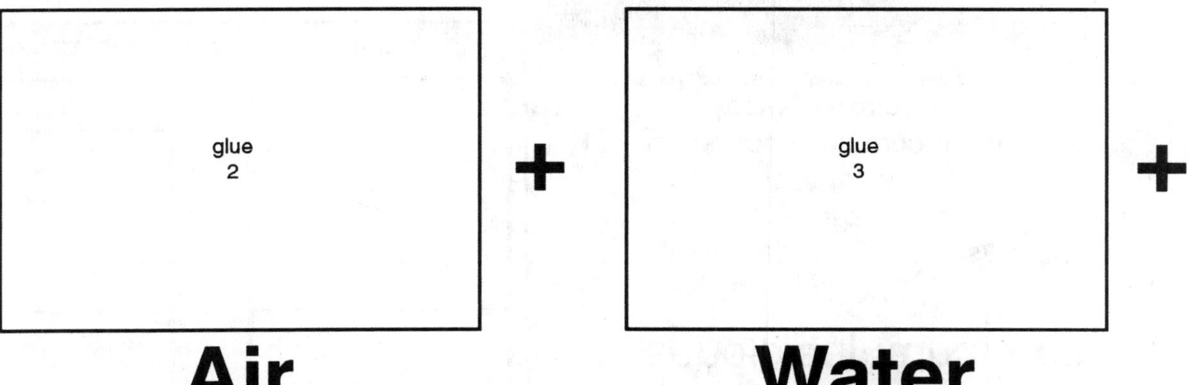
glue
2
glue
3

Air

Water

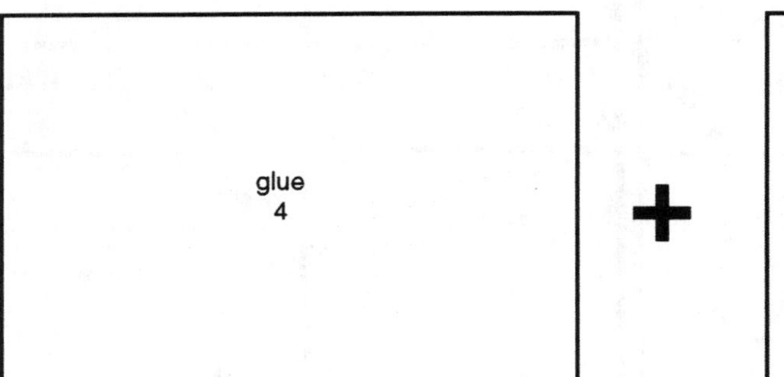
glue
4

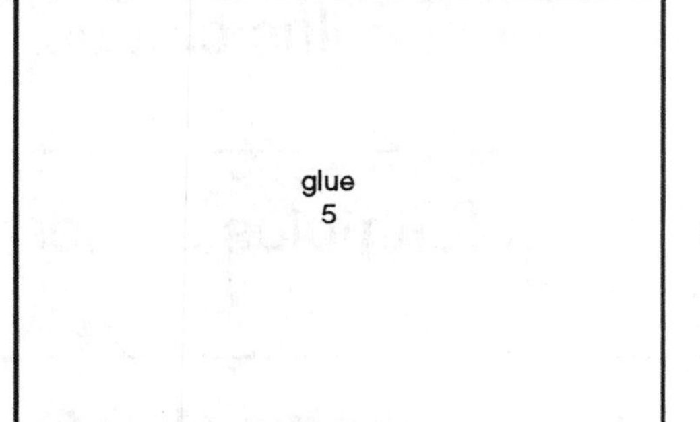
glue
5

Rotation & Revolution

Land

Cut, fold and glue pages from "Weather Recipe" (page 2). On each cover, draw the appropriate symbol (sun, air, etc.).

Cloud Cover

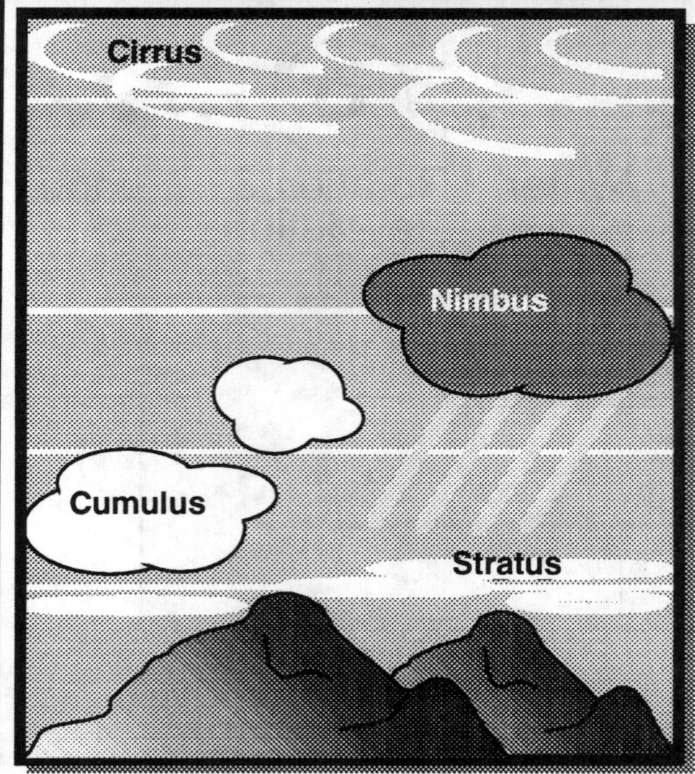

Cirrus
Nimbus
Cumulus
Stratus

The Three Basic Cloud Types:

(Use the clues and the picture to figure out the answers.)

20,000

____________________: **"wispy"**
High frozen clouds of ice crystals. Look like curls or horses' tails.

6,000 ____________________: **"layer"**
Wide flat-bottomed clouds. On ground is called fog.

4,000 ____________________: **"puffed-up"**
Fluffy heaps of brilliant white clouds without rain. Look like mountains.

2,000 **Two More Cloud Terms**

__________= **"dark rain"**
Rain or snow cloud

Alto = "high"— 6,000 to 20,000 ft.

(Use the meaning of these words to figure out the type of cloud.)

cirrus or cirro-: "wispy"
cumulus or cumulo-" puffed up"
stratus or strato-: "layer"
alto: "higher"
nimbus or nimbo-: "dark rain"

cirro | cumulus clouds

____

alto | cumulus clouds

____

strato | cumulus clouds

____

nimbo | stratus clouds

____

cumulo | nimbus clouds

____

Draw these cloud combinations

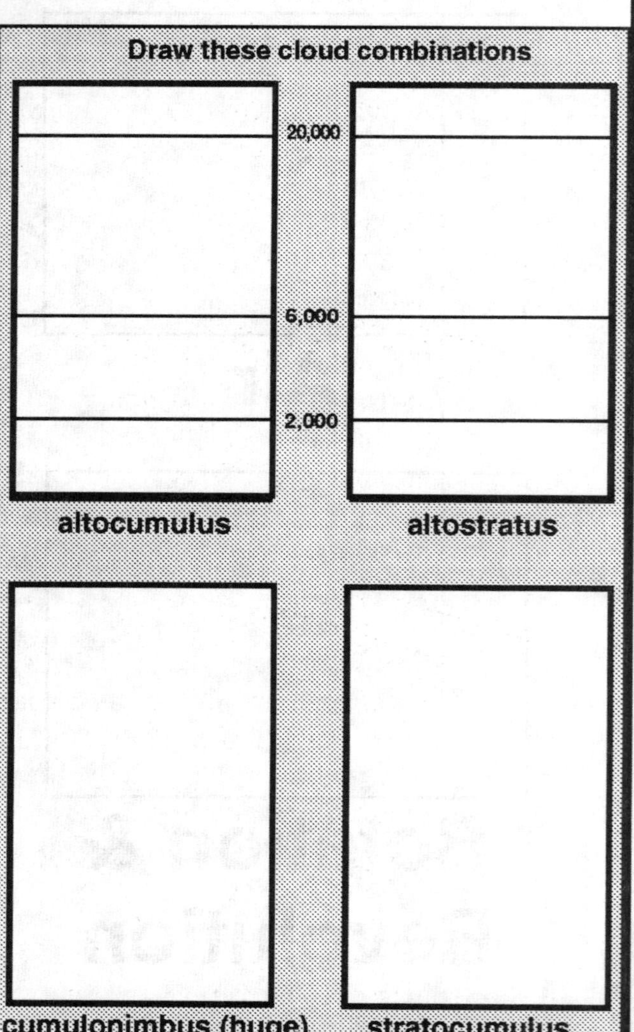

20,000
6,000
2,000
altocumulus
altostratus
cumulonimbus (huge)
stratocumulus

Weather Recipe (page 2)

The ____ heats up ________, ________ and ________. This causes wind and ocean currents and evaporation. Temperatures are warmest at the __________ due to the direct rays of sunlight.	1 sun air equator water land
Air can be calm or violent. Warm air is _________, cold air is ____________. When cold air moves into the warm air spaces, it causes wind. If the wind is at your back, in front is a low pressure area.	2 warm air heavy light cold air
Water is important to all life. Water falls as precipitation, which means ________ or __________. It evaporates, forms _______________ and falls again. Water currents in the oceans can cool or warm land.	3 snow rain clouds evaporate ocean
The earth is moving in two paths at the same time. It spins like a top on its axis which makes _______________ and _____________. It also travels in a large orbit around the sun causing the _____________.	4 fall summer winter day night spring Seasons
Mountains have a strong effect on the weather. When clouds approach ___________, they often drop their _________ on that side. Therefore the other side of the mountain is much _____________.	wetter 5 dryer rain

Cloud Detective

Cloud Name:____________________________ **Date:**_______________

Basic Cloud Shape:

- ❐ cirrus (wispy, feathery, icy, "mares' tails")
- ❐ cumulus (puffed up)
- ❐ stratus (layer, "blanket")

Altitude:

❐ cirro- "wispy", (icy, extremely high, over 20,000 ft.)	cirrus	cirrocumulus	cirrostratus
20,000 ft. ❐ alto- "higher" (higher than usual, between 6-20,000 ft.)	X	altocumulus	altostratus
6,000 ft. ❐ strato- "layer" (low layer, below 6,000 ft.)	X	cumulus (not a layer) stratocumulus (layer)	stratus

Predicting the Weather:

Cloud Color:
[indicates fair (white) versus foul (black) weather]

- ❐ white
- ❐ gray
- ❐ black:
  - ❐ shapeless = nimbus
  - ❐ thunderhead = cumulonimbus
  - ❐ low layer = nimbostratus

Cloud Movement:
[indicates rate of weather change]

- ❐ stationary
- ❐ moving slowly
- ❐ moving rapidly

Wind Speed:_______

Wind Direction:

N NE E SE S SW W NW

Observe a cloud. Choose the basic shape, altitude, color, movement. Point the compass to the north, then draw an arrow for wind direction. Estimate wind speed from chart on "Speed Detective" page.

Cloud Detective

Cloud Name:________________________ **Date:**____________

Basic Cloud Shape:

- ❒ cirrus (wispy, feathery, icy, "mares' tails")
- ❒ cumulus (puffed up)
- ❒ stratus (layer, "blanket")

Altitude:

- ❒ cirro- "wispy", (icy, extremely high, over 20,000 ft.)
- ❒ alto- "higher" (higher than usual, between 6-20,000 ft.)
- ❒ strato- "layer" (low layer, below 6,000 ft.)

Altitude			
above 20,000 ft.	cirrus	cirrocumulus	cirrostratus
6,000–20,000 ft.	X	altocumulus	altostratus
below 6,000 ft.	X	cumulus (not a layer) stratocumulus (layer)	stratus

Predicting the Weather:

Cloud Color:
[indicates fair (white) versus foul (black) weather]

- ❒ white
- ❒ gray
- ❒ black:
  - ❒ shapeless = nimbus
  - ❒ thunderhead = cumulonimbus
  - ❒ low layer = nimbostratus

Cloud Movement:
[indicates rate of weather change]

- ❒ stationary
- ❒ moving slowly
- ❒ moving rapidly

Wind Speed:_______

Wind Direction:

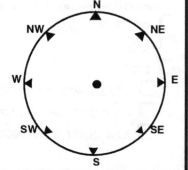

N
NE
E
SE
S
SW
W
NW

Observe a cloud. Choose the basic shape, altitude, color, movement. Point the compass to the north, then draw an arrow for wind direction. Estimate wind speed from chart on "Speed Detective" page.

Cloud Detective

Cloud Name:________________________________ **Date:**________________

Basic Cloud Shape:

- ❒ cirrus (wispy, feathery, icy, "mares' tails")
- ❒ cumulus (puffed up)
- ❒ stratus (layer, "blanket")

Altitude:

❒ cirro- "wispy", (icy, extremely high, over 20,000 ft.)	cirrus	cirrocumulus	cirrostratus
20,000 ft. ❒ alto- "higher" (higher than usual, between 6-20,000 ft.)	X	altocumulus	altostratus
6,000 ft. ❒ strato- "layer" (low layer, below 6,000 ft.)	X	cumulus (not a layer) / stratocumulus (layer)	stratus

Predicting the Weather:

Cloud Color:

[indicates fair (white) versus foul (black) weather]

- ❒ white
- ❒ gray
- ❒ black:
  - ❒ shapeless = nimbus
  - ❒ thunderhead = cumulonimbus
  - ❒ low layer = nimbostratus

Cloud Movement:

[indicates rate of weather change]

- ❒ stationary
- ❒ moving slowly
- ❒ moving rapidly

Wind Speed:_______

Wind Direction:

N NW NE W E SW SE S

Observe a cloud. Choose the basic shape, altitude, color, movement. Point the compass to the north, then draw an arrow for wind direction. Estimate wind speed from chart on "Speed Detective" page.

Cloud Detective

Cloud Name: ______________________ **Date:** ____________

Basic Cloud Shape:

- ❐ cirrus (wispy, feathery, icy, "mares' tails")
- ❐ cumulus (puffed up)
- ❐ stratus (layer, "blanket")

Altitude:

❐ cirro- "wispy", (icy, extremely high, over 20,000 ft.)	cirrus	cirrocumulus	cirrostratus
20,000 ft.			
❐ alto- "higher" (higher than usual, between 6-20,000 ft.)	X	altocumulus	altostratus
6,000 ft.			
❐ strato- "layer" (low layer, below 6,000 ft.)	X	cumulus (not a layer) stratocumulus (layer)	stratus

Predicting the Weather:

Cloud Color:
[indicates fair (white) versus foul (black) weather]

- ❐ white
- ❐ gray
- ❐ black:
  - ❐ shapeless = nimbus
  - ❐ thunderhead = cumulonimbus
  - ❐ low layer = nimbostratus

Cloud Movement:
[indicates rate of weather change]

- ❐ stationary
- ❐ moving slowly
- ❐ moving rapidly

Wind Speed:________

Wind Direction:

N
NE
E
SE
S
SW
W
NW

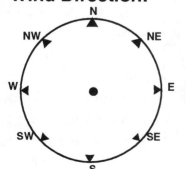

 Observe a cloud. Choose the basic shape, altitude, color, movement. Point the compass to the north, then draw an arrow for wind direction. Estimate wind speed from chart on "Speed Detective" page.

Two Week Weather Chart

Sunny Cloudy Partly Cloudy Rainy Stormy Snowy Windy

Month:

Sunday	Monday	Tuesday	Wednesday	Thursday	Friday	Saturday
Date:	Date:	Date:	Date:	Date:	Date:	Date:
Temperature:	Temperature:	Temperature:	Temperature:	Temperature:	Temperature:	Temperature:
Date:	Date:	Date:	Date:	Date:	Date:	Date:
Temperature:	Temperature:	Temperature:	Temperature:	Temperature:	Temperature:	Temperature:

Fill in date, temperature and draw one or more symbols for daily weather.

Scientist Detective

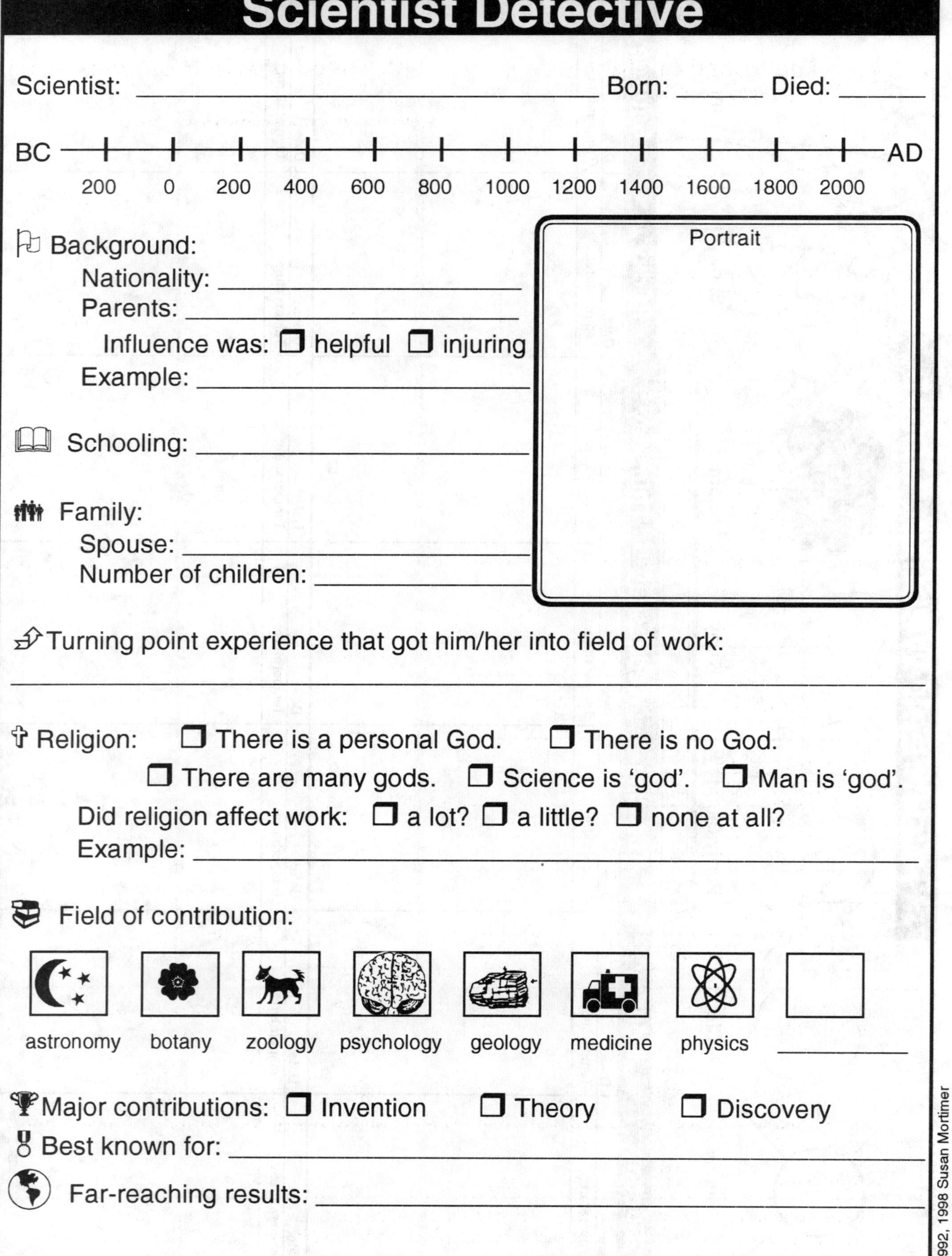

Scientist: ______________________ Born: ______ Died: ______

BC — 200 — 0 — 200 — 400 — 600 — 800 — 1000 — 1200 — 1400 — 1600 — 1800 — 2000 — AD

Portrait

Background:
Nationality: ______________________
Parents: ______________________
Influence was: ❑ helpful ❑ injuring
Example: ______________________

Schooling: ______________________

Family:
Spouse: ______________________
Number of children: ______________________

Turning point experience that got him/her into field of work:

____

Religion: ❑ There is a personal God. ❑ There is no God.
❑ There are many gods. ❑ Science is 'god'. ❑ Man is 'god'.
Did religion affect work: ❑ a lot? ❑ a little? ❑ none at all?
Example: ______________________

Field of contribution:

astronomy botany zoology psychology geology medicine physics ______

Major contributions: ❑ Invention ❑ Theory ❑ Discovery

Best known for: ______________________

Far-reaching results: ______________________

Speed Detective

The Speed of Light

(186,000 miles/second)

STOP

Seconds	Miles light traveled	Times around the earth at speed of light
1	186,300	7 1/3
5	931,500	36 2/3
10	1,863,000	73 1/3
15	2,794,500	110
20	3,726,000	146 2/3
25	4,657,500	183 1/3
30	5,589,000	220
35	6,520,500	256 2/3
40	7,452,000	293 1/3
45	8,383,500	330

The Speed of Wind (Beaufort's Scale)

Wind Speed/mph		Fill in wind speed by picture.
0	Smoke rises up	____
1-3	Smoke drifts	____
4-7	Leaves rustle; flags stir	____
8-12	Leaves and twigs move	____
13-18	Moves small branches	____
19-24	Small trees sway	____
25-31	Large branches move	____
32-38	Whole trees move	____
39-46	Twigs break walking hard	____
47-54	Signs blow down	____
55-up	Widespread damage	____

The Speed of Sound (1/5 mile per second) Finish graph.

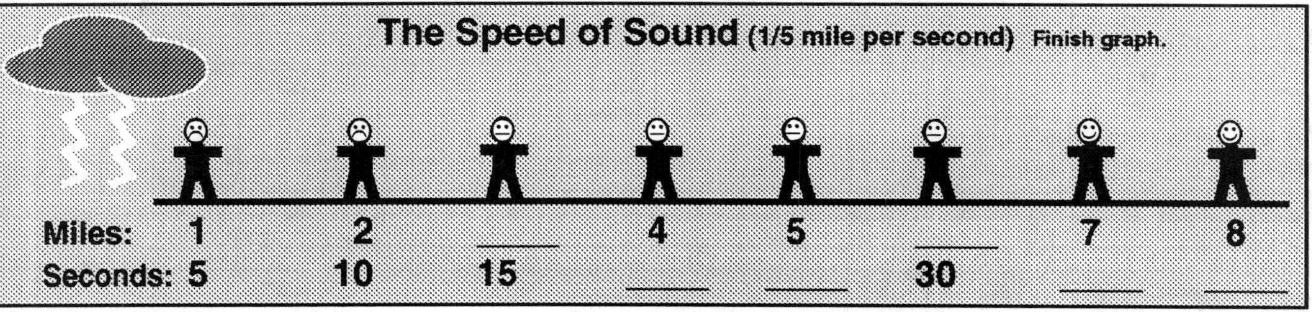
Miles: 1 2 ____ 4 5 ____ 7 8
Seconds: 5 10 15 ____ ____ 30 ____ ____

Sound travels one mile every five seconds. To tell how far away the lightening is, from the moment you see the lightening until you hear the thunder, count each second by saying "Thunderstorm One, Thunderstorm Two", etc. Then divide the total by five to get the miles.

For "Speed of Light": Trace the loops as the teacher calls out the seconds. Then color in how many second it took to complete. Discuss how far light has traveled and how many times around the earth you could have gone in that time.

Plant Parts

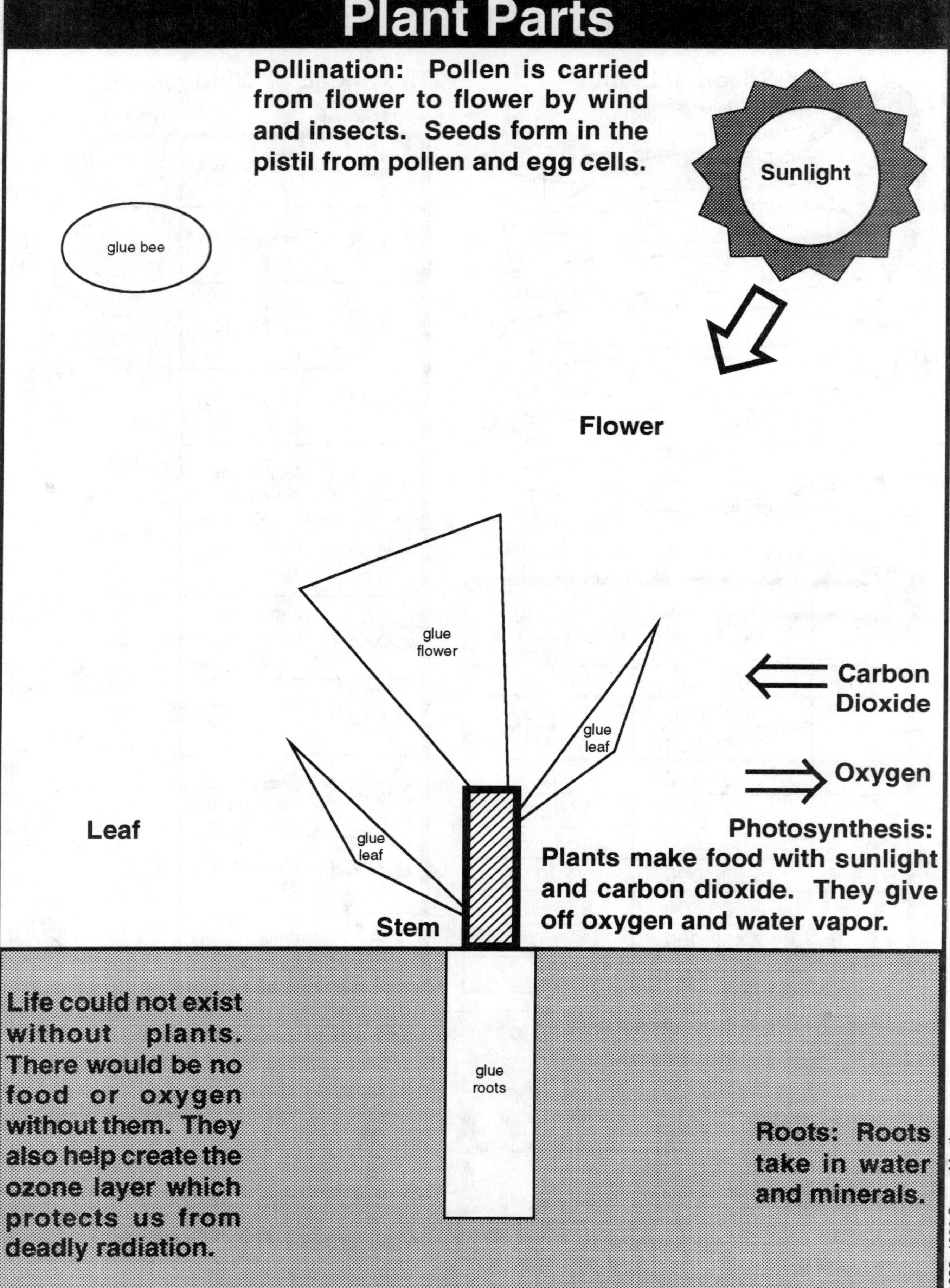

Pollination: Pollen is carried from flower to flower by wind and insects. Seeds form in the pistil from pollen and egg cells.
Sunlight
glue bee
Flower
glue flower
Carbon Dioxide
glue leaf
Oxygen
glue leaf
Leaf
Photosynthesis: Plants make food with sunlight and carbon dioxide. They give off oxygen and water vapor.
Stem
glue roots
Life could not exist without plants. There would be no food or oxygen without them. They also help create the ozone layer which protects us from deadly radiation.
Roots: Roots take in water and minerals.

 Color, then cut out flower parts and bee from “Plant Parts” (page 2). Fold on dotted lines, then glue onto this page.

Plant Parts (page 2)

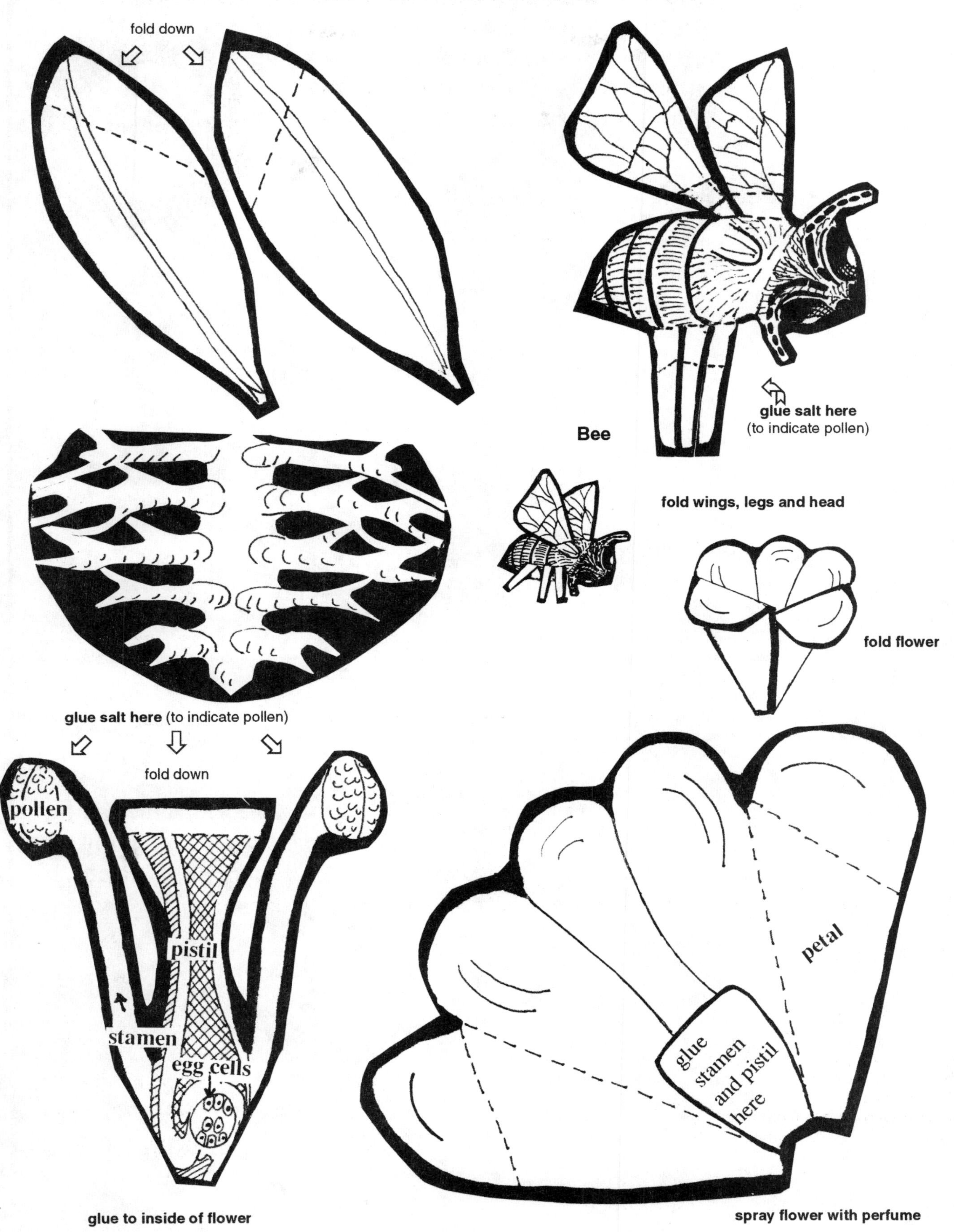
fold down
Bee
glue salt here
(to indicate pollen)
fold wings, legs and head
fold flower
glue salt here (to indicate pollen)
fold down
pollen
pistil
stamen
egg cells
petal
glue stamen and pistil here
glue to inside of flower
spray flower with perfume

Color, cut and fold, then glue on "Plant Parts" page.

Scientist Detective

Scientist: ______________________ Born: ______ Died: ______

BC —|—|—|—|—|—|—|—|—|—|—|—|— AD

200 0 200 400 600 800 1000 1200 1400 1600 1800 2000

Portrait

Background:

Nationality: ______________________

Parents: ______________________

Influence was: ❐ helpful ❐ injuring

Example: ______________________

Schooling: ______________________

Family:

Spouse: ______________________

Number of children: ______________________

Turning point experience that got him/her into field of work:

____

Religion: ❐ There is a personal God. ❐ There is no God.

❐ There are many gods. ❐ Science is 'god'. ❐ Man is 'god'.

Did religion affect work: ❐ a lot? ❐ a little? ❐ none at all?

Example: ______________________

Field of contribution:

astronomy botany zoology psychology geology medicine physics ______

Major contributions: ❐ Invention ❐ Theory ❐ Discovery

Best known for: ______________________

Far-reaching results: ______________________

Portrait of a Flower

Name of specimen: ____________________

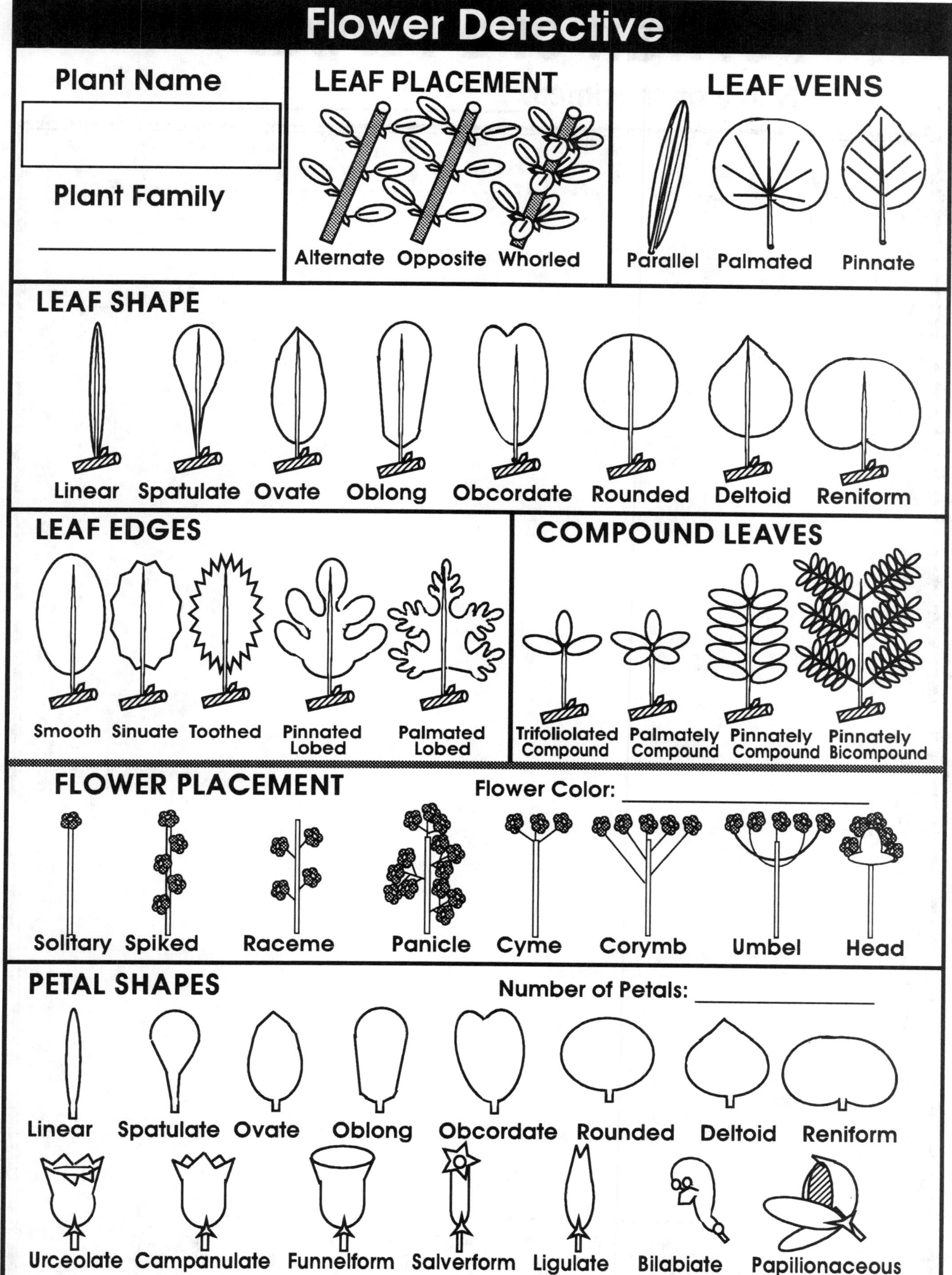
Flower Detective
Plant Name
Plant Family
LEAF PLACEMENT
Alternate
Opposite
Whorled
LEAF VEINS
Parallel
Palmated
Pinnate
LEAF SHAPE
Linear
Spatulate
Ovate
Oblong
Obcordate
Rounded
Deltoid
Reniform
LEAF EDGES
Smooth
Sinuate
Toothed
Pinnated Lobed
Palmated Lobed
COMPOUND LEAVES
Trifoliolated Compound
Palmately Compound
Pinnately Compound
Pinnately Bicompound
FLOWER PLACEMENT
Flower Color: ____________
Solitary
Spiked
Raceme
Panicle
Cyme
Corymb
Umbel
Head
PETAL SHAPES
Number of Petals: ____________
Linear
Spatulate
Ovate
Oblong
Obcordate
Rounded
Deltoid
Reniform
Urceolate
Campanulate
Funnelform
Salverform
Ligulate
Bilabiate
Papilionaceous

Choose a flowering plant and analyze its leaf and flower structure. Color the closest match in each category. Draw or place pressed plant on preceding page. Do not pick plants from state or national parks.

Portrait of a Flower

Name of specimen:__________________________

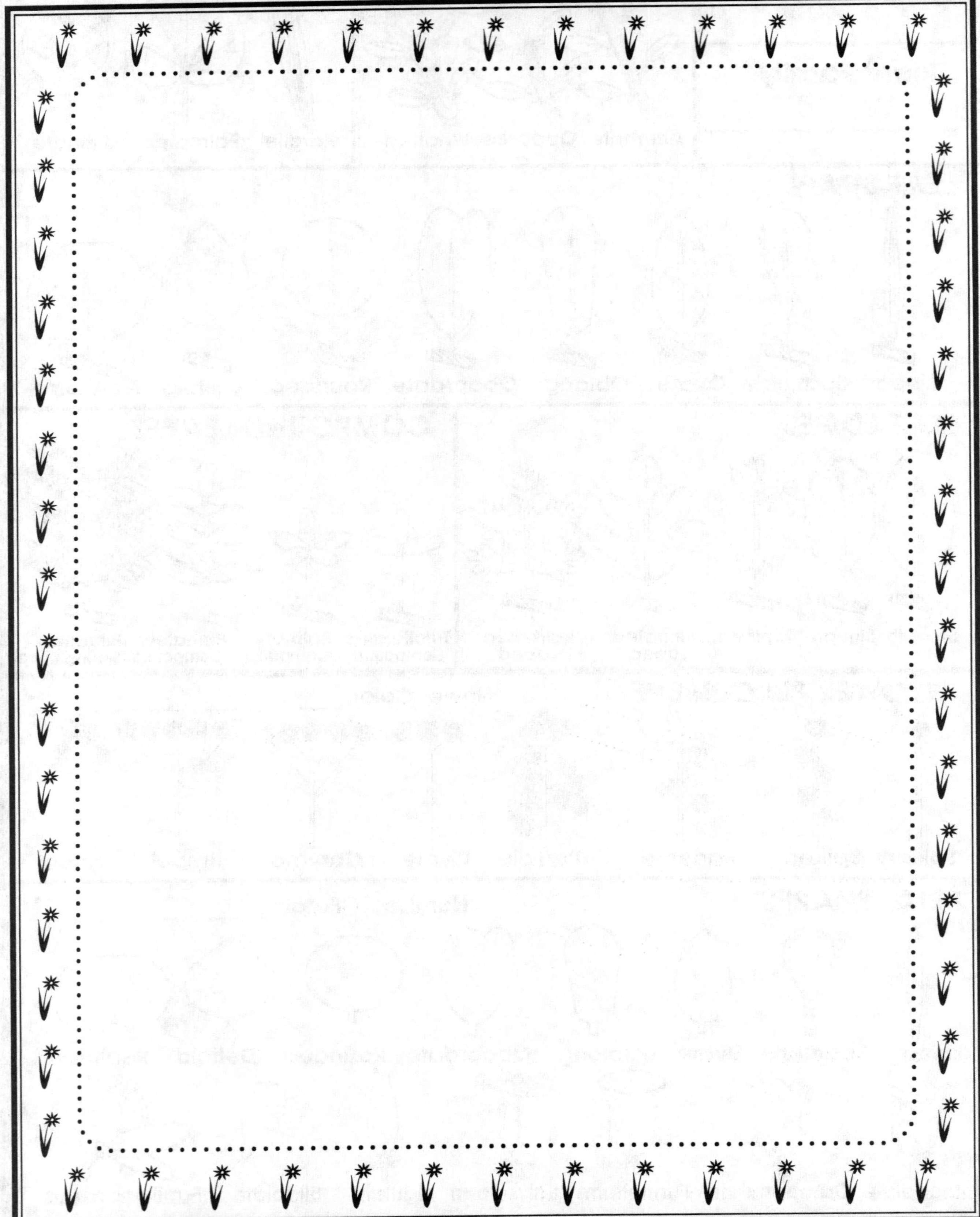

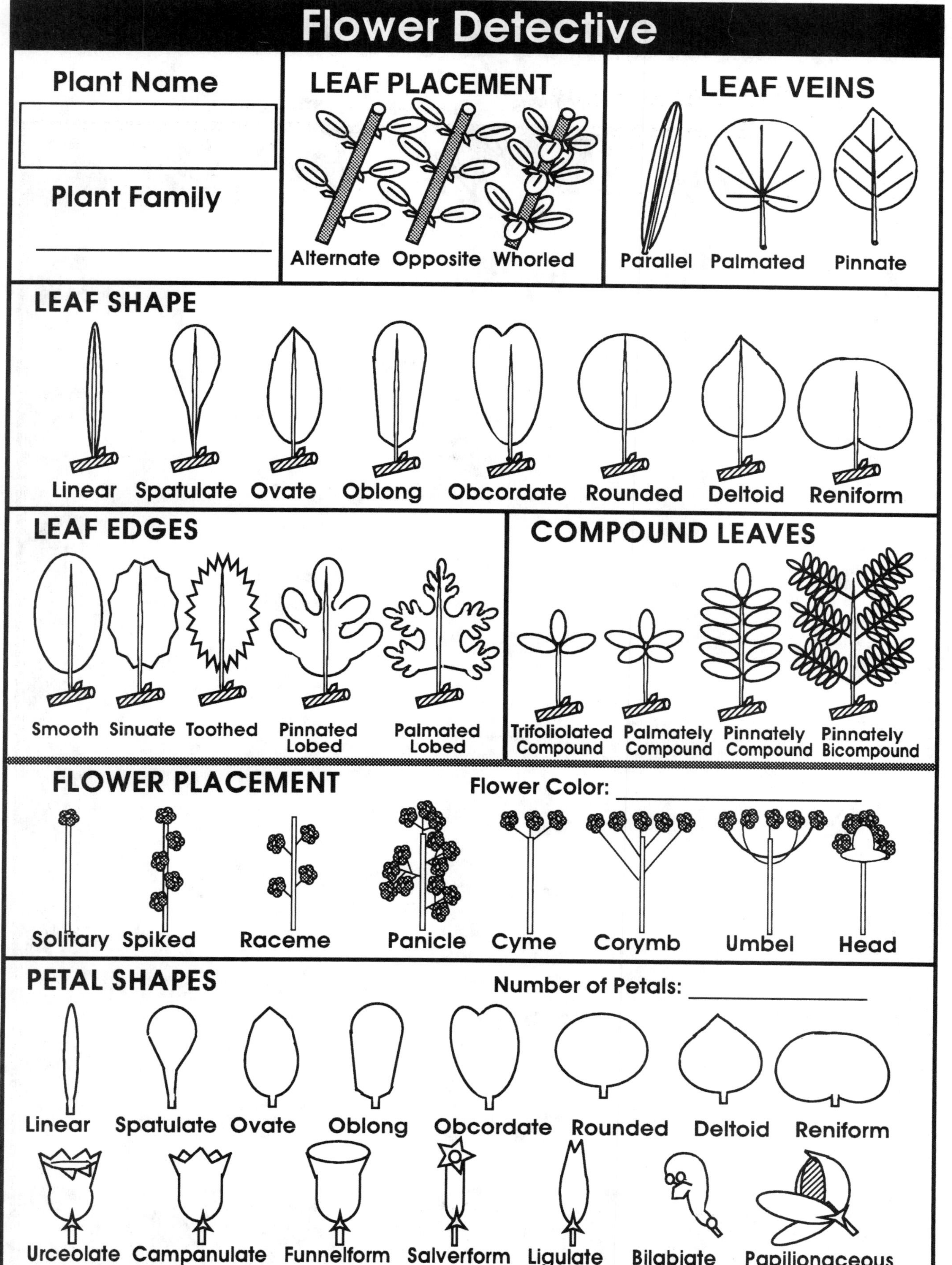
Flower Detective
Plant Name
Plant Family
LEAF PLACEMENT
Alternate
Opposite
Whorled
LEAF VEINS
Parallel
Palmated
Pinnate
LEAF SHAPE
Linear
Spatulate
Ovate
Oblong
Obcordate
Rounded
Deltoid
Reniform
LEAF EDGES
Smooth
Sinuate
Toothed
Pinnated Lobed
Palmated Lobed
COMPOUND LEAVES
Trifoliolated Compound
Palmately Compound
Pinnately Compound
Pinnately Bicompound
FLOWER PLACEMENT
Flower Color:
Solitary
Spiked
Raceme
Panicle
Cyme
Corymb
Umbel
Head
PETAL SHAPES
Number of Petals:
Linear
Spatulate
Ovate
Oblong
Obcordate
Rounded
Deltoid
Reniform
Urceolate
Campanulate
Funnelform
Salverform
Ligulate
Bilabiate
Papilionaceous

Choose a flowering plant and analyze its leaf and flower structure. Color the closest match in each category. Draw or place pressed plant on preceding page. Do not pick plants from state or national parks.

Portrait of a Flower

Name of specimen: ____________________

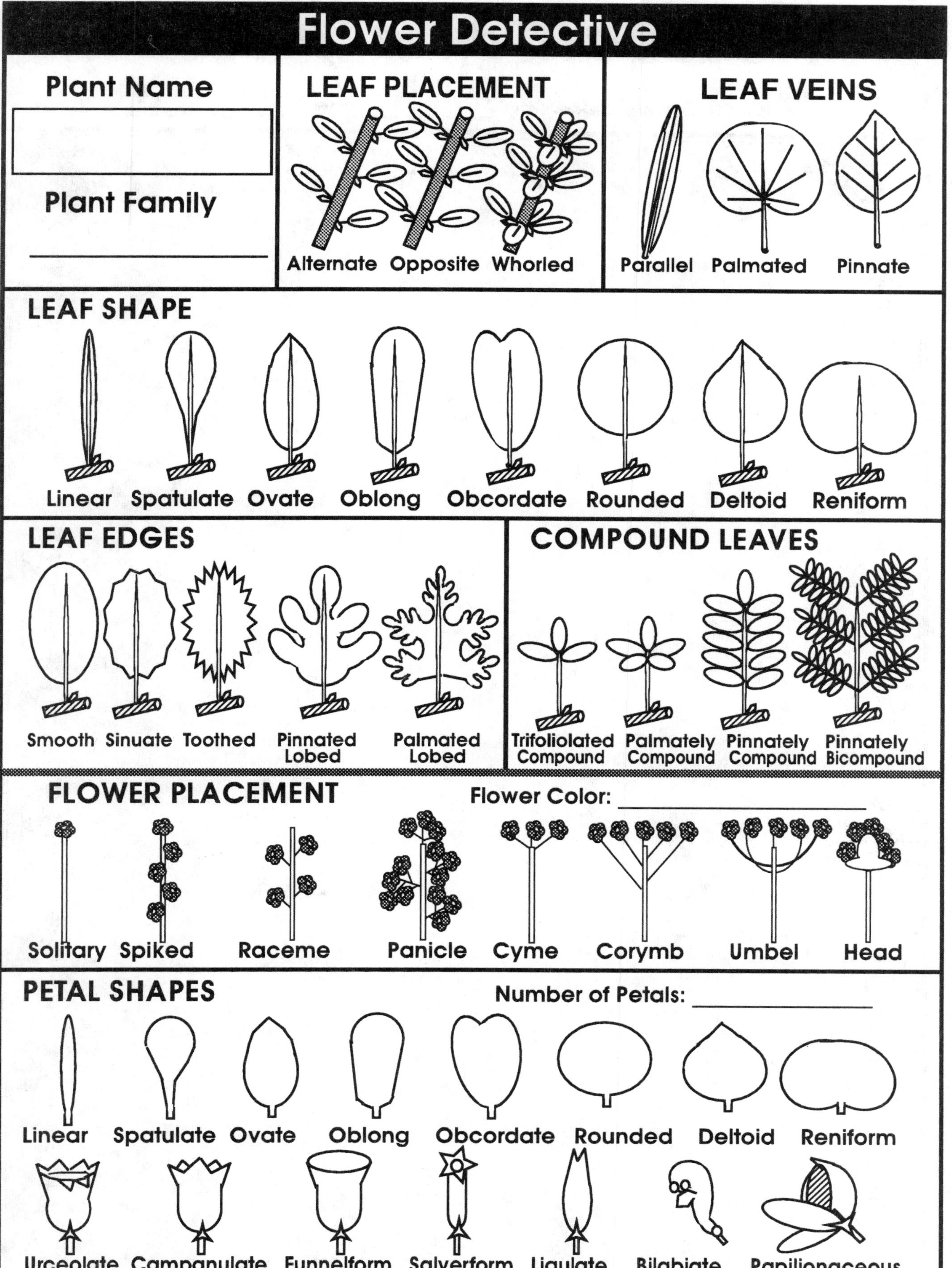
Flower Detective
Plant Name
Plant Family
LEAF PLACEMENT
Alternate
Opposite
Whorled
LEAF VEINS
Parallel
Palmated
Pinnate
LEAF SHAPE
Linear
Spatulate
Ovate
Oblong
Obcordate
Rounded
Deltoid
Reniform
LEAF EDGES
Smooth
Sinuate
Toothed
Pinnated Lobed
Palmated Lobed
COMPOUND LEAVES
Trifoliolated Compound
Palmately Compound
Pinnately Compound
Pinnately Bicompound
FLOWER PLACEMENT
Flower Color: ____________
Solitary
Spiked
Raceme
Panicle
Cyme
Corymb
Umbel
Head
PETAL SHAPES
Number of Petals: ____________
Linear
Spatulate
Ovate
Oblong
Obcordate
Rounded
Deltoid
Reniform
Urceolate
Campanulate
Funnelform
Salverform
Ligulate
Bilabiate
Papilionaceous

Choose a flowering plant and analyze its leaf and flower structure. Color the closest match in each category. Draw or place pressed plant on preceding page. Do not pick plants from state or national parks.

Portrait of a Flower

Name of specimen: ______________________________

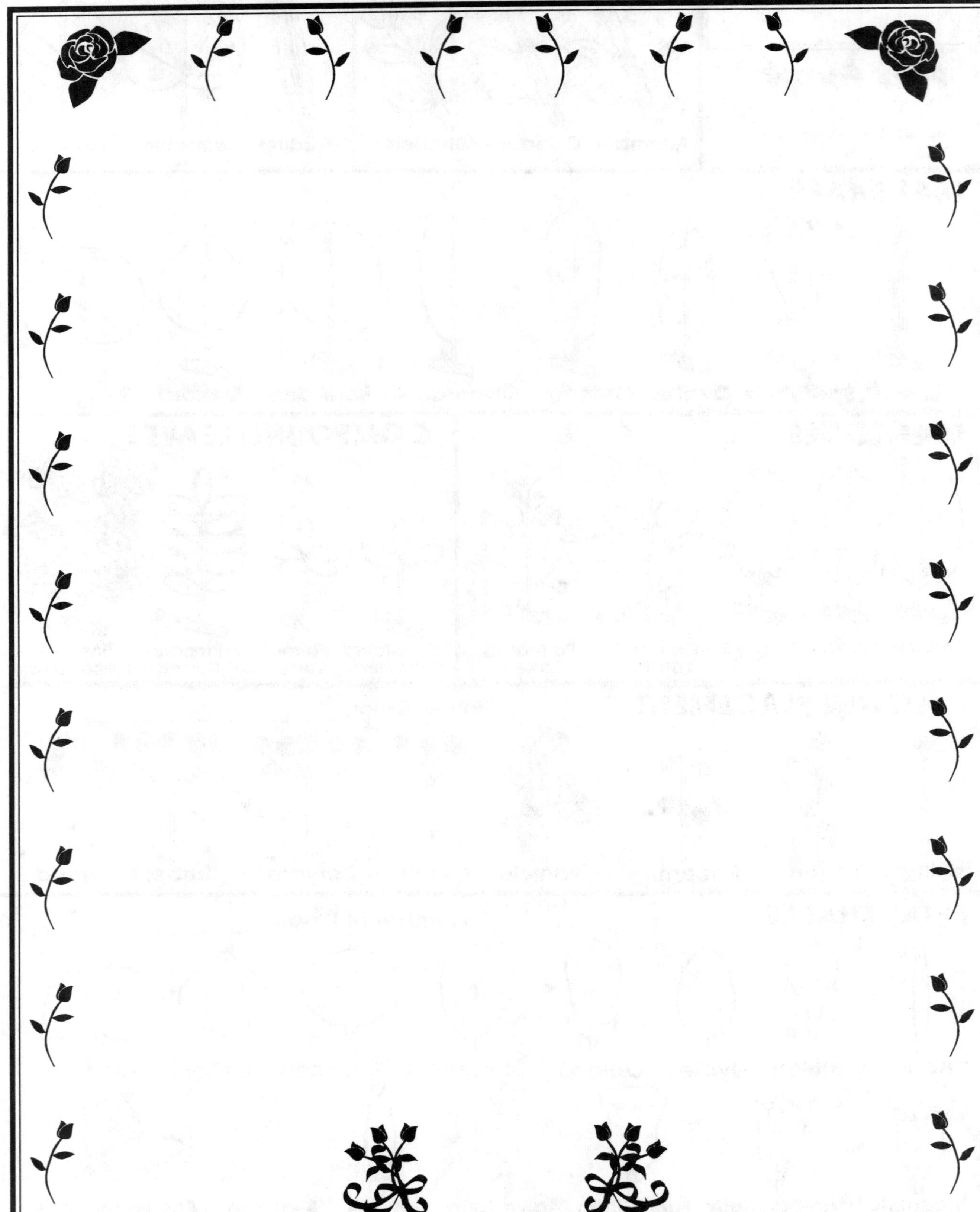

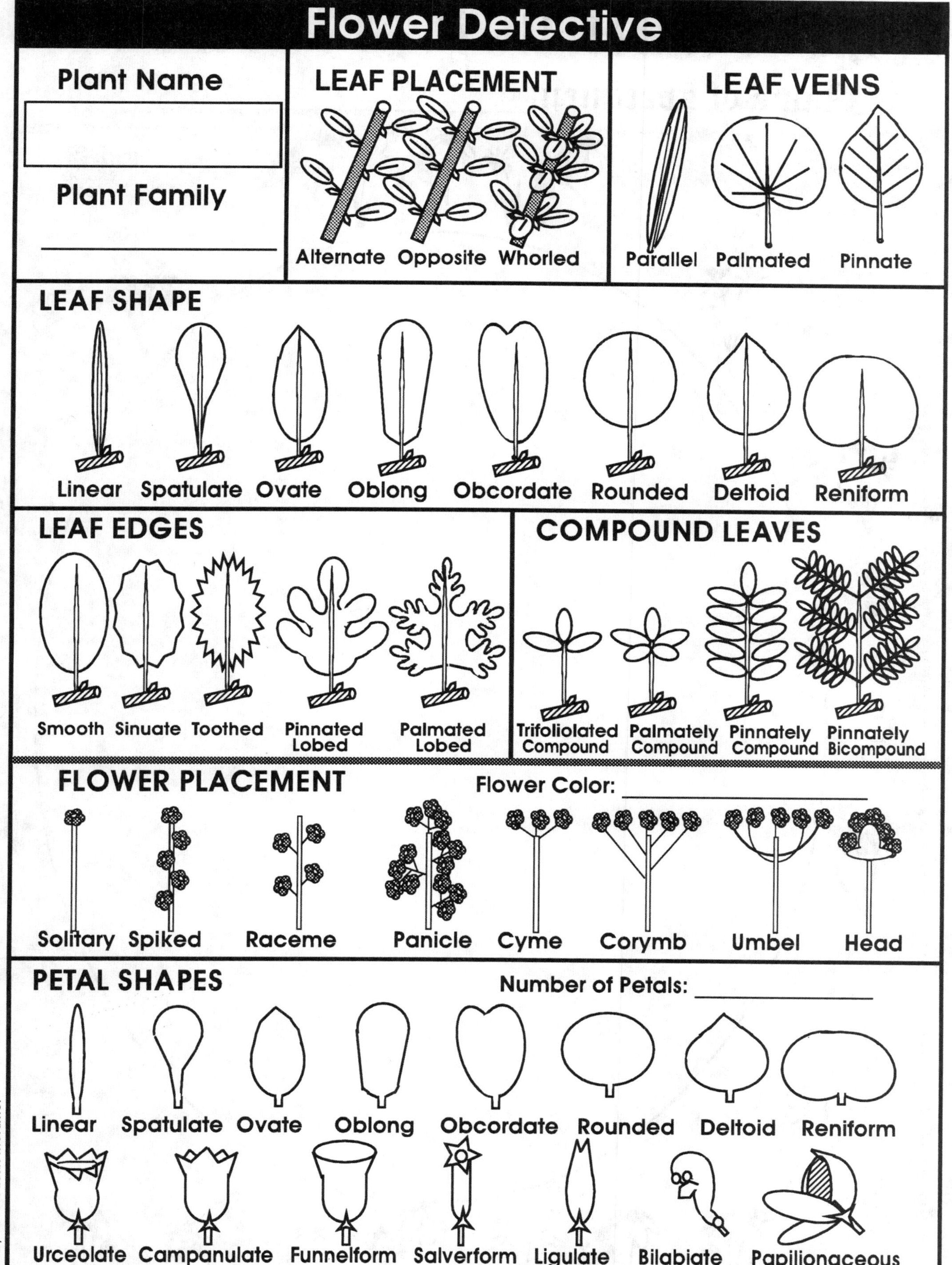
Flower Detective
Plant Name
Plant Family
LEAF PLACEMENT
Alternate
Opposite
Whorled
LEAF VEINS
Parallel
Palmated
Pinnate
LEAF SHAPE
Linear
Spatulate
Ovate
Oblong
Obcordate
Rounded
Deltoid
Reniform
LEAF EDGES
Smooth
Sinuate
Toothed
Pinnated Lobed
Palmated Lobed
COMPOUND LEAVES
Trifoliolated Compound
Palmately Compound
Pinnately Compound
Pinnately Bicompound
FLOWER PLACEMENT
Flower Color: ____________
Solitary
Spiked
Raceme
Panicle
Cyme
Corymb
Umbel
Head
PETAL SHAPES
Number of Petals: ____________
Linear
Spatulate
Ovate
Oblong
Obcordate
Rounded
Deltoid
Reniform
Urceolate
Campanulate
Funnelform
Salverform
Ligulate
Bilabiate
Papilionaceous

Choose a flowering plant and analyze its leaf and flower structure. Color the closest match in each category. Draw or place pressed plant on preceding page. Do not pick plants from state or national parks.

Portrait of a Flower

Name of specimen: ______________________________

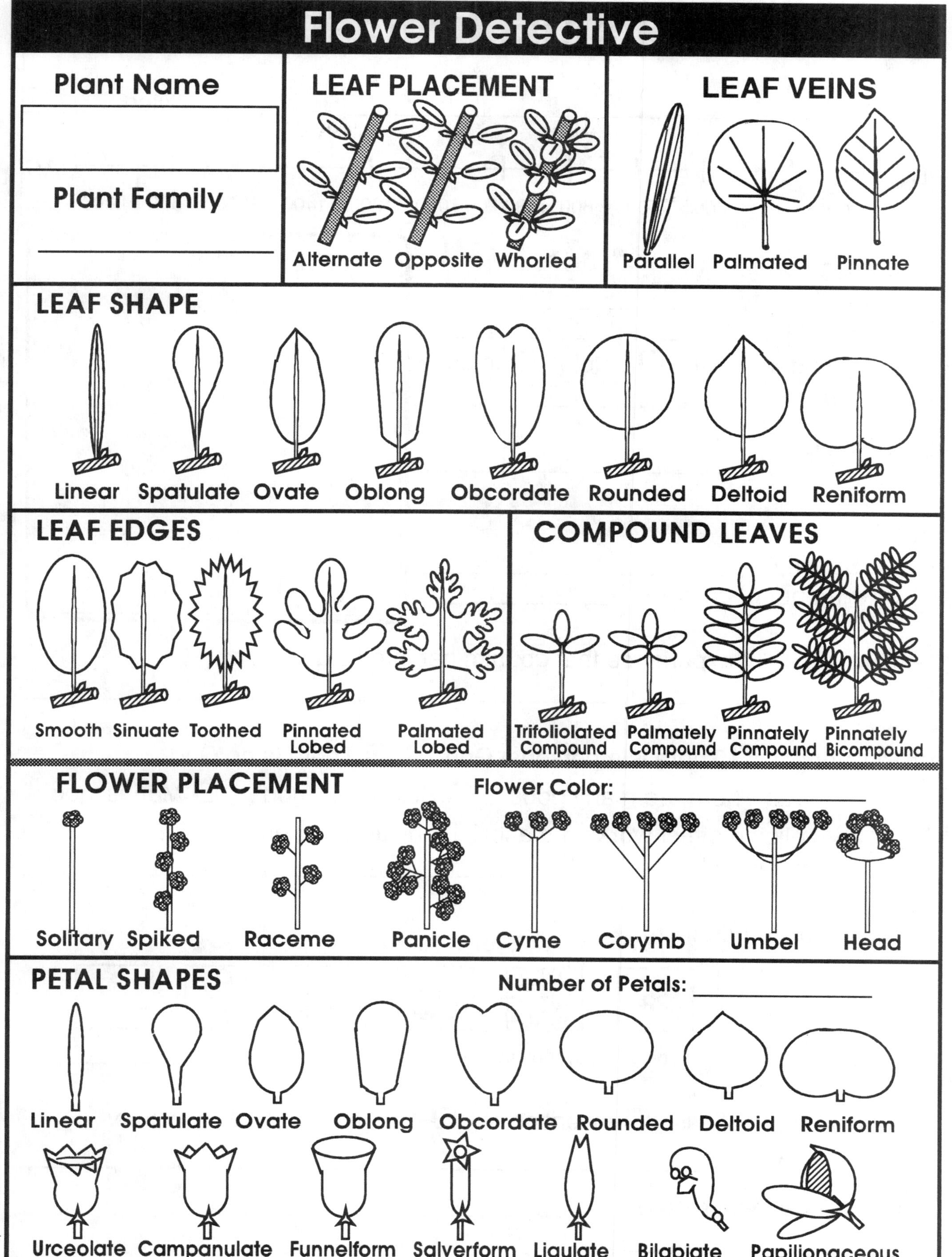
Flower Detective
Plant Name
Plant Family
LEAF PLACEMENT
Alternate
Opposite
Whorled
LEAF VEINS
Parallel
Palmated
Pinnate
LEAF SHAPE
Linear
Spatulate
Ovate
Oblong
Obcordate
Rounded
Deltoid
Reniform
LEAF EDGES
Smooth
Sinuate
Toothed
Pinnated Lobed
Palmated Lobed
COMPOUND LEAVES
Trifoliolated Compound
Palmately Compound
Pinnately Compound
Pinnately Bicompound
FLOWER PLACEMENT
Flower Color:
Solitary
Spiked
Raceme
Panicle
Cyme
Corymb
Umbel
Head
PETAL SHAPES
Number of Petals:
Linear
Spatulate
Ovate
Oblong
Obcordate
Rounded
Deltoid
Reniform
Urceolate
Campanulate
Funnelform
Salverform
Ligulate
Bilabiate
Papilionaceous

Choose a flowering plant and analyze its leaf and flower structure. Color the closest match in each category. Draw or place pressed plant on preceding page. Do not pick plants from state or national parks.

Scientist Detective

Scientist: ______________________ Born: ______ Died: ______

BC — 200 — 0 — 200 — 400 — 600 — 800 — 1000 — 1200 — 1400 — 1600 — 1800 — 2000 — AD

Portrait

Background:
Nationality: ______________________
Parents: ______________________
Influence was: ❒ helpful ❒ injuring
Example: ______________________

Schooling: ______________________

Family:
Spouse: ______________________
Number of children: ______________________

Turning point experience that got him/her into field of work:

____

Religion: ❒ There is a personal God. ❒ There is no God.
❒ There are many gods. ❒ Science is 'god'. ❒ Man is 'god'.
Did religion affect work: ❒ a lot? ❒ a little? ❒ none at all?
Example: ______________________

Field of contribution:

astronomy | botany | zoology | psychology | geology | medicine | physics | ______

Major contributions: ❒ Invention ❒ Theory ❒ Discovery
Best known for: ______________________
Far-reaching results: ______________________

Mold Detective

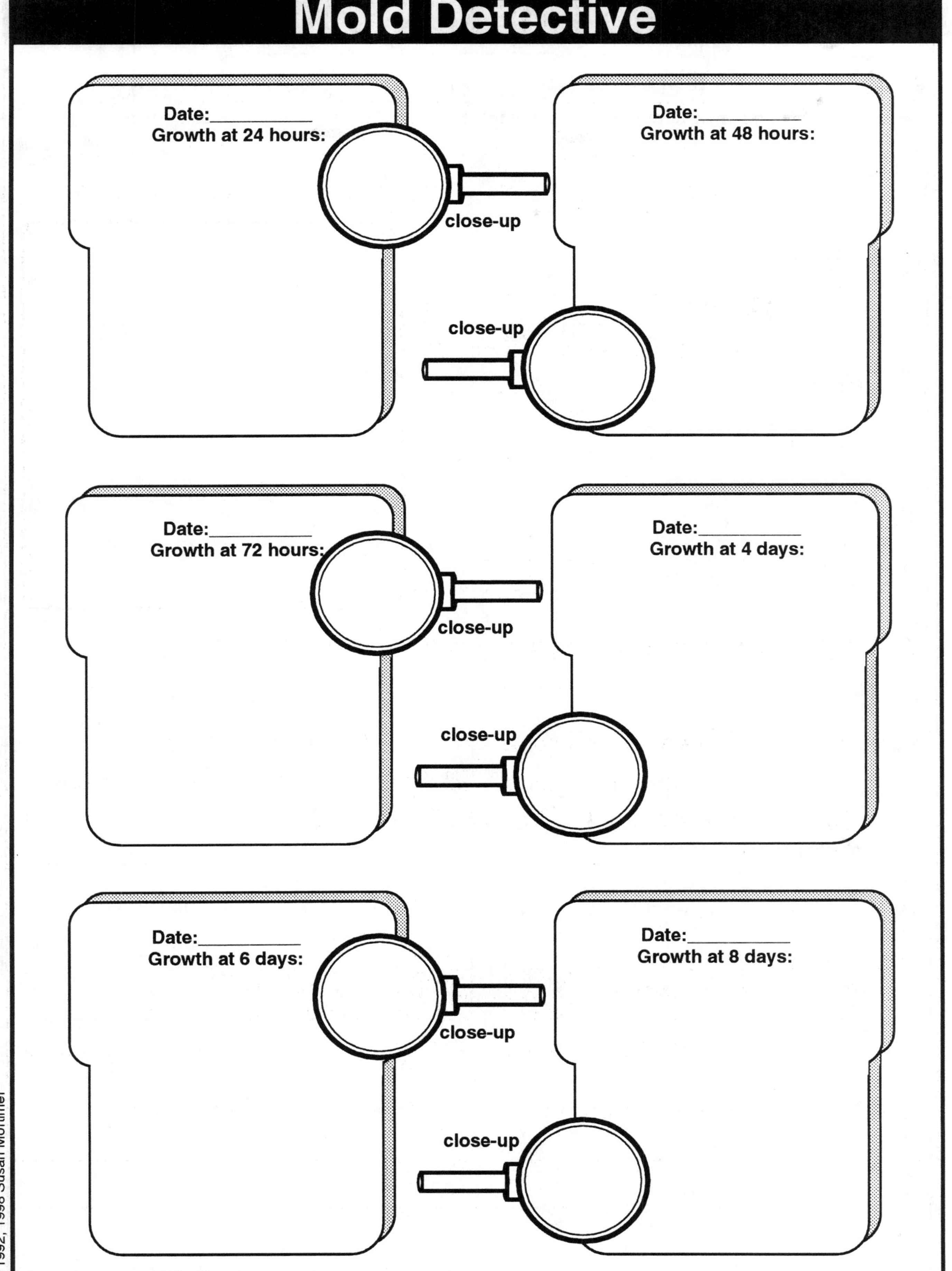
Date:__________
Growth at 24 hours:
close-up
Date:__________
Growth at 48 hours:
close-up
Date:__________
Growth at 72 hours:
close-up
Date:__________
Growth at 4 days:
close-up
Date:__________
Growth at 6 days:
close-up
Date:__________
Growth at 8 days:
close-up

Place a slice of bread in a container with moldy bread. Observe at intervals and record the growth in the rectangle. In the circles, draw what you see with a magnifying glass.

Sketch of a Tree

Name of Specimen ____________

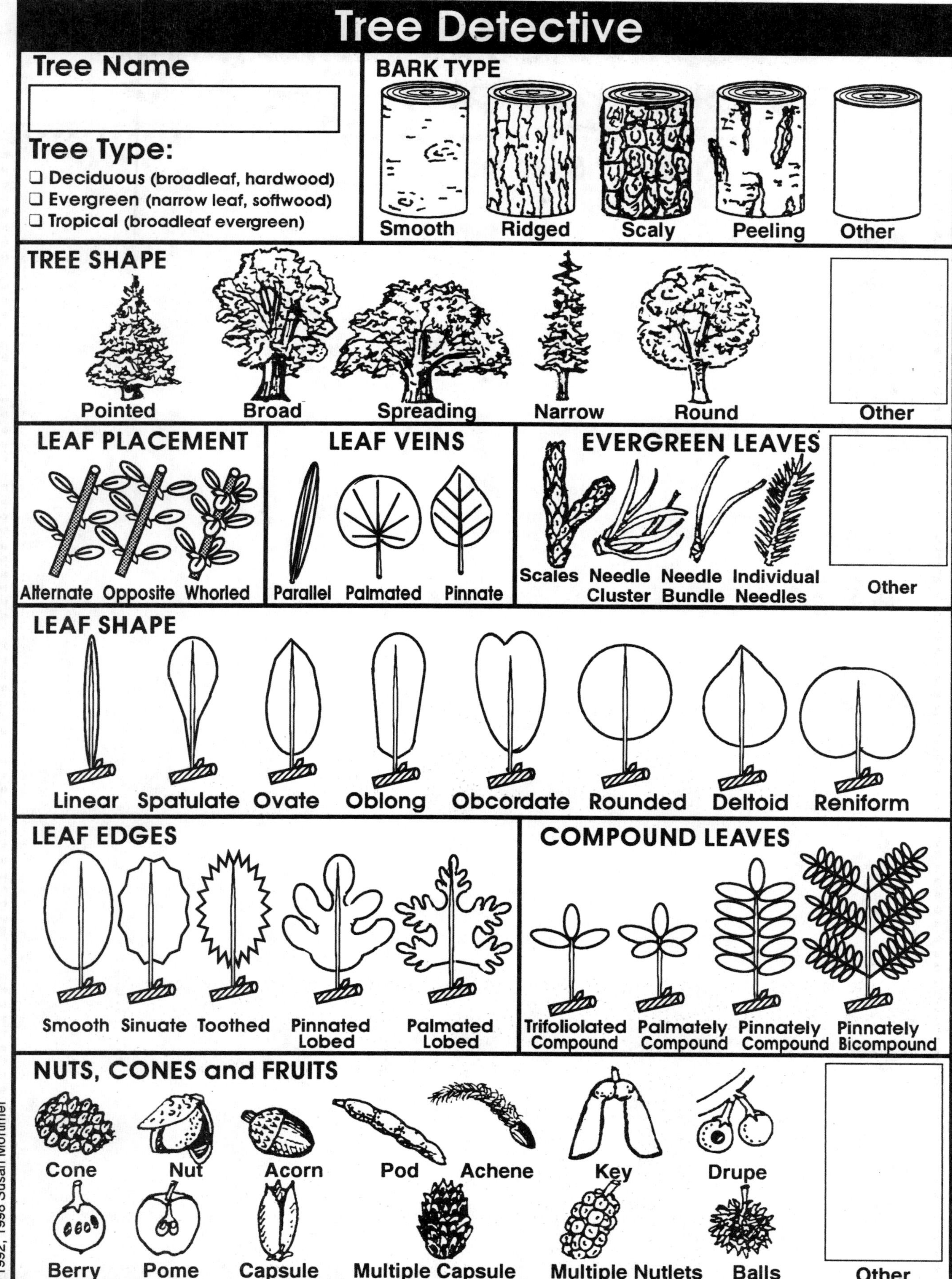
Tree Detective
Tree Name
Tree Type:
❑ Deciduous (broadleaf, hardwood)
❑ Evergreen (narrow leaf, softwood)
❑ Tropical (broadleaf evergreen)
BARK TYPE
Smooth
Ridged
Scaly
Peeling
Other
TREE SHAPE
Pointed
Broad
Spreading
Narrow
Round
Other
LEAF PLACEMENT
Alternate
Opposite
Whorled
LEAF VEINS
Parallel
Palmated
Pinnate
EVERGREEN LEAVES
Scales
Needle Cluster
Needle Bundle
Individual Needles
Other
LEAF SHAPE
Linear
Spatulate
Ovate
Oblong
Obcordate
Rounded
Deltoid
Reniform
LEAF EDGES
Smooth
Sinuate
Toothed
Pinnated Lobed
Palmated Lobed
COMPOUND LEAVES
Trifoliolated Compound
Palmately Compound
Pinnately Compound
Pinnately Bicompound
NUTS, CONES and FRUITS
Cone
Nut
Acorn
Pod
Achene
Key
Drupe
Berry
Pome
Capsule
Multiple Capsule
Multiple Nutlets
Balls
Other
© 1992, 1998 Susan Mortimer

Choose a tree and analyze its leaves, shape, trunk and structure. Color the closest match in each category. Draw or place pressed leaves on preceding page. Do not pick leaves from state or national parks.

Sketch of a Tree

Name of Specimen ______________

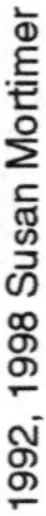

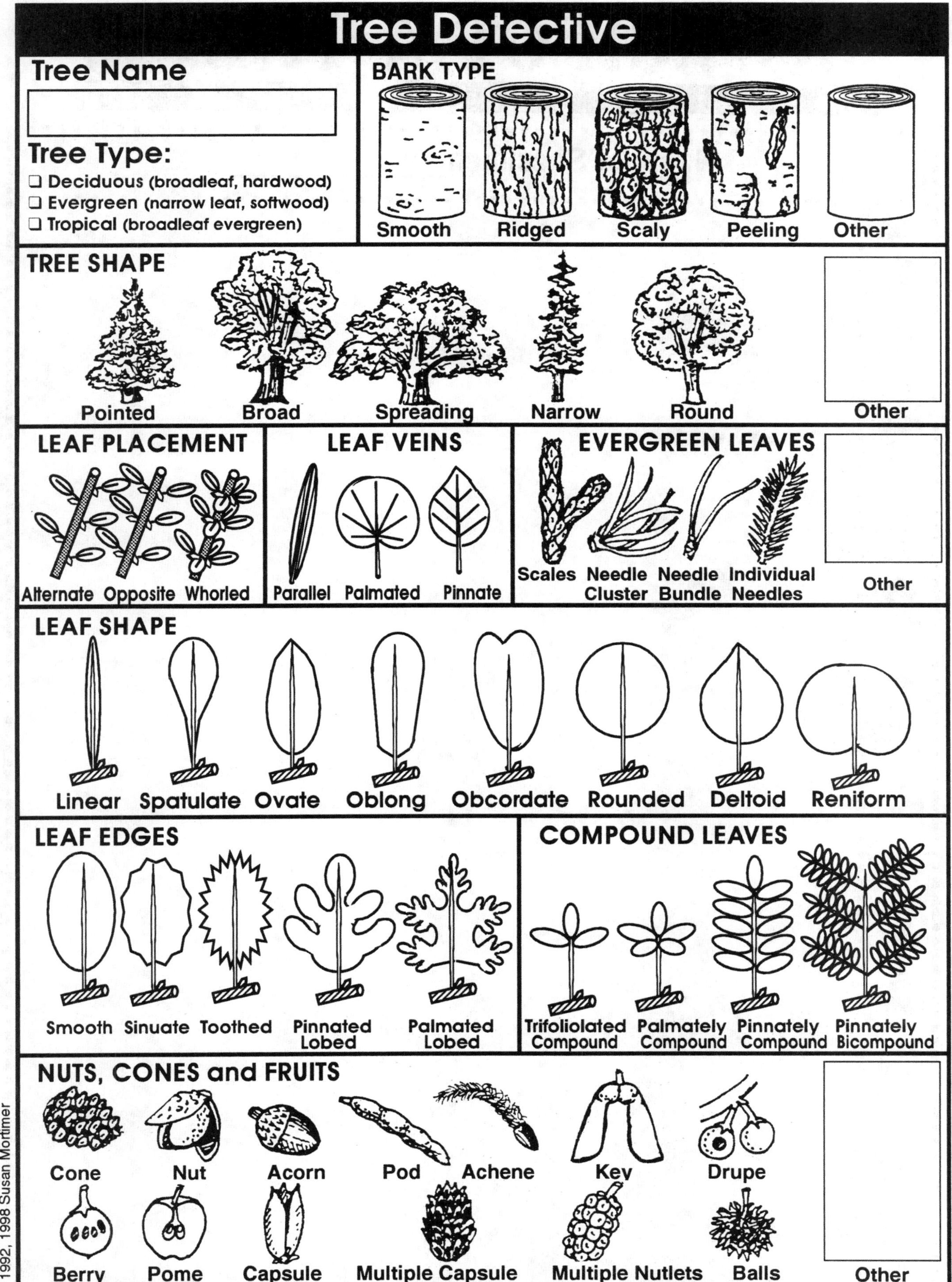
Tree Detective
Tree Name
Tree Type:
❑ Deciduous (broadleaf, hardwood)
❑ Evergreen (narrow leaf, softwood)
❑ Tropical (broadleaf evergreen)
BARK TYPE
Smooth
Ridged
Scaly
Peeling
Other
TREE SHAPE
Pointed
Broad
Spreading
Narrow
Round
Other
LEAF PLACEMENT
Alternate
Opposite
Whorled
LEAF VEINS
Parallel
Palmated
Pinnate
EVERGREEN LEAVES
Scales
Needle Cluster
Needle Bundle
Individual Needles
Other
LEAF SHAPE
Linear
Spatulate
Ovate
Oblong
Obcordate
Rounded
Deltoid
Reniform
LEAF EDGES
Smooth
Sinuate
Toothed
Pinnated Lobed
Palmated Lobed
COMPOUND LEAVES
Trifoliolated Compound
Palmately Compound
Pinnately Compound
Pinnately Bicompound
NUTS, CONES and FRUITS
Cone
Nut
Acorn
Pod
Achene
Key
Drupe
Berry
Pome
Capsule
Multiple Capsule
Multiple Nutlets
Balls
Other

Choose a tree and analyze its leaves, shape, trunk and structure. Color the closest match in each category. Draw or place pressed leaves on preceding page. Do not pick leaves from state or national parks.

SKETCH OF A TREE

Name of Specimen______________

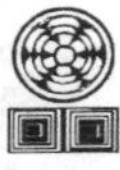

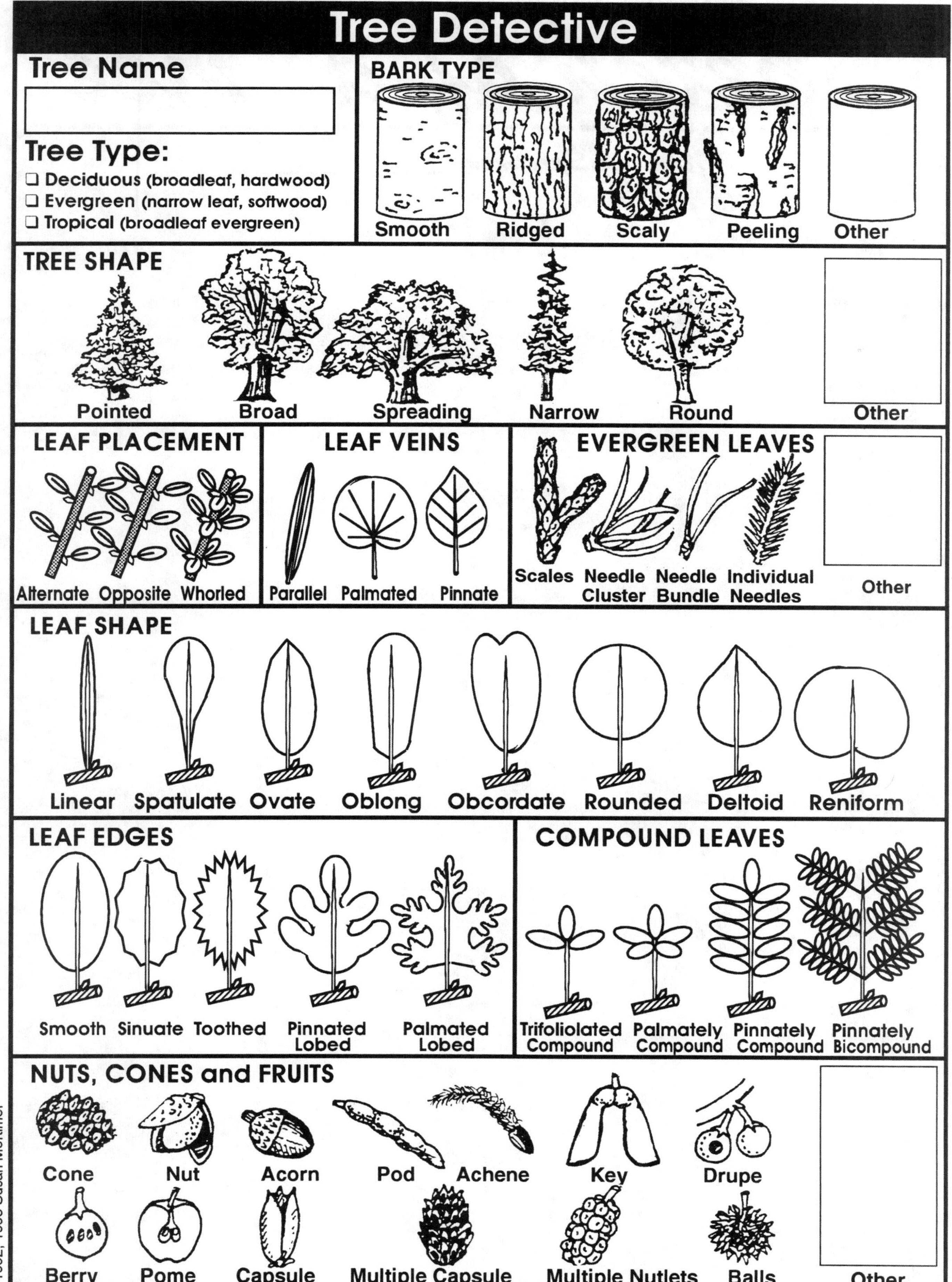
Tree Detective
Tree Name
Tree Type:
❑ Deciduous (broadleaf, hardwood)
❑ Evergreen (narrow leaf, softwood)
❑ Tropical (broadleaf evergreen)
BARK TYPE
Smooth
Ridged
Scaly
Peeling
Other
TREE SHAPE
Pointed
Broad
Spreading
Narrow
Round
Other
LEAF PLACEMENT
Alternate
Opposite
Whorled
LEAF VEINS
Parallel
Palmated
Pinnate
EVERGREEN LEAVES
Scales
Needle Cluster
Needle Bundle
Individual Needles
Other
LEAF SHAPE
Linear
Spatulate
Ovate
Oblong
Obcordate
Rounded
Deltoid
Reniform
LEAF EDGES
Smooth
Sinuate
Toothed
Pinnated Lobed
Palmated Lobed
COMPOUND LEAVES
Trifoliolated Compound
Palmately Compound
Pinnately Compound
Pinnately Bicompound
NUTS, CONES and FRUITS
Cone
Nut
Acorn
Pod
Achene
Key
Drupe
Berry
Pome
Capsule
Multiple Capsule
Multiple Nutlets
Balls
Other

Choose a tree and analyze its leaves, shape, trunk and structure. Color the closest match in each category. Draw or place pressed leaves on preceding page. Do not pick leaves from state or national parks.

Sketch of a Tree

*Name of Specimen*________________

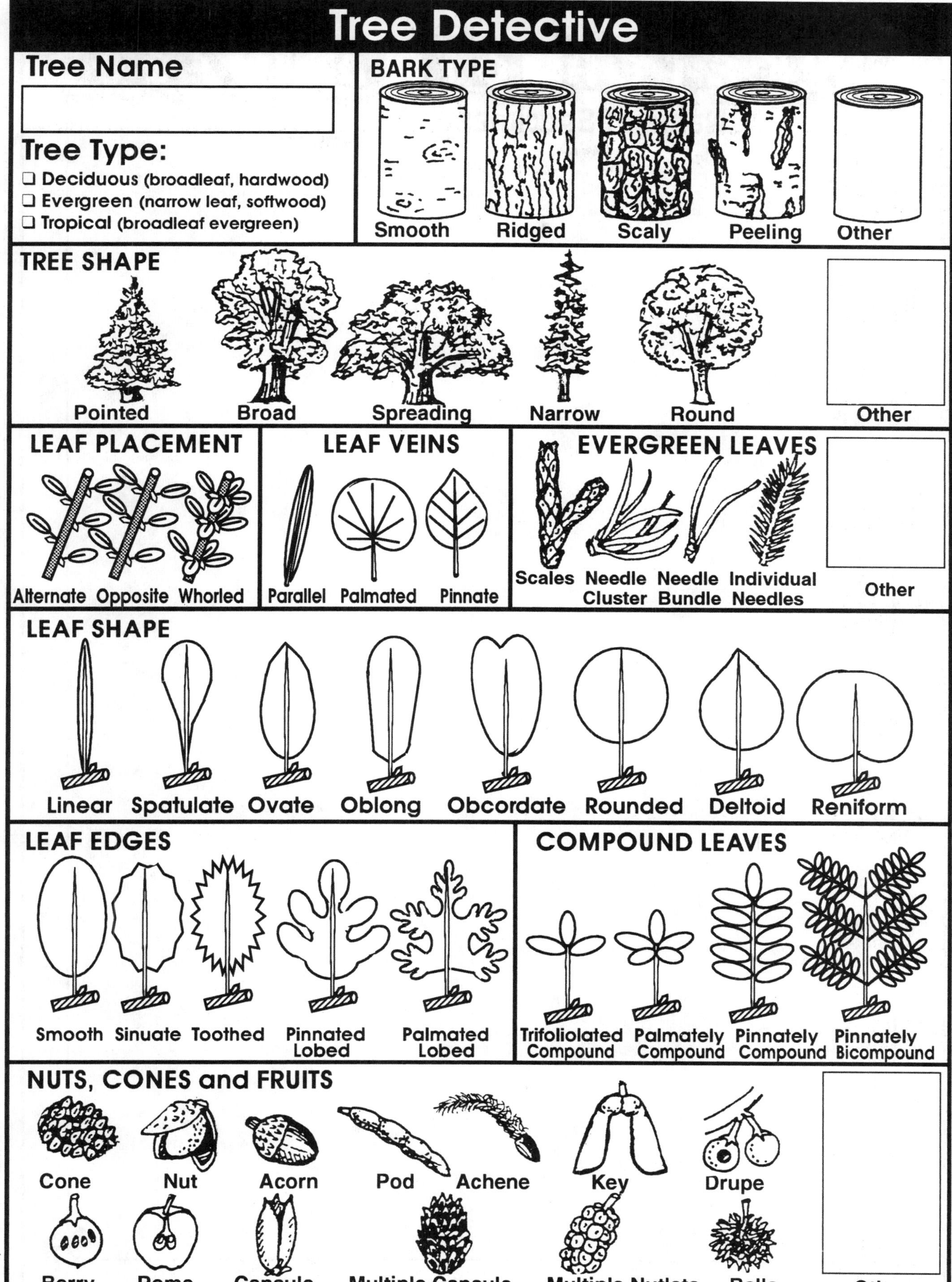
Tree Detective
Tree Name
Tree Type:
❑ Deciduous (broadleaf, hardwood)
❑ Evergreen (narrow leaf, softwood)
❑ Tropical (broadleaf evergreen)
BARK TYPE
Smooth
Ridged
Scaly
Peeling
Other
TREE SHAPE
Pointed
Broad
Spreading
Narrow
Round
Other
LEAF PLACEMENT
Alternate
Opposite
Whorled
LEAF VEINS
Parallel
Palmated
Pinnate
EVERGREEN LEAVES
Scales
Needle Cluster
Needle Bundle
Individual Needles
Other
LEAF SHAPE
Linear
Spatulate
Ovate
Oblong
Obcordate
Rounded
Deltoid
Reniform
LEAF EDGES
Smooth
Sinuate
Toothed
Pinnated Lobed
Palmated Lobed
COMPOUND LEAVES
Trifoliolated Compound
Palmately Compound
Pinnately Compound
Pinnately Bicompound
NUTS, CONES and FRUITS
Cone
Nut
Acorn
Pod
Achene
Key
Drupe
Berry
Pome
Capsule
Multiple Capsule
Multiple Nutlets
Balls
Other

Choose a tree and analyze its leaves, shape, trunk and structure. Color the closest match in each category. Draw or place pressed leaves on preceding page. Do not pick leaves from state or national parks.

Sketch of a Tree

Name of Specimen____________

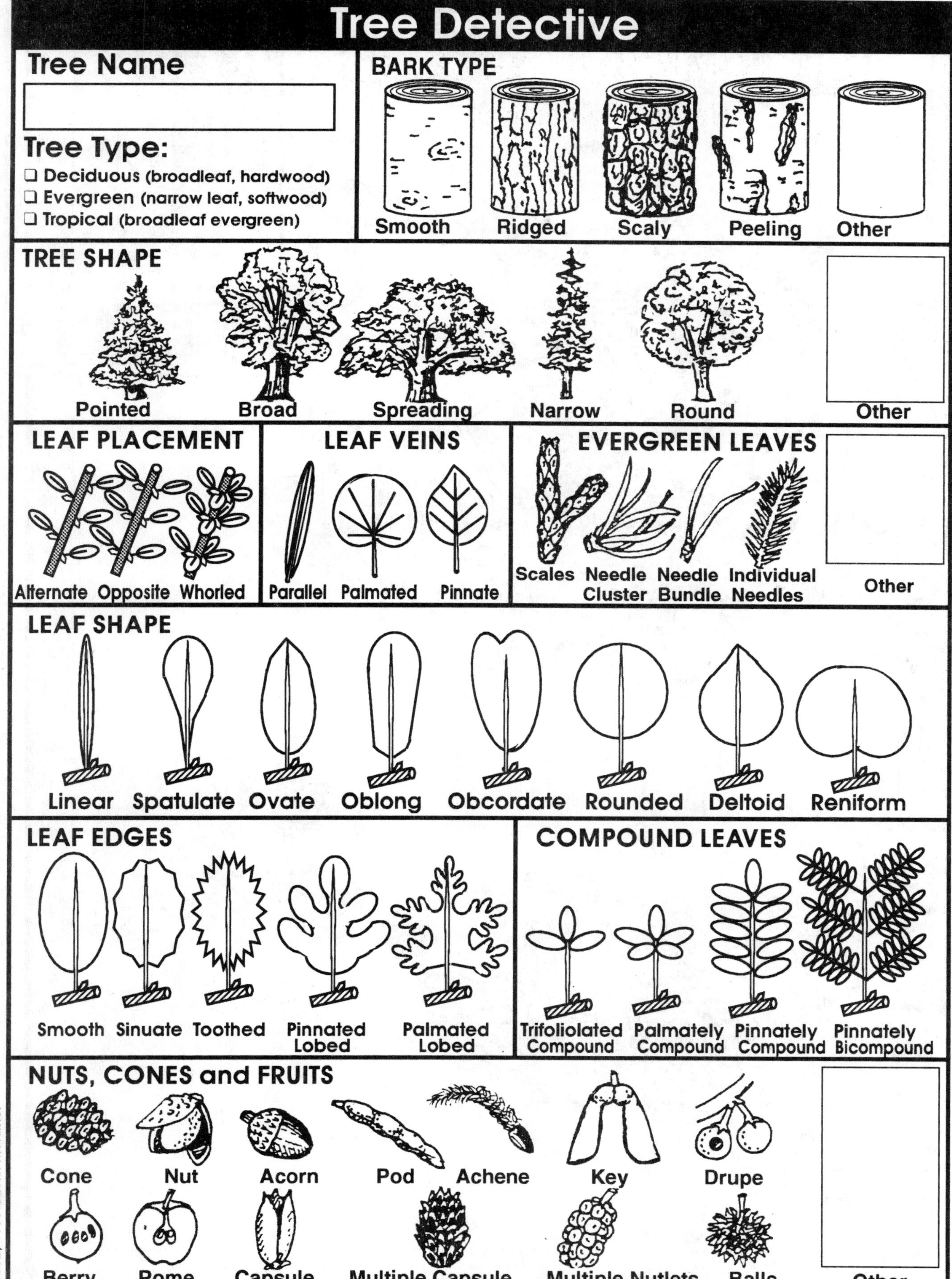
Tree Detective
Tree Name
Tree Type:
❑ Deciduous (broadleaf, hardwood)
❑ Evergreen (narrow leaf, softwood)
❑ Tropical (broadleaf evergreen)
BARK TYPE
Smooth
Ridged
Scaly
Peeling
Other
TREE SHAPE
Pointed
Broad
Spreading
Narrow
Round
Other
LEAF PLACEMENT
Alternate
Opposite
Whorled
LEAF VEINS
Parallel
Palmated
Pinnate
EVERGREEN LEAVES
Scales
Needle Cluster
Needle Bundle
Individual Needles
Other
LEAF SHAPE
Linear
Spatulate
Ovate
Oblong
Obcordate
Rounded
Deltoid
Reniform
LEAF EDGES
Smooth
Sinuate
Toothed
Pinnated Lobed
Palmated Lobed
COMPOUND LEAVES
Trifoliolated Compound
Palmately Compound
Pinnately Compound
Pinnately Bicompound
NUTS, CONES and FRUITS
Cone
Nut
Acorn
Pod
Achene
Key
Drupe
Berry
Pome
Capsule
Multiple Capsule
Multiple Nutlets
Balls
Other
© 1992, 1998 Susan Mortimer

Choose a tree and analyze its leaves, shape, trunk and structure. Color the closest match in each category. Draw or place pressed leaves on preceding page. Do not pick leaves from state or national parks.

Plant Life on our Planet

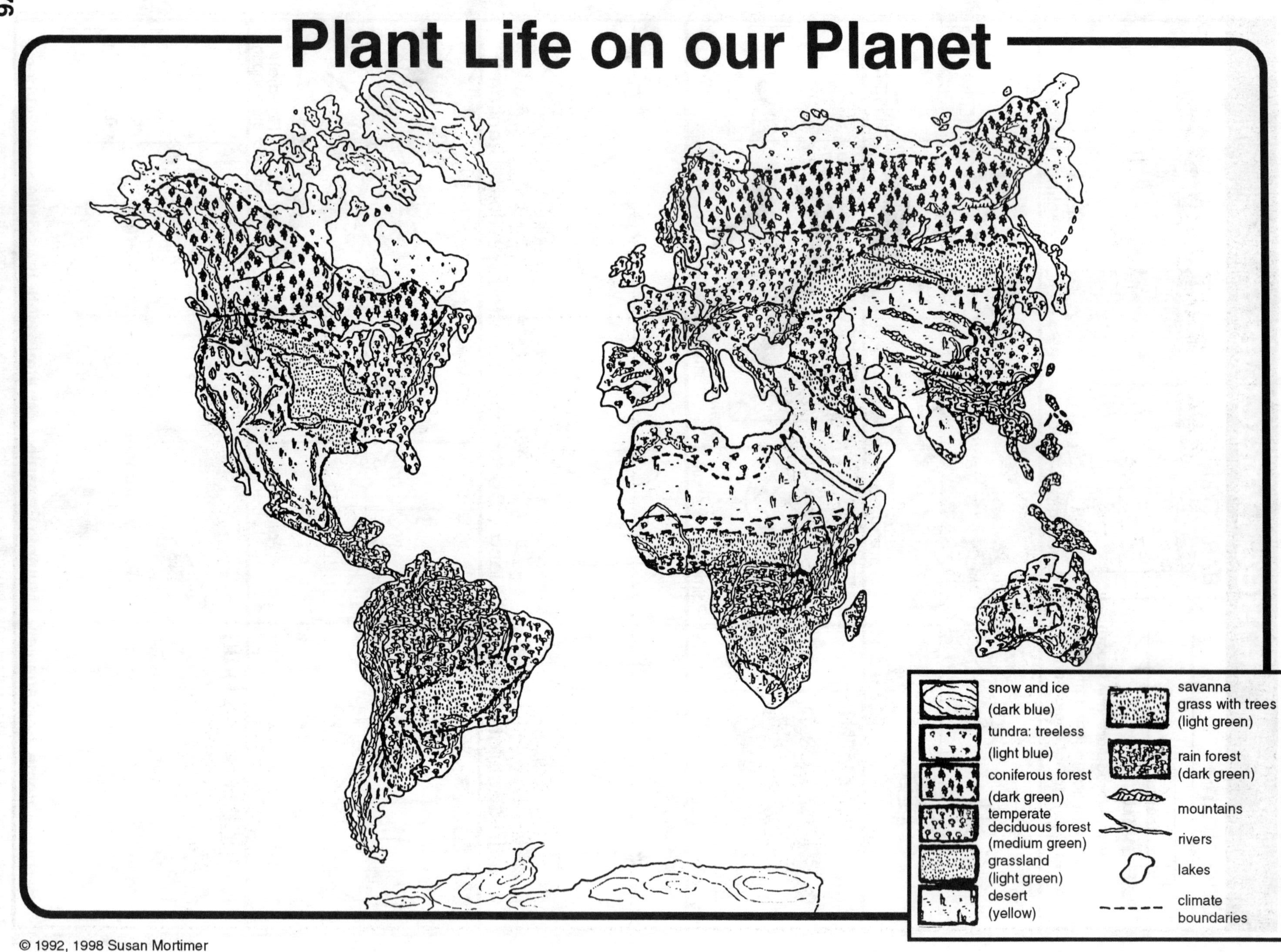
snow and ice
(dark blue)
tundra: treeless
(light blue)
coniferous forest
(dark green)
temperate
deciduous forest
(medium green)
grassland
(light green)
desert
(yellow)
savanna
grass with trees
(light green)
rain forest
(dark green)
mountains
rivers
lakes
climate
boundaries

Making Sense of Insects

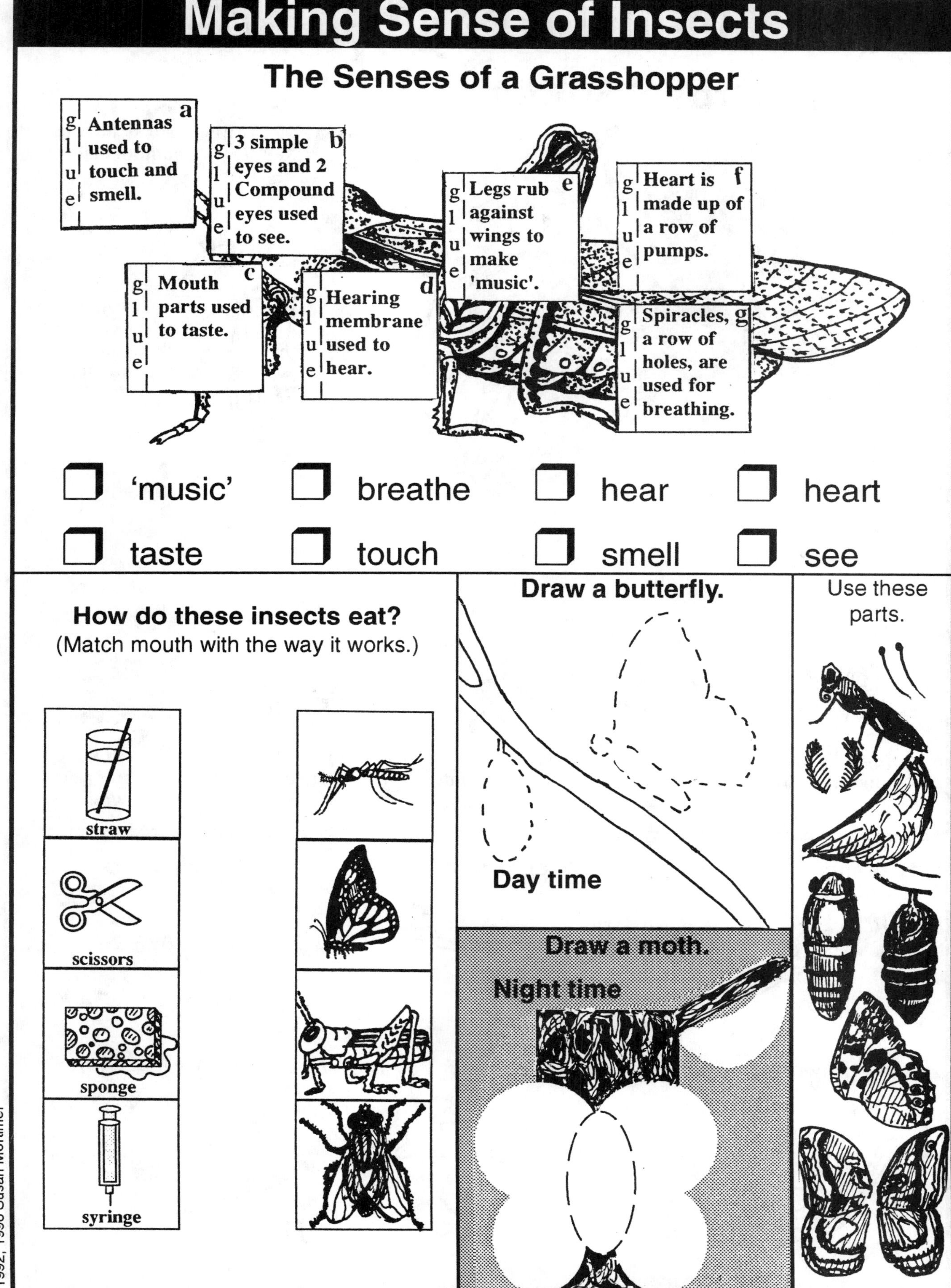
The Senses of a Grasshopper
glue Antennas used to touch and smell. a
glue 3 simple eyes and 2 Compound eyes used to see. b
glue Mouth parts used to taste. c
glue Hearing membrane used to hear. d
glue Legs rub against wings to make 'music'. e
glue Heart is made up of a row of pumps. f
glue Spiracles, a row of holes, are used for breathing. g
❐ 'music' ❐ breathe ❐ hear ❐ heart
❐ taste ❐ touch ❐ smell ❐ see
How do these insects eat?
(Match mouth with the way it works.)
straw
scissors
sponge
syringe
Draw a butterfly.
Day time
Draw a moth.
Night time
Use these parts.

Cut and glue puzzle pieces from "Making Sense of Insects" (page 2) on the top of this page. Then write the letter in the box that applies to each of the senses listed.

Caught in a Spider's Web

Garden Cross Spider

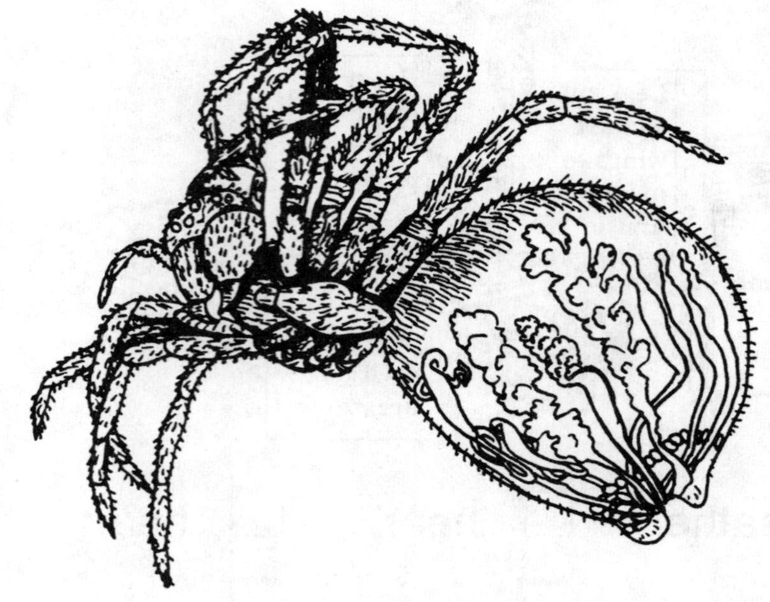

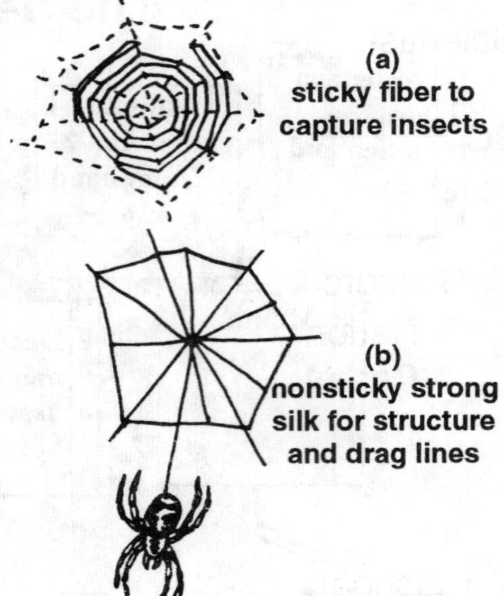

(a)
sticky fiber to capture insects

(b)
nonsticky strong silk for structure and drag lines

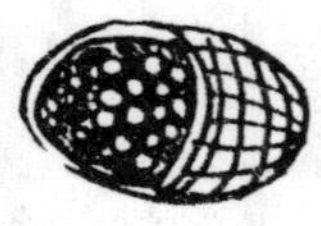

(c)
soft silk to line egg sac

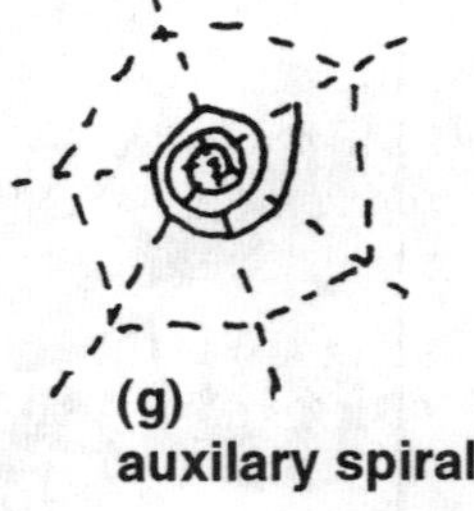

(g)
auxilary spiral

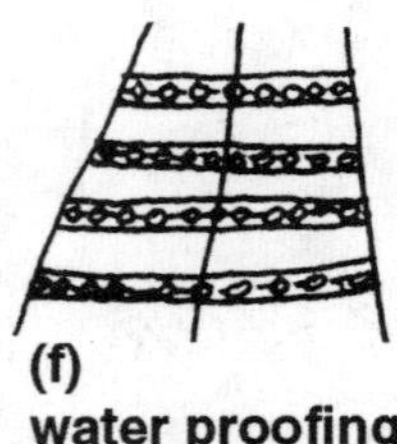

(f)
water proofing

(e)
cement joints

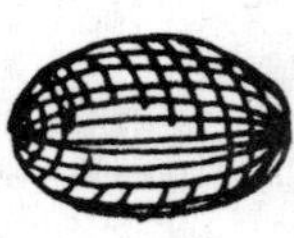

(d)
tough outer silk for egg sac

(c)
soft silk to wrap prey

---

1) orange—a

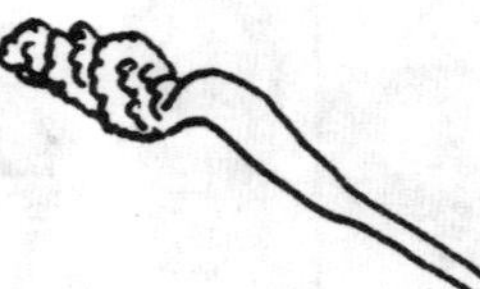

2) purple—b

3) yellow—c

4) brown—d

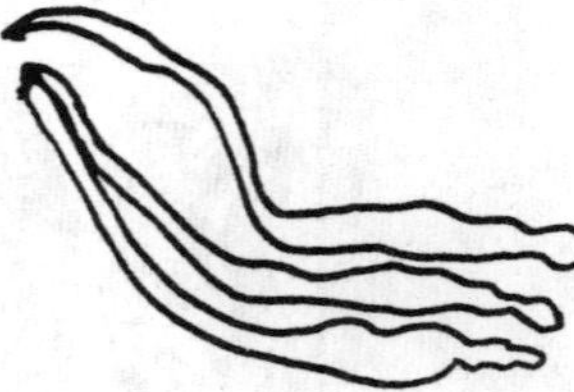

5) green—e

6) red—f

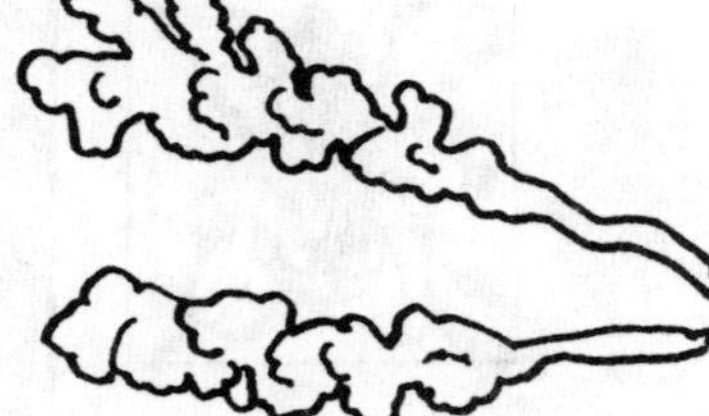

7) blue—g

Locate the glands pictured under number (1) on the spider. Draw an orange 'thread' from the spider's rear to the object marked (a) to see what the thread is used for. Do the same with each of the rest.

Scientist Detective

Scientist: ______________________ Born: _______ Died: _______

BC —|—|—|—|—|—|—|—|—|—|—|—|— AD

200 0 200 400 600 800 1000 1200 1400 1600 1800 2000

Background:

Nationality: ______________________

Parents: ______________________

Influence was: ❑ helpful ❑ injuring

Example: ______________________

Portrait

Schooling: ______________________

Family:

Spouse: ______________________

Number of children: ______________________

Turning point experience that got him/her into field of work:

____

Religion: ❑ There is a personal God. ❑ There is no God.

❑ There are many gods. ❑ Science is 'god'. ❑ Man is 'god'.

Did religion affect work: ❑ a lot? ❑ a little? ❑ none at all?

Example: ______________________

Field of contribution:

astronomy botany zoology psychology geology medicine physics ______

Major contributions: ❑ Invention ❑ Theory ❑ Discovery

Best known for: ______________________

Far-reaching results: ______________________

Word Search—FISH

Circle the words that describe a fish

a w b l a k e a w l y f l y
i o v o v i v i p a r o u s
r a s c a l e s l d f s s e
b c c u f l o a t h i n w a
l i h s b a c k b o n e i w
a l o g m a e r t b s k m e
d f o c r o a a h t r e d e
d w l e a t n e r y e g d d
e y s c o l d b l o o d e d
r i x s e g i l l s n t t x
y j e l l y l i k e e g g s
n l a t e r a l l i n e s o

Word Bank

(Cross out each word as you find it above.)

ovoviviparous	backbone	cold-blooded	gills	air bladder
jellylike eggs	fins	scales	float	swim
ocean	lake	lateral lines	schools	sea weed

Animal Detective

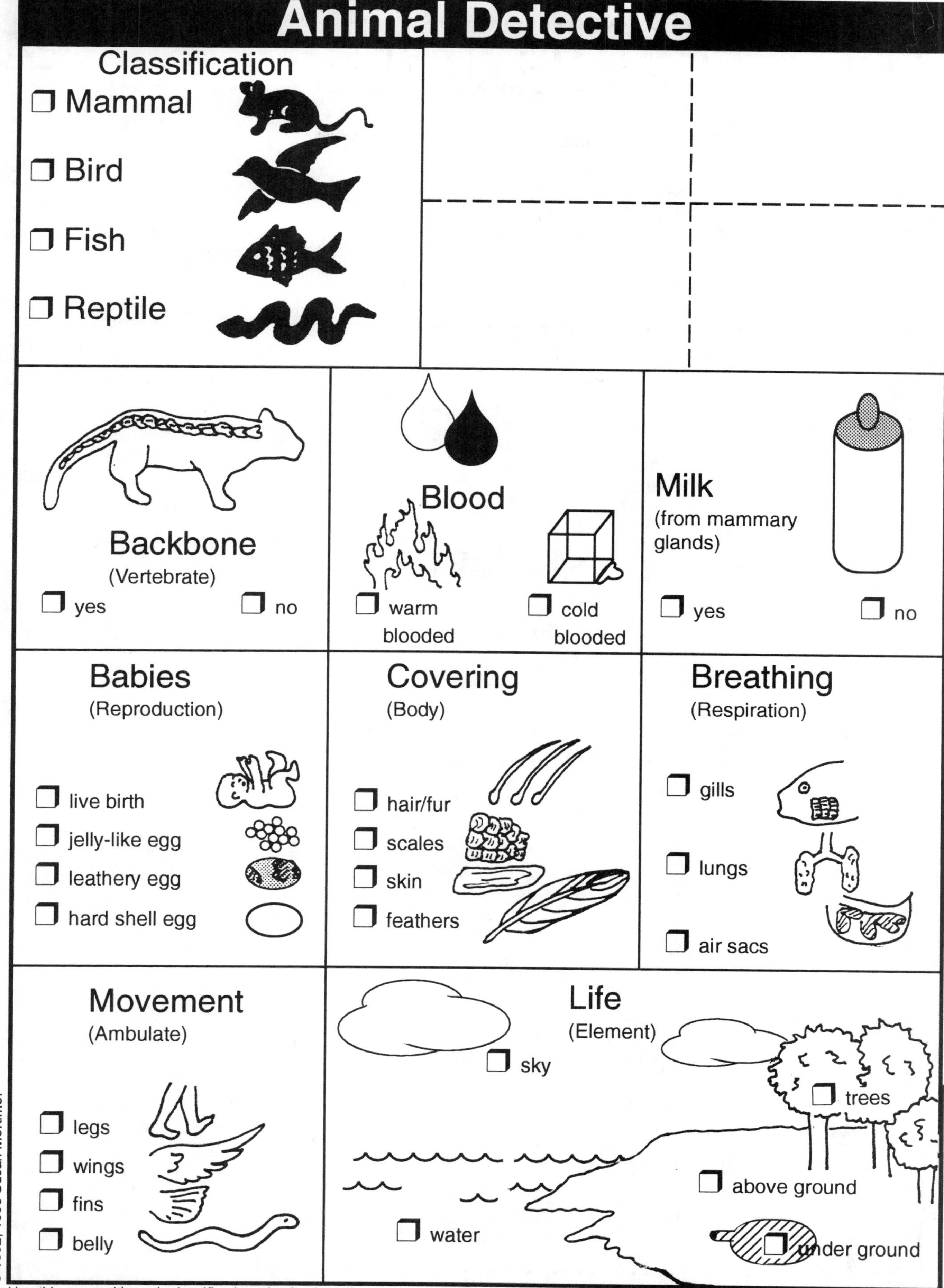

Classification
Mammal
Bird
Fish
Reptile
Backbone
(Vertebrate)
yes
no
Blood
warm blooded
cold blooded
Milk
(from mammary glands)
yes
no
Babies
(Reproduction)
live birth
jelly-like egg
leathery egg
hard shell egg
Covering
(Body)
hair/fur
scales
skin
feathers
Breathing
(Respiration)
gills
lungs
air sacs
Movement
(Ambulate)
legs
wings
fins
belly
Life
(Element)
sky
trees
above ground
water
under ground

Use this page with each classification of animal studied. Check the appropriate squares for each category. From "Animal Detective" (page 2) cut and glue the related animals in the top right hand boxes.

My Animal Cards

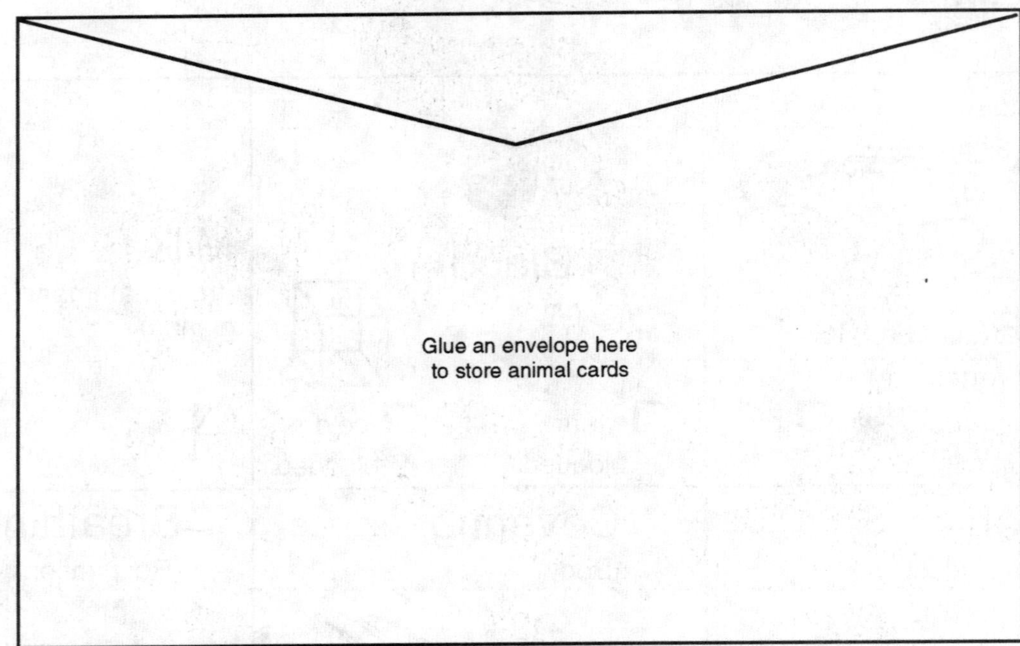
Glue an envelope here
to store animal cards

Representing Reptiles (page 2)

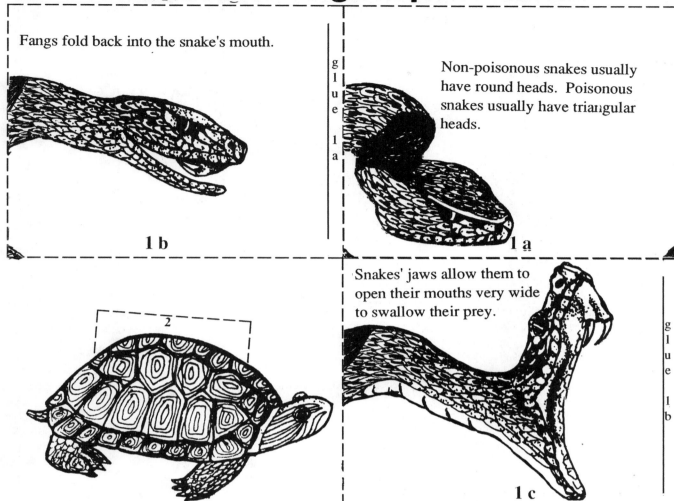

Fangs fold back into the snake's mouth.

glue 1a

1 b

Non-poisonous snakes usually have round heads. Poisonous snakes usually have triangular heads.

1 a

Snakes' jaws allow them to open their mouths very wide to swallow their prey.

glue 1b

1 c

2

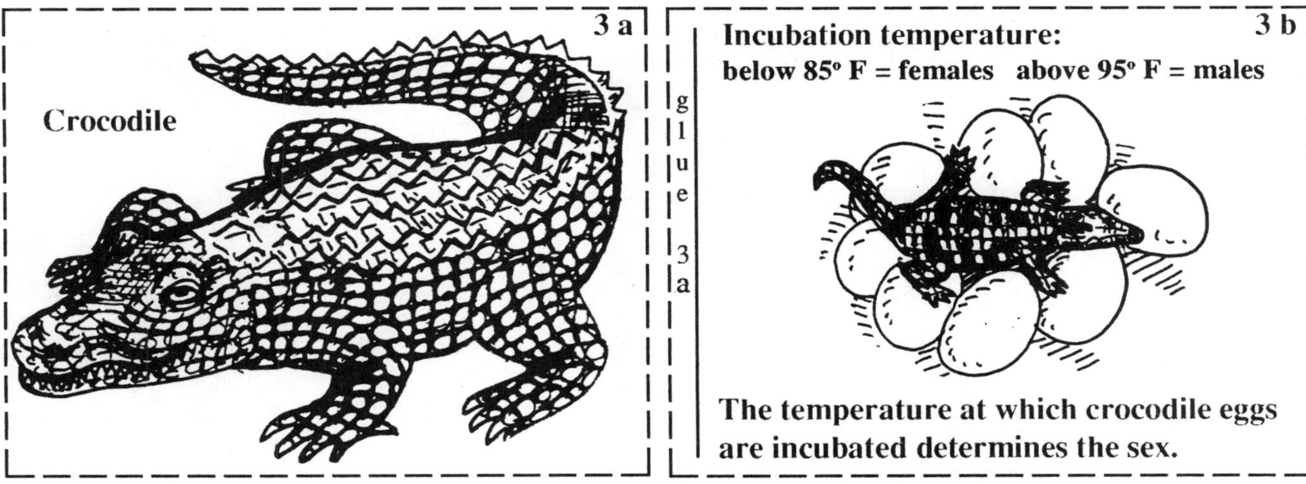
3 a
Crocodile
glue 3a
3 b
Incubation temperature:
below 85° F = females above 95° F = males
The temperature at which crocodile eggs are incubated determines the sex.

Scientist Detective

Scientist: ______________________ Born: _______ Died: _______

BC ―+―+―+―+―+―+―+―+―+―+―+―+― AD

200 0 200 400 600 800 1000 1200 1400 1600 1800 2000

Background:

Nationality: ______________________

Parents: ______________________

Influence was: ❐ helpful ❐ injuring

Example: ______________________

Portrait

Schooling: ______________________

Family:

Spouse: ______________________

Number of children: ______________________

Turning point experience that got him/her into field of work:

____

Religion: ❐ There is a personal God. ❐ There is no God.

❐ There are many gods. ❐ Science is 'god'. ❐ Man is 'god'.

Did religion affect work: ❐ a lot? ❐ a little? ❐ none at all?

Example: ______________________

Field of contribution:

astronomy | botany | zoology | psychology | geology | medicine | physics | __________

Major contributions: ❐ Invention ❐ Theory ❐ Discovery

Best known for: ______________________

Far-reaching results: ______________________

Word Search—BIRDS

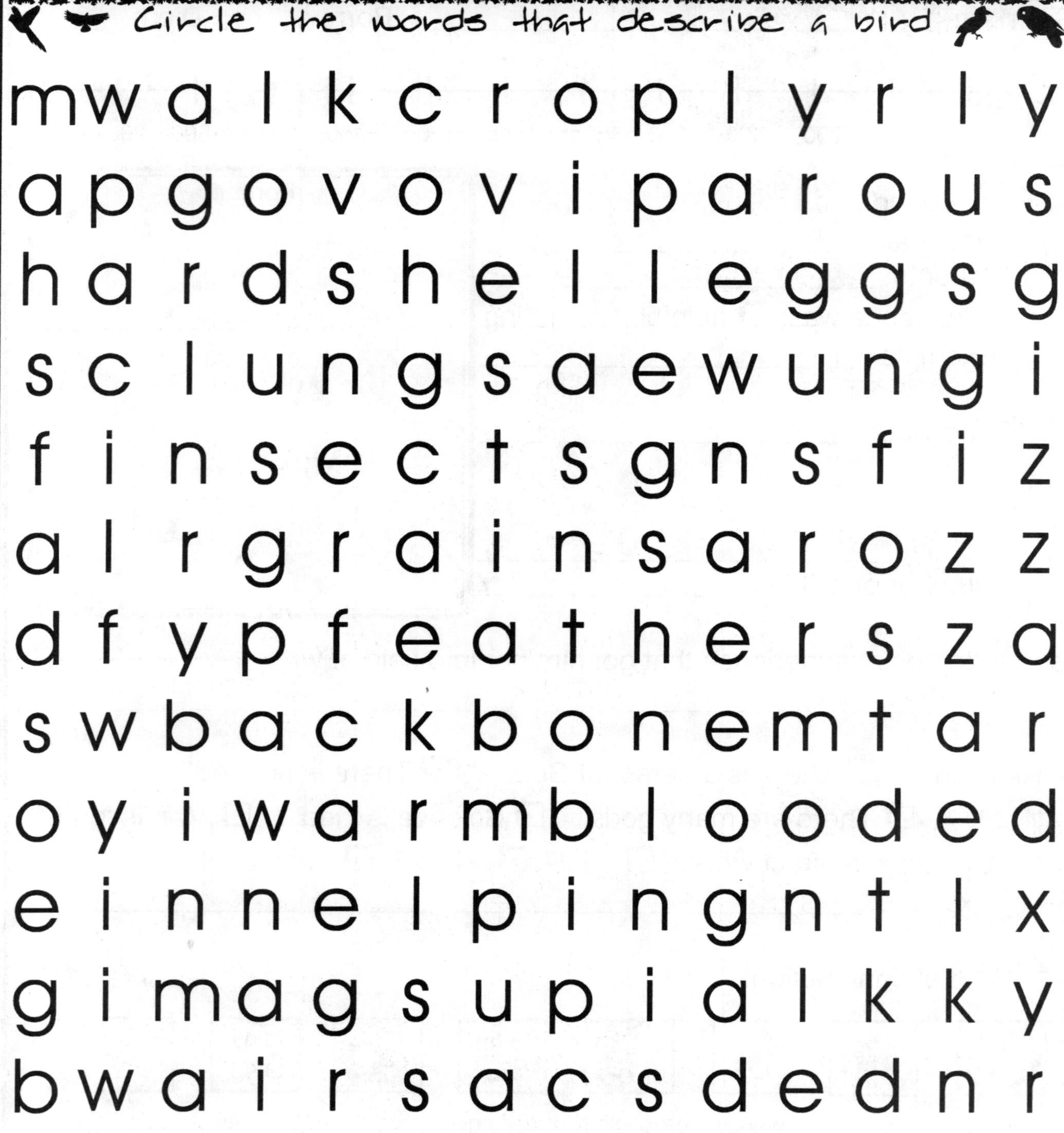

Circle the words that describe a bird
m w a l k c r o p l y r l y
a p g o v o v i p a r o u s
h a r d s h e l l e g g s g
s c l u n g s a e w u n g i
f i n s e c t s g n s f i z
a l r g r a i n s a r o z z
d f y p f e a t h e r s z a
s w b a c k b o n e m t a r
o y i w a r m b l o o d e d
e i n n e l p i n g n t l x
g i m a g s u p i a l k k y
b w a i r s a c s d e d n r

Word Bank

(Cross out each word as you find it above.)

oviparous	backbone	lungs	legs	wings
insects	warmblooded	feathers	walk	fly
air sacs	hard-shell eggs	crop	grains	gizzard

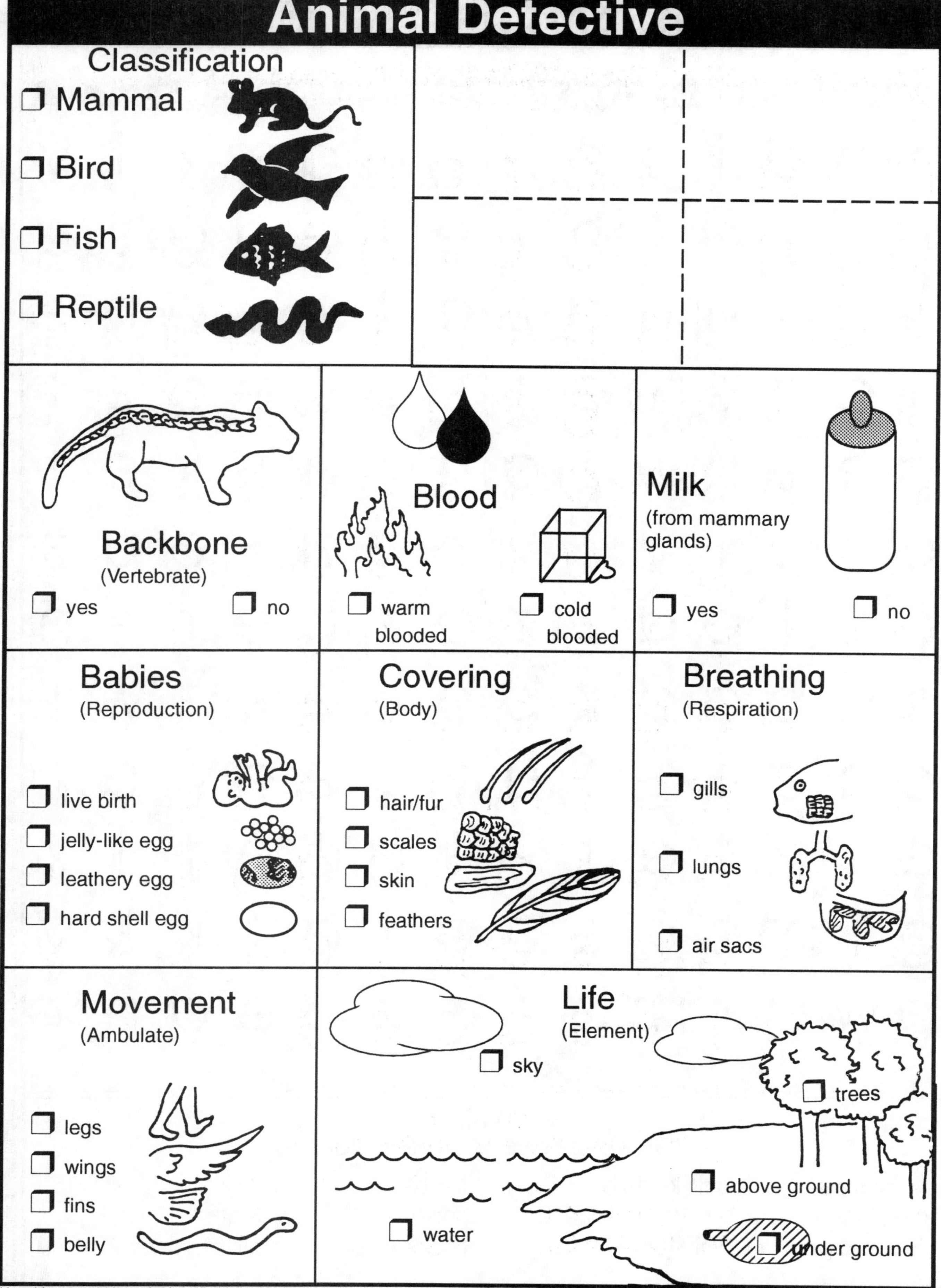
Animal Detective
Classification
❒ Mammal
❒ Bird
❒ Fish
❒ Reptile
Backbone
(Vertebrate)
❒ yes
❒ no
Blood
❒ warm blooded
❒ cold blooded
Milk
(from mammary glands)
❒ yes
❒ no
Babies
(Reproduction)
❒ live birth
❒ jelly-like egg
❒ leathery egg
❒ hard shell egg
Covering
(Body)
❒ hair/fur
❒ scales
❒ skin
❒ feathers
Breathing
(Respiration)
❒ gills
❒ lungs
❒ air sacs
Movement
(Ambulate)
❒ legs
❒ wings
❒ fins
❒ belly
Life
(Element)
❒ sky
❒ trees
❒ above ground
❒ water
❒ under ground

Use this page with each classification of animal studied. Check the appropriate squares for each category. From "Animal Detective" (page 2) cut and glue the related animals in the top right hand boxes.

Word Search—MAMMALS

Circle the words that describe a mammal

m	p	d	i	a	p	h	r	a	g	m	r	l	y
h	l	r	d	f	h	i	e	t	e	d	g	s	u
s	a	l	u	n	g	s	a	l	w	i	b	h	s
h	c	n	s	m	c	t	s	x	l	e	g	s	l
g	e	e	n	w	m	a	h	i	n	s	k	e	l
a	n	g	i	v	i	v	i	p	a	r	o	u	s
d	t	l	p	d	l	t	a	t	h	e	r	s	n
s	a	b	a	c	k	b	o	n	e	s	t	w	j
o	h	a	i	r	f	u	r	l	e	d	n	a	r
e	i	n	t	e	l	l	i	g	e	n	t	l	x
g	i	m	a	r	s	u	p	i	a	l	k	k	y
b	w	a	r	m	b	l	o	o	d	e	d	n	r

Word Bank

(Cross out each word as you find it above.)

viviparous	backbone	lungs	legs
intelligent	warm-blooded	milk	walk
diaphragm	hair/fur	marsupial	placenta

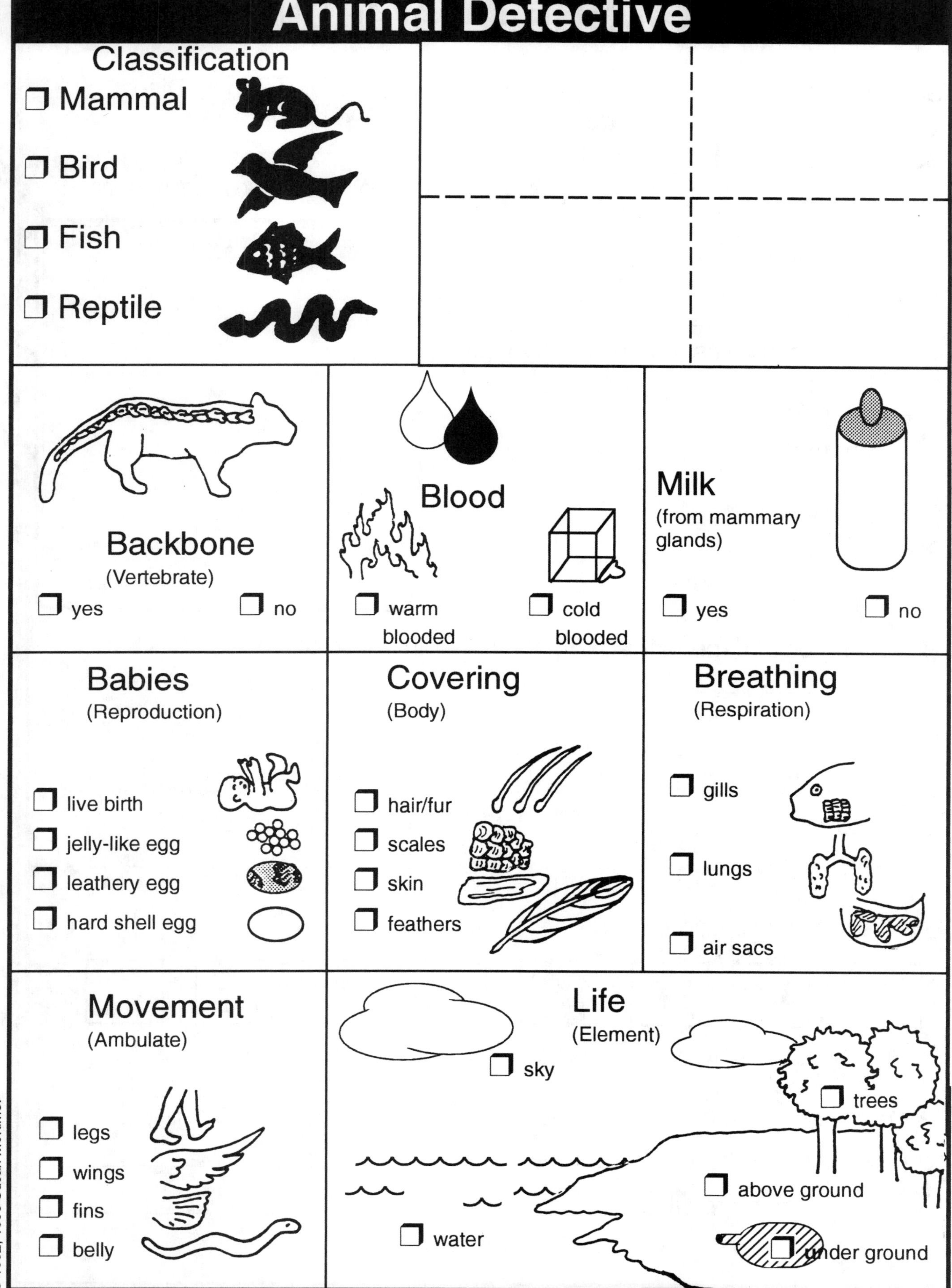
Animal Detective
Classification
❒ Mammal
❒ Bird
❒ Fish
❒ Reptile
Backbone
(Vertebrate)
❒ yes
❒ no
Blood
❒ warm blooded
❒ cold blooded
Milk
(from mammary glands)
❒ yes
❒ no
Babies
(Reproduction)
❒ live birth
❒ jelly-like egg
❒ leathery egg
❒ hard shell egg
Covering
(Body)
❒ hair/fur
❒ scales
❒ skin
❒ feathers
Breathing
(Respiration)
❒ gills
❒ lungs
❒ air sacs
Movement
(Ambulate)
❒ legs
❒ wings
❒ fins
❒ belly
Life
(Element)
❒ sky
❒ trees
❒ above ground
❒ water
❒ under ground

Use this page with each classification of animal studied. Check the appropriate squares for each category. From "Animal Detective" (page 2) cut and glue the related animals in the top right hand boxes.

Scientist Detective

Scientist: ______________________________ Born: ______ Died: ______

BC —|—|—|—|—|—|—|—|—|—|—|—|— AD

200 0 200 400 600 800 1000 1200 1400 1600 1800 2000

Portrait

Background:

Nationality: ______________________

Parents: ______________________

Influence was: ❐ helpful ❐ injuring

Example: ______________________

Schooling: ______________________

Family:

Spouse: ______________________

Number of children: ______________

Turning point experience that got him/her into field of work:

____

Religion: ❐ There is a personal God. ❐ There is no God.

❐ There are many gods. ❐ Science is 'god'. ❐ Man is 'god'.

Did religion affect work: ❐ a lot? ❐ a little? ❐ none at all?

Example: ______________________________________

Field of contribution:

astronomy botany zoology psychology geology medicine physics ______

Major contributions: ❐ Invention ❐ Theory ❐ Discovery

Best known for: ______________________________________

Far-reaching results: ______________________________________

My Zoo Adventure

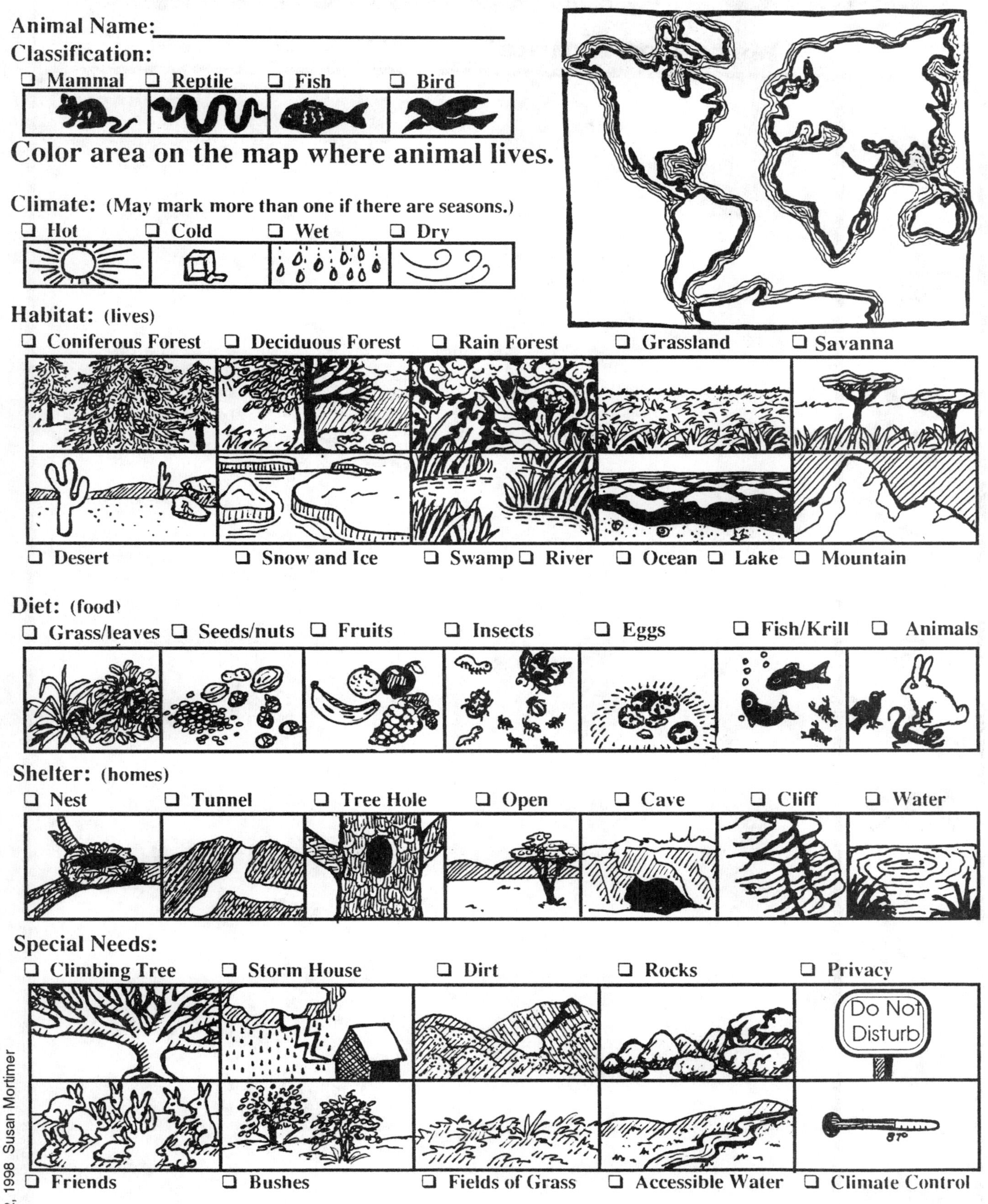

Animal Name:______________________
Classification:
❑ Mammal ❑ Reptile ❑ Fish ❑ Bird
Color area on the map where animal lives.
Climate: (May mark more than one if there are seasons.)
❑ Hot ❑ Cold ❑ Wet ❑ Dry
Habitat: (lives)
❑ Coniferous Forest ❑ Deciduous Forest ❑ Rain Forest ❑ Grassland ❑ Savanna
❑ Desert ❑ Snow and Ice ❑ Swamp ❑ River ❑ Ocean ❑ Lake ❑ Mountain
Diet: (food)
❑ Grass/leaves ❑ Seeds/nuts ❑ Fruits ❑ Insects ❑ Eggs ❑ Fish/Krill ❑ Animals
Shelter: (homes)
❑ Nest ❑ Tunnel ❑ Tree Hole ❑ Open ❑ Cave ❑ Cliff ❑ Water
Special Needs:
❑ Climbing Tree ❑ Storm House ❑ Dirt ❑ Rocks ❑ Privacy
Do Not Disturb
❑ Friends ❑ Bushes ❑ Fields of Grass ❑ Accessible Water ❑ Climate Control

Zoo Creatures

Name of Animal____________________

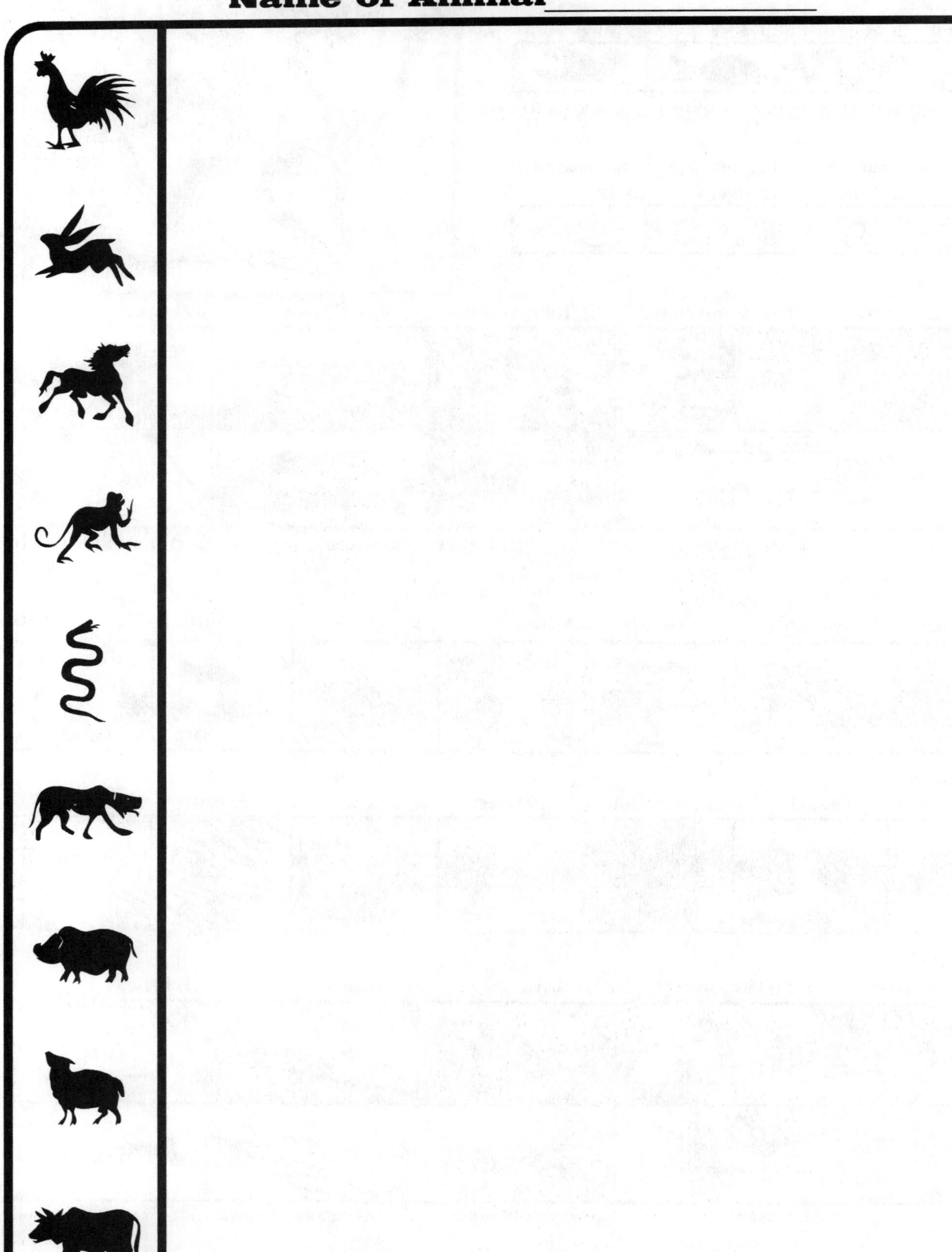

My Zoo Adventure

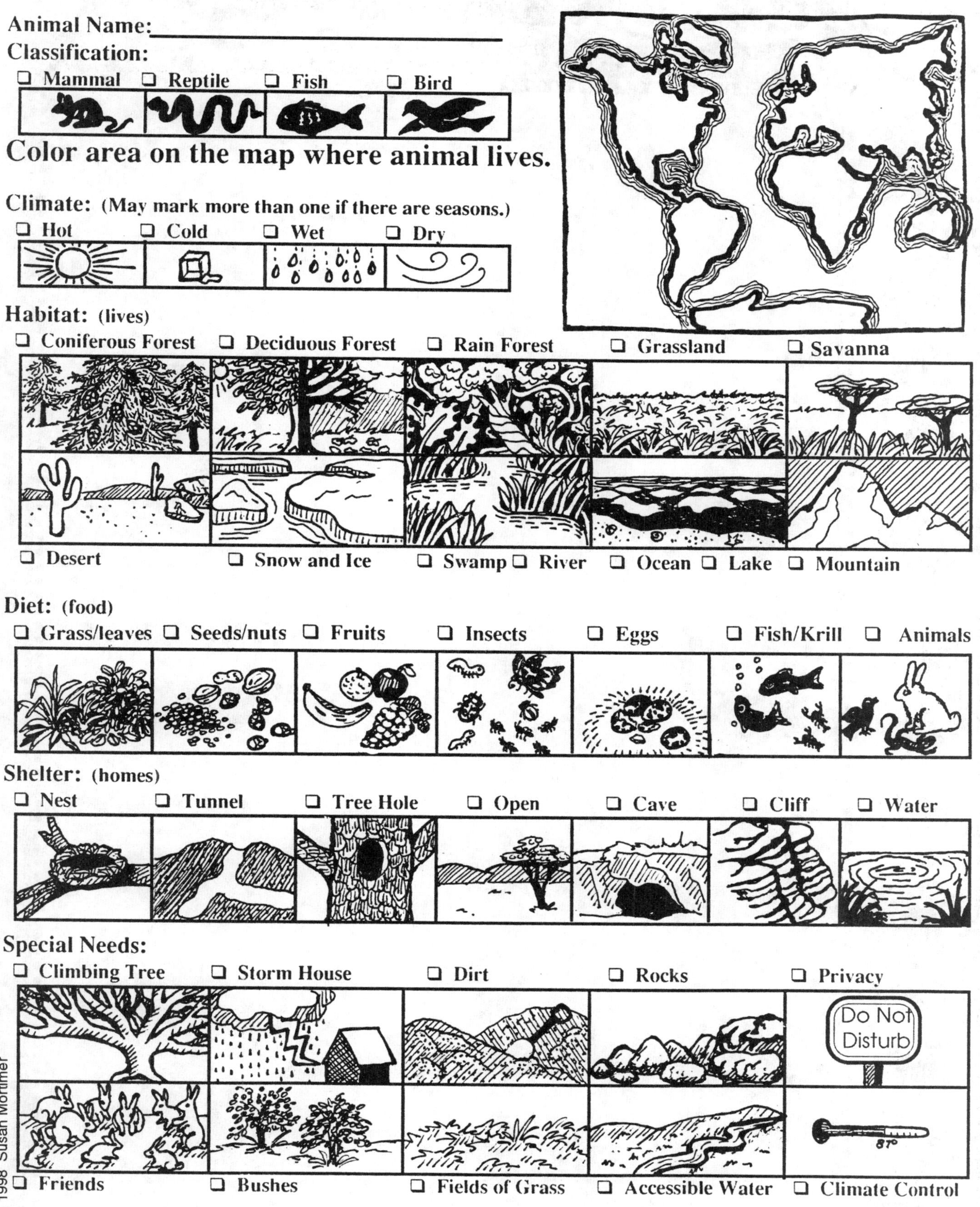

Animal Name: ______________________

Classification:

❑ Mammal ❑ Reptile ❑ Fish ❑ Bird

Color area on the map where animal lives.

Climate: (May mark more than one if there are seasons.)

❑ Hot ❑ Cold ❑ Wet ❑ Dry

Habitat: (lives)

❑ Coniferous Forest ❑ Deciduous Forest ❑ Rain Forest ❑ Grassland ❑ Savanna

❑ Desert ❑ Snow and Ice ❑ Swamp ❑ River ❑ Ocean ❑ Lake ❑ Mountain

Diet: (food)

❑ Grass/leaves ❑ Seeds/nuts ❑ Fruits ❑ Insects ❑ Eggs ❑ Fish/Krill ❑ Animals

Shelter: (homes)

❑ Nest ❑ Tunnel ❑ Tree Hole ❑ Open ❑ Cave ❑ Cliff ❑ Water

Special Needs:

❑ Climbing Tree ❑ Storm House ❑ Dirt ❑ Rocks ❑ Privacy

Do Not Disturb
87°

❑ Friends ❑ Bushes ❑ Fields of Grass ❑ Accessible Water ❑ Climate Control

ZOO CREATURES

Name of Animal ____________________

My Zoo Adventure

Animal Name:___________________________

Classification:

❑ Mammal ❑ Reptile ❑ Fish ❑ Bird

Color area on the map where animal lives.

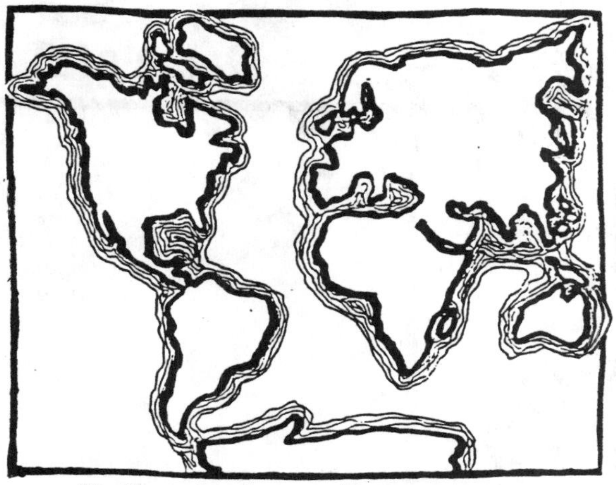

Climate: (May mark more than one if there are seasons.)

❑ Hot ❑ Cold ❑ Wet ❑ Dry

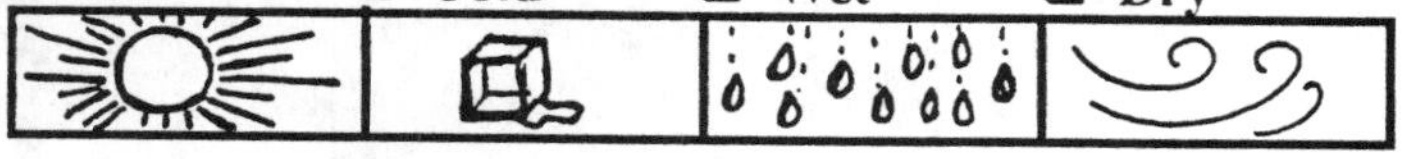

Habitat: (lives)

❑ Coniferous Forest ❑ Deciduous Forest ❑ Rain Forest ❑ Grassland ❑ Savanna

❑ Desert ❑ Snow and Ice ❑ Swamp ❑ River ❑ Ocean ❑ Lake ❑ Mountain

Diet: (food)

❑ Grass/leaves ❑ Seeds/nuts ❑ Fruits ❑ Insects ❑ Eggs ❑ Fish/Krill ❑ Animals

Shelter: (homes)

❑ Nest ❑ Tunnel ❑ Tree Hole ❑ Open ❑ Cave ❑ Cliff ❑ Water

Special Needs:

❑ Climbing Tree ❑ Storm House ❑ Dirt ❑ Rocks ❑ Privacy

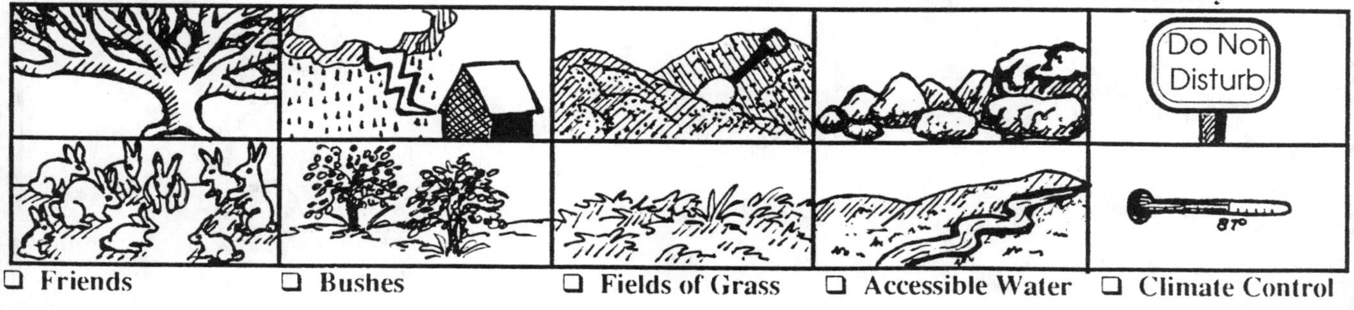

Do Not Disturb

❑ Friends ❑ Bushes ❑ Fields of Grass ❑ Accessible Water ❑ Climate Control

Zoo Creatures

Name of Animal ______________

My Zoo Adventure

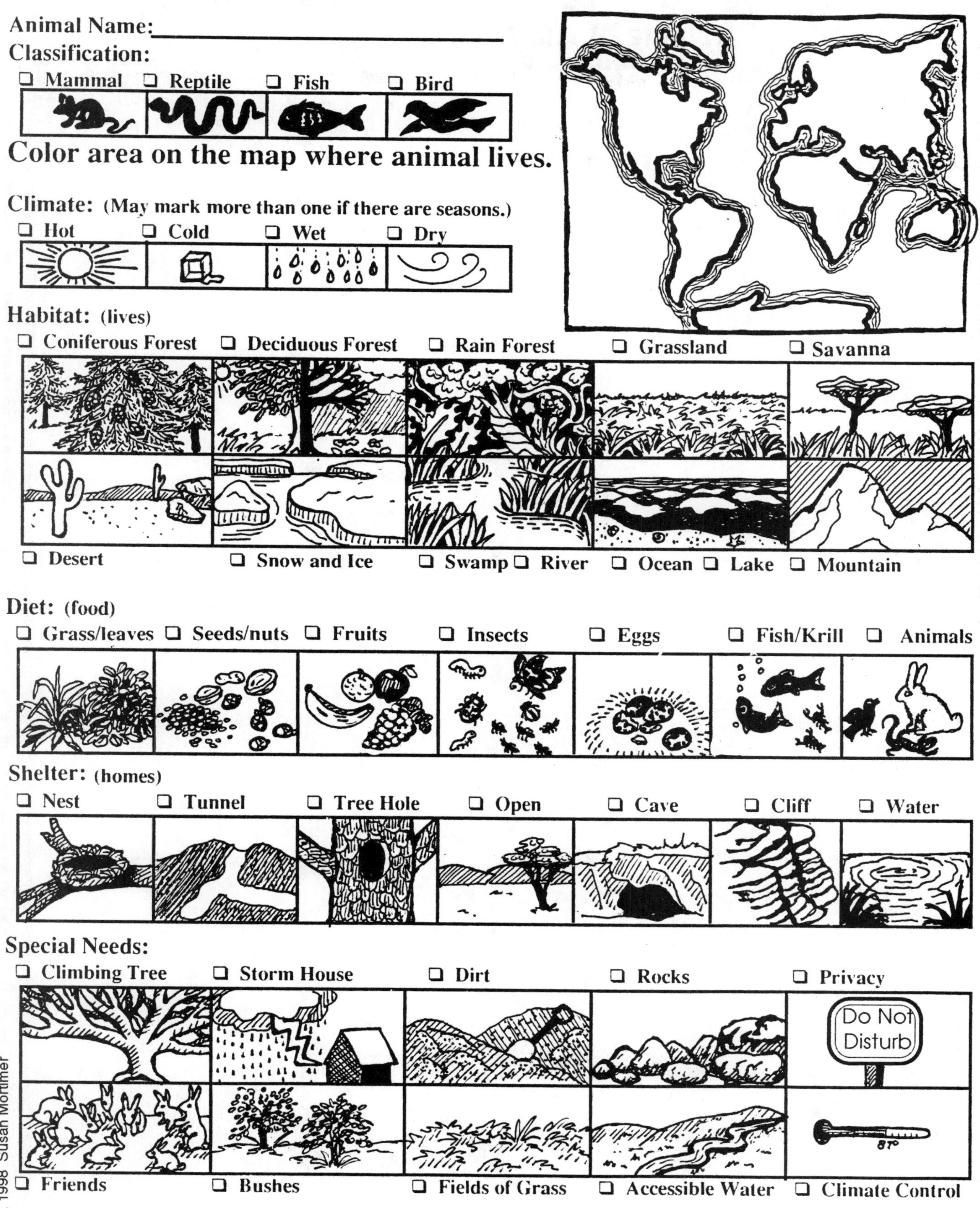

Animal Name:____________________

Classification:

❑ Mammal ❑ Reptile ❑ Fish ❑ Bird

Color area on the map where animal lives.

Climate: (May mark more than one if there are seasons.)

❑ Hot ❑ Cold ❑ Wet ❑ Dry

Habitat: (lives)

❑ Coniferous Forest ❑ Deciduous Forest ❑ Rain Forest ❑ Grassland ❑ Savanna

❑ Desert ❑ Snow and Ice ❑ Swamp ❑ River ❑ Ocean ❑ Lake ❑ Mountain

Diet: (food)

❑ Grass/leaves ❑ Seeds/nuts ❑ Fruits ❑ Insects ❑ Eggs ❑ Fish/Krill ❑ Animals

Shelter: (homes)

❑ Nest ❑ Tunnel ❑ Tree Hole ❑ Open ❑ Cave ❑ Cliff ❑ Water

Special Needs:

❑ Climbing Tree ❑ Storm House ❑ Dirt ❑ Rocks ❑ Privacy

Do Not
Disturb

❑ Friends ❑ Bushes ❑ Fields of Grass ❑ Accessible Water ❑ Climate Control

Zoo Creatures

Name of Animal ____________

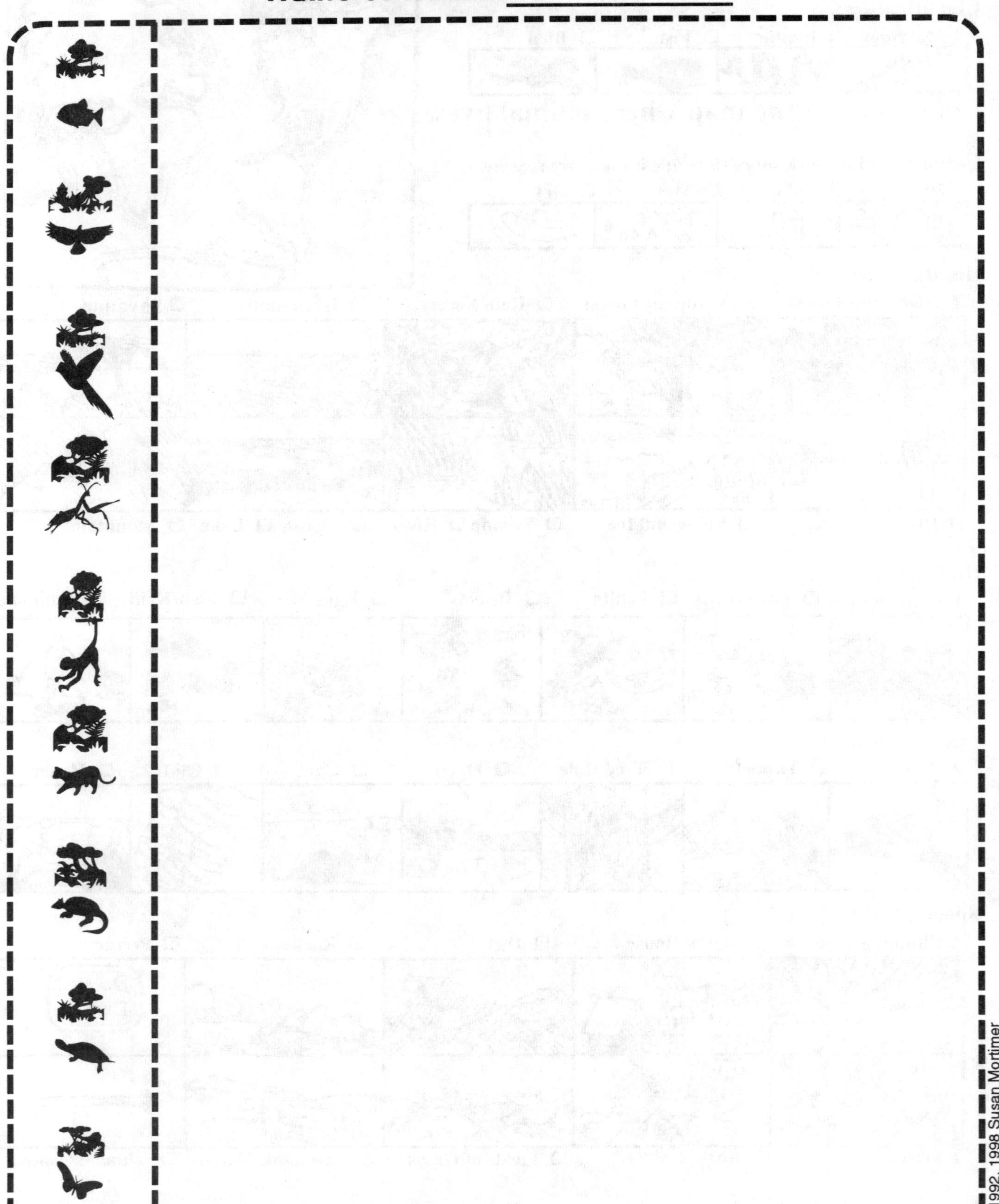

My Zoo Adventure

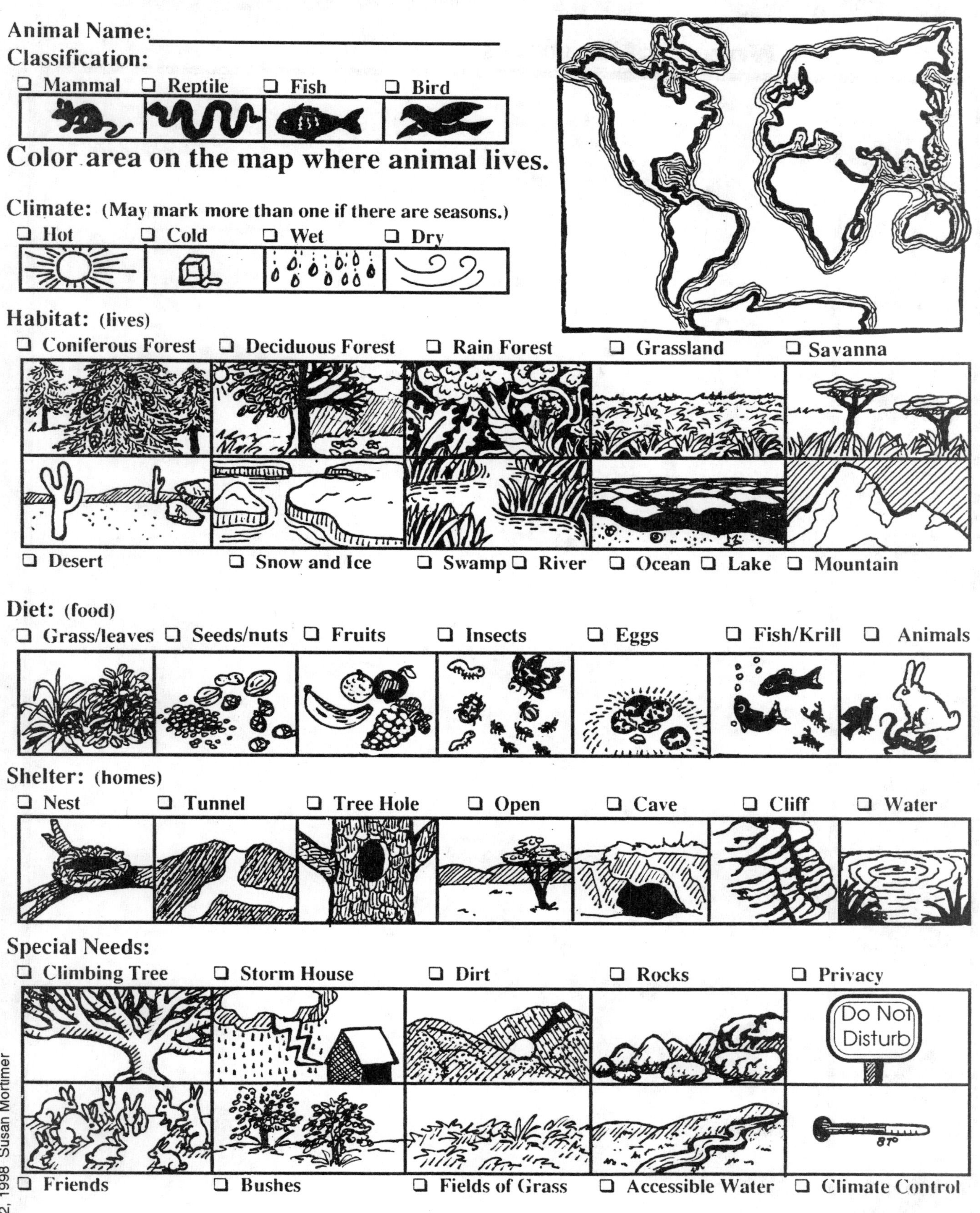

Animal Name:______________________

Classification:

❑ Mammal ❑ Reptile ❑ Fish ❑ Bird

Color area on the map where animal lives.

Climate: (May mark more than one if there are seasons.)

❑ Hot ❑ Cold ❑ Wet ❑ Dry

Habitat: (lives)

❑ Coniferous Forest ❑ Deciduous Forest ❑ Rain Forest ❑ Grassland ❑ Savanna

❑ Desert ❑ Snow and Ice ❑ Swamp ❑ River ❑ Ocean ❑ Lake ❑ Mountain

Diet: (food)

❑ Grass/leaves ❑ Seeds/nuts ❑ Fruits ❑ Insects ❑ Eggs ❑ Fish/Krill ❑ Animals

Shelter: (homes)

❑ Nest ❑ Tunnel ❑ Tree Hole ❑ Open ❑ Cave ❑ Cliff ❑ Water

Special Needs:

❑ Climbing Tree ❑ Storm House ❑ Dirt ❑ Rocks ❑ Privacy

❑ Friends ❑ Bushes ❑ Fields of Grass ❑ Accessible Water ❑ Climate Control

Do Not Disturb
87°

Zoo Creatures

Name of Animal____________________

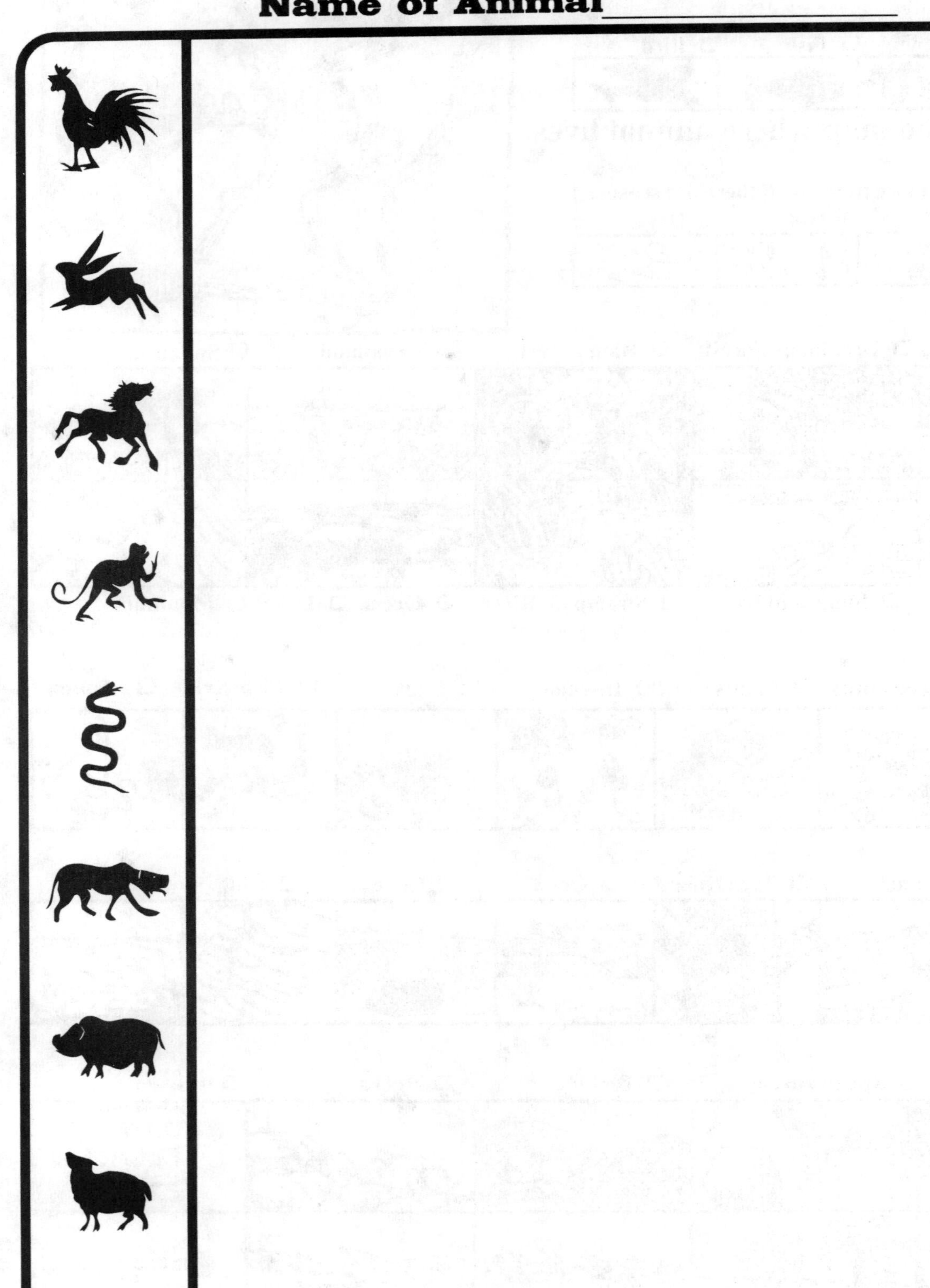

My Zoo Adventure

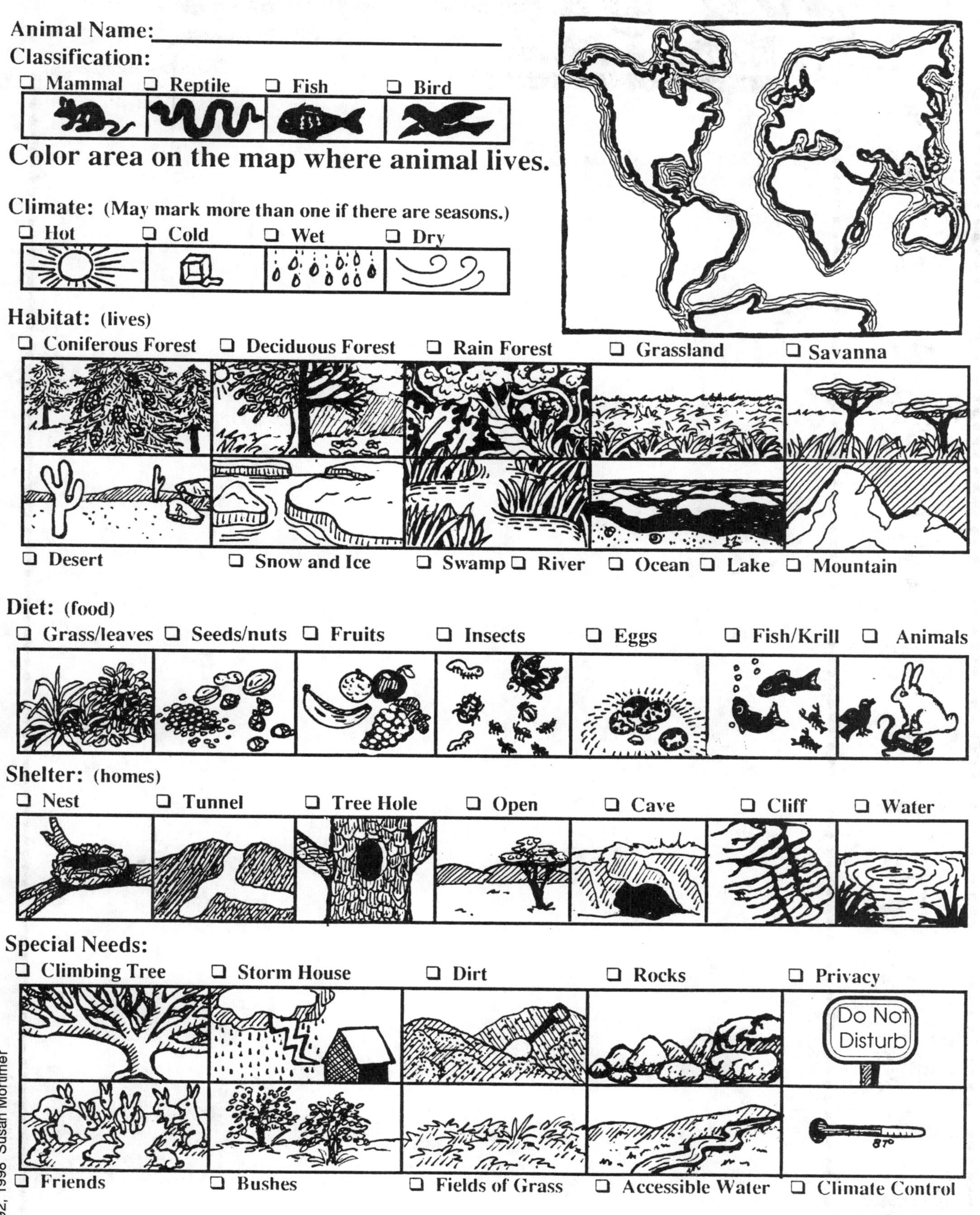

Animal Name: ______________________

Classification:

❑ Mammal ❑ Reptile ❑ Fish ❑ Bird

Color area on the map where animal lives.

Climate: (May mark more than one if there are seasons.)

❑ Hot ❑ Cold ❑ Wet ❑ Dry

Habitat: (lives)

❑ Coniferous Forest ❑ Deciduous Forest ❑ Rain Forest ❑ Grassland ❑ Savanna

❑ Desert ❑ Snow and Ice ❑ Swamp ❑ River ❑ Ocean ❑ Lake ❑ Mountain

Diet: (food)

❑ Grass/leaves ❑ Seeds/nuts ❑ Fruits ❑ Insects ❑ Eggs ❑ Fish/Krill ❑ Animals

Shelter: (homes)

❑ Nest ❑ Tunnel ❑ Tree Hole ❑ Open ❑ Cave ❑ Cliff ❑ Water

Special Needs:

❑ Climbing Tree ❑ Storm House ❑ Dirt ❑ Rocks ❑ Privacy

Do Not Disturb
87°

❑ Friends ❑ Bushes ❑ Fields of Grass ❑ Accessible Water ❑ Climate Control

ZOO CREATURES

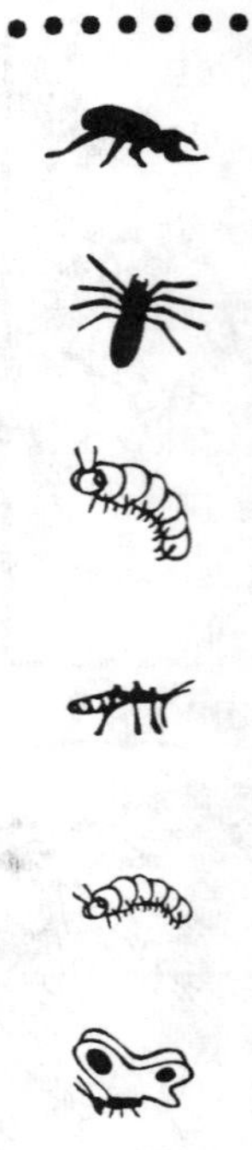

Name of Animal ____________________

My Zoo Adventure

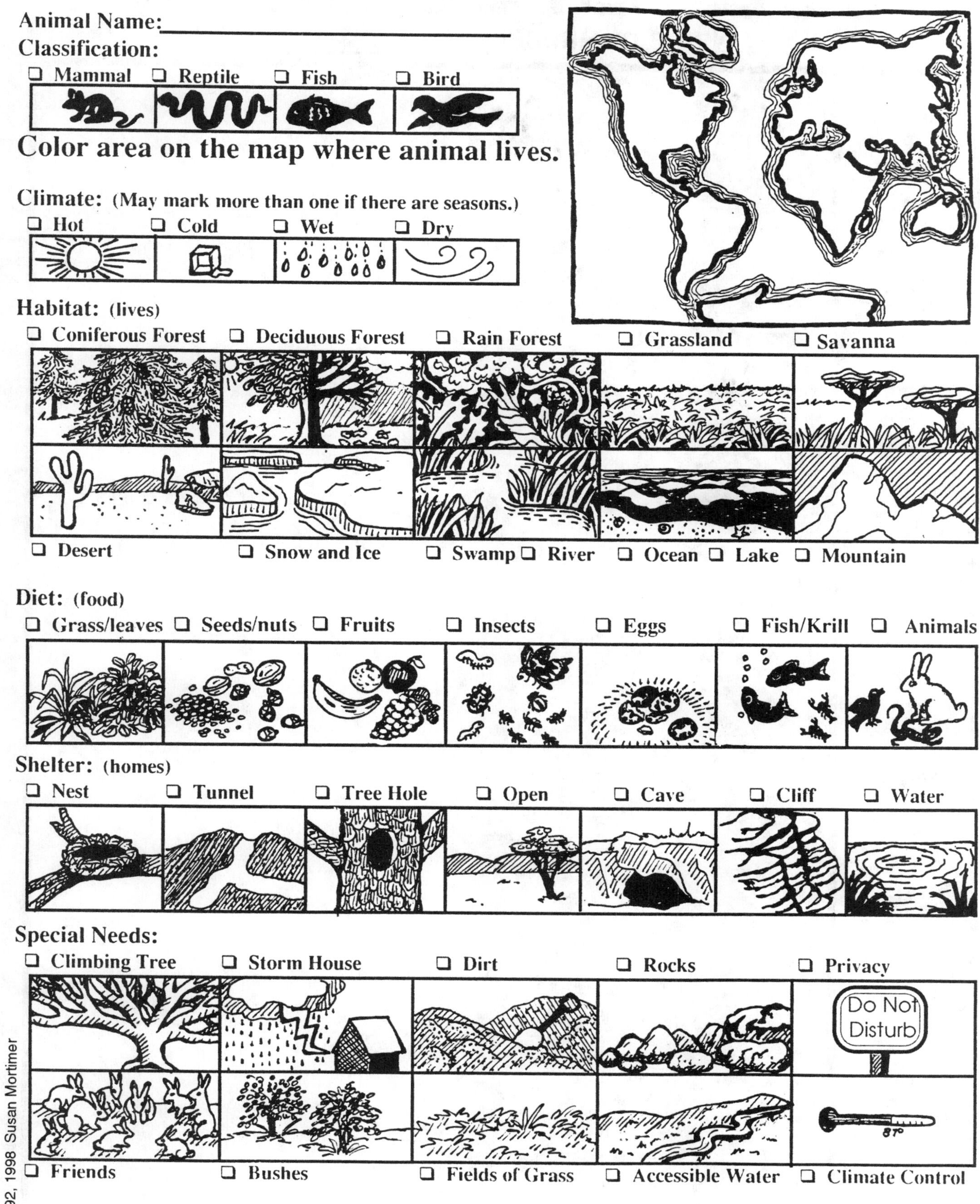

Animal Name:____________________

Classification:

❑ Mammal ❑ Reptile ❑ Fish ❑ Bird

Color area on the map where animal lives.

Climate: (May mark more than one if there are seasons.)

❑ Hot ❑ Cold ❑ Wet ❑ Dry

Habitat: (lives)

❑ Coniferous Forest ❑ Deciduous Forest ❑ Rain Forest ❑ Grassland ❑ Savanna

❑ Desert ❑ Snow and Ice ❑ Swamp ❑ River ❑ Ocean ❑ Lake ❑ Mountain

Diet: (food)

❑ Grass/leaves ❑ Seeds/nuts ❑ Fruits ❑ Insects ❑ Eggs ❑ Fish/Krill ❑ Animals

Shelter: (homes)

❑ Nest ❑ Tunnel ❑ Tree Hole ❑ Open ❑ Cave ❑ Cliff ❑ Water

Special Needs:

❑ Climbing Tree ❑ Storm House ❑ Dirt ❑ Rocks ❑ Privacy

Do Not
Disturb

❑ Friends ❑ Bushes ❑ Fields of Grass ❑ Accessible Water ❑ Climate Control

Zoo Creatures

Name of Animal ____________

My Zoo Adventure

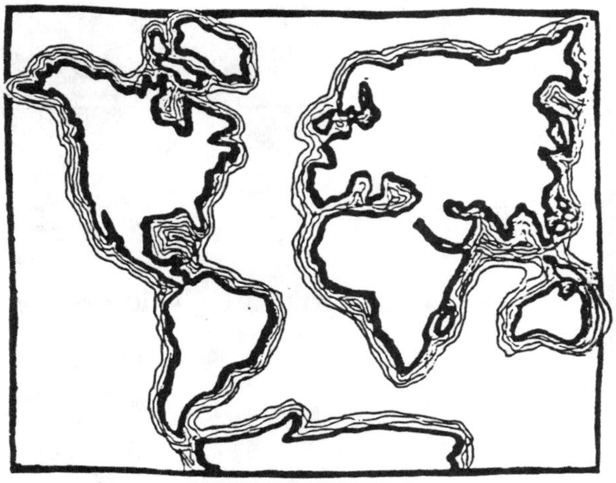

Animal Name:________________________

Classification:

❑ Mammal ❑ Reptile ❑ Fish ❑ Bird

Color area on the map where animal lives.

Climate: (May mark more than one if there are seasons.)

❑ Hot ❑ Cold ❑ Wet ❑ Dry

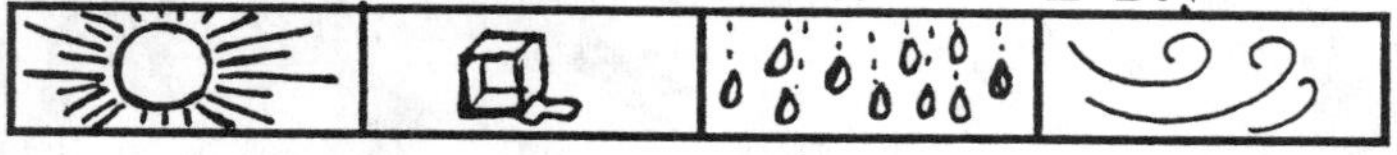

Habitat: (lives)

❑ Coniferous Forest ❑ Deciduous Forest ❑ Rain Forest ❑ Grassland ❑ Savanna

❑ Desert ❑ Snow and Ice ❑ Swamp ❑ River ❑ Ocean ❑ Lake ❑ Mountain

Diet: (food)

❑ Grass/leaves ❑ Seeds/nuts ❑ Fruits ❑ Insects ❑ Eggs ❑ Fish/Krill ❑ Animals

Shelter: (homes)

❑ Nest ❑ Tunnel ❑ Tree Hole ❑ Open ❑ Cave ❑ Cliff ❑ Water

Special Needs:

❑ Climbing Tree ❑ Storm House ❑ Dirt ❑ Rocks ❑ Privacy

Do Not Disturb

87°

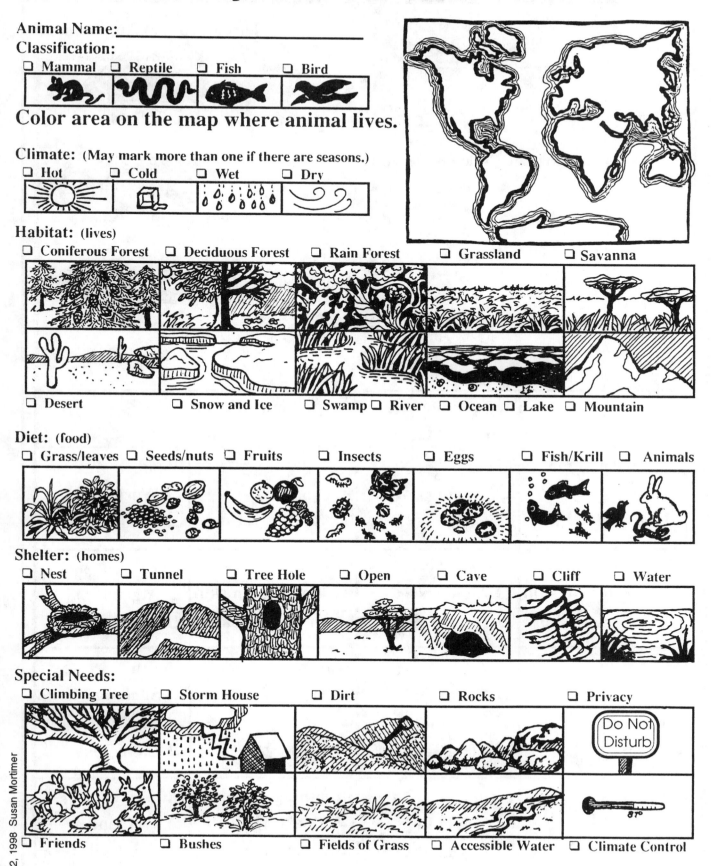

❑ Friends ❑ Bushes ❑ Fields of Grass ❑ Accessible Water ❑ Climate Control

Amphibian Detective

Glue Frog Life Cycle Booklet here.

Three Types of Amphibians

Frogs/Toads

Salamanders/Newts

Caecilians

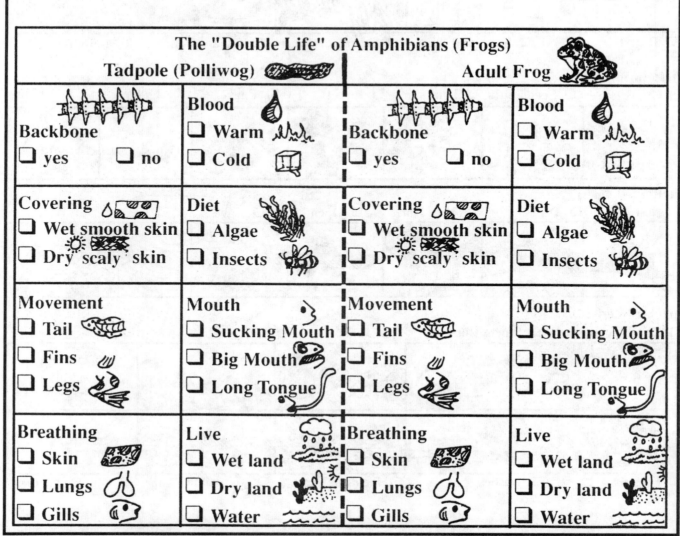

The "Double Life" of Amphibians (Frogs)

Tadpole (Polliwog)		Adult Frog	
Backbone ❑ yes ❑ no	Blood ❑ Warm ❑ Cold	Backbone ❑ yes ❑ no	Blood ❑ Warm ❑ Cold
Covering ❑ Wet smooth skin ❑ Dry scaly skin	Diet ❑ Algae ❑ Insects	Covering ❑ Wet smooth skin ❑ Dry scaly skin	Diet ❑ Algae ❑ Insects
Movement ❑ Tail ❑ Fins ❑ Legs	Mouth ❑ Sucking Mouth ❑ Big Mouth ❑ Long Tongue	Movement ❑ Tail ❑ Fins ❑ Legs	Mouth ❑ Sucking Mouth ❑ Big Mouth ❑ Long Tongue
Breathing ❑ Skin ❑ Lungs ❑ Gills	Live ❑ Wet land ❑ Dry land ❑ Water	Breathing ❑ Skin ❑ Lungs ❑ Gills	Live ❑ Wet land ❑ Dry land ❑ Water

 Color, cut, fold and glue booklet from "Amphibian Detective" (page 2) on top left corner of page. Complete the drawings of amphibians. Then mark the characteristics of tadpoles and adult frogs.

Amphibian Detective (page 2)

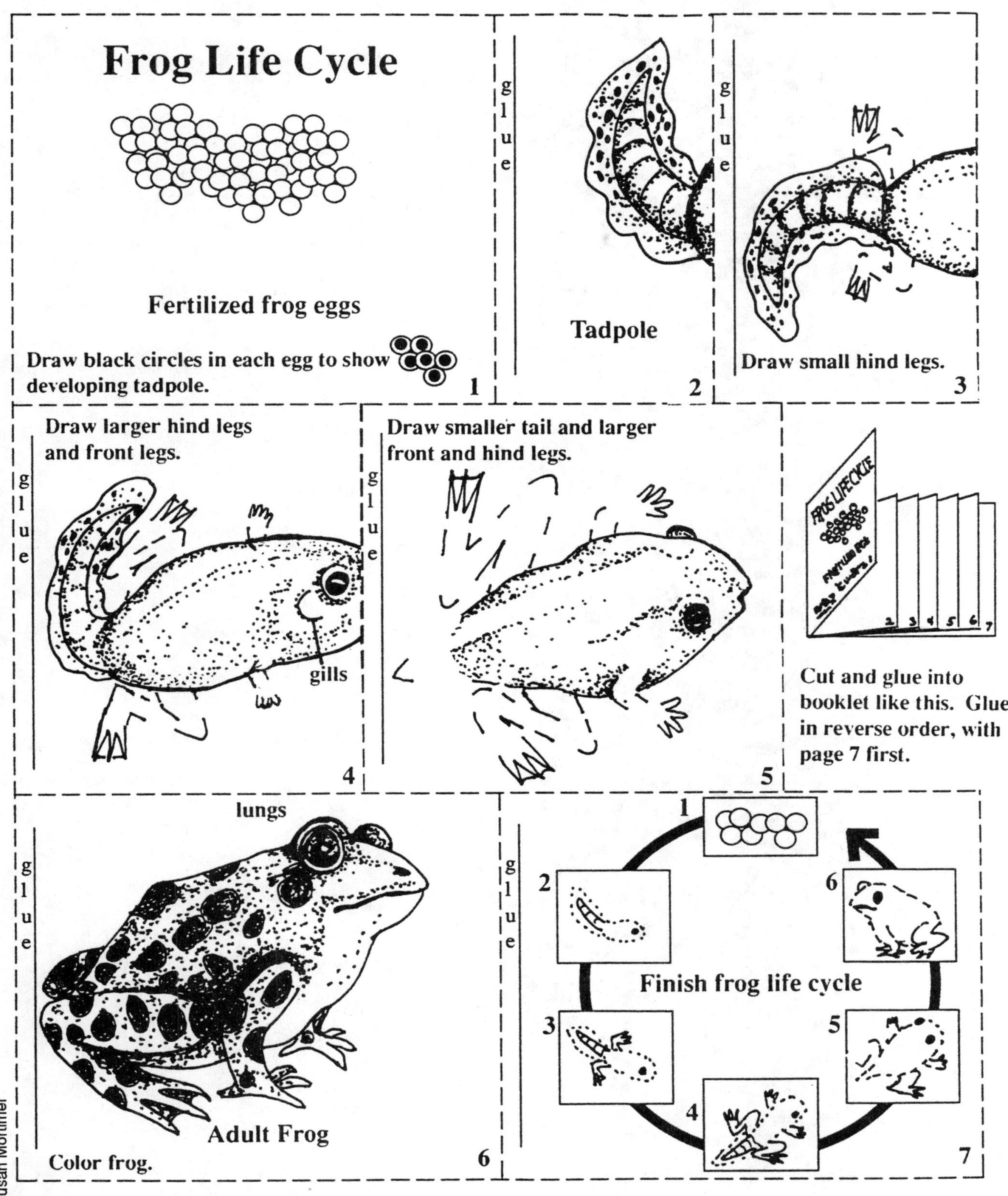

Frog Life Cycle
Fertilized frog eggs
Draw black circles in each egg to show developing tadpole.
1
glue
Tadpole
2
glue
Draw small hind legs.
3
glue
Draw larger hind legs and front legs.
gills
4
glue
Draw smaller tail and larger front and hind legs.
5
Cut and glue into booklet like this. Glue in reverse order, with page 7 first.
glue
lungs
Adult Frog
Color frog.
6
glue
Finish frog life cycle
1
2
3
4
5
6
7

Horns and Antlers (page 2)

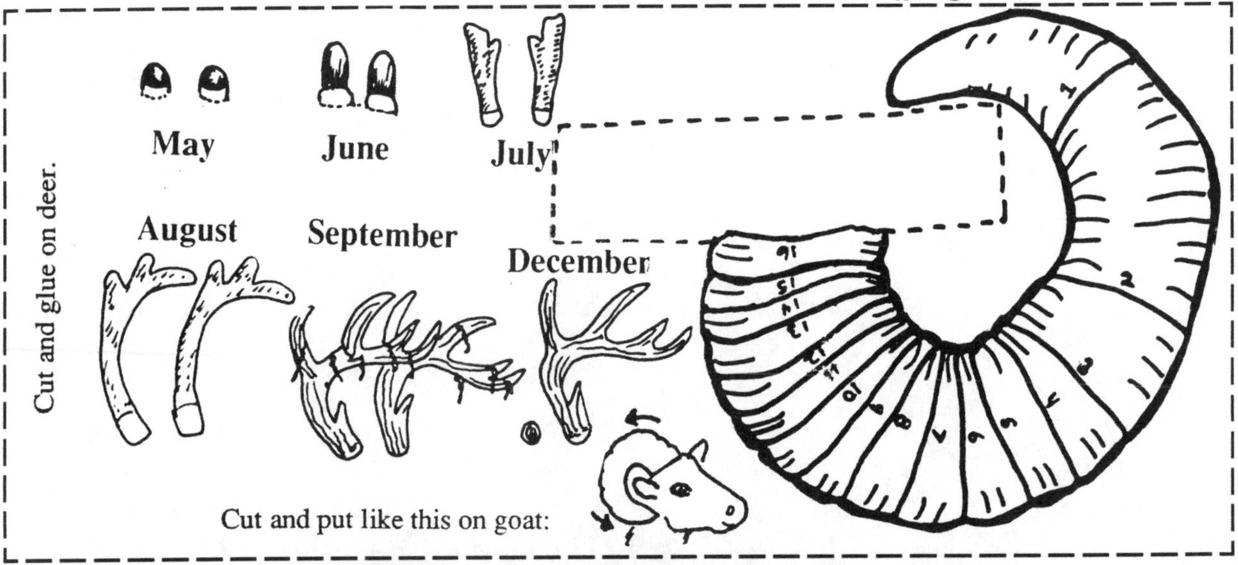

Cut and glue on deer.

May

June

July

August

September

December

Cut and put like this on goat:

1 2 3 4 5 6 7 8 9 10 11 12 13 14 15 16

A Pile of Bones

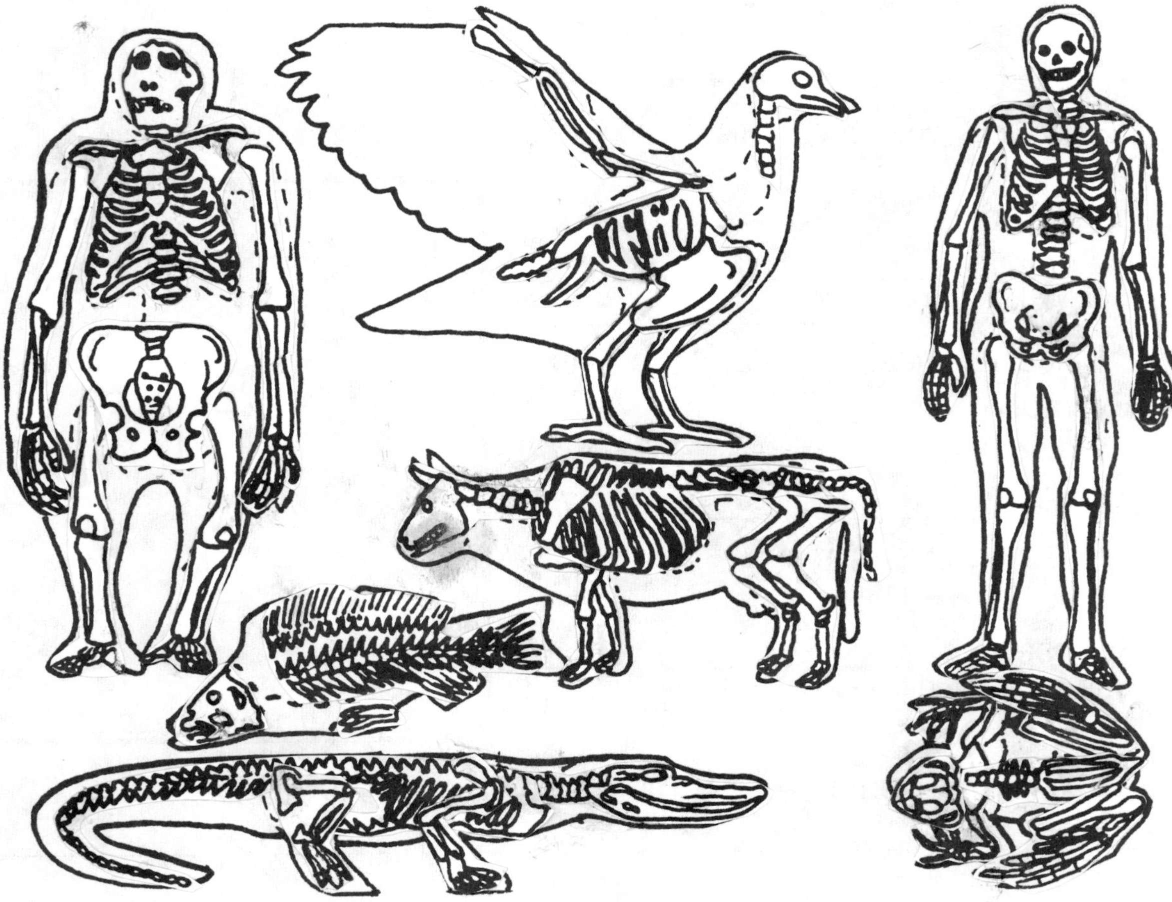

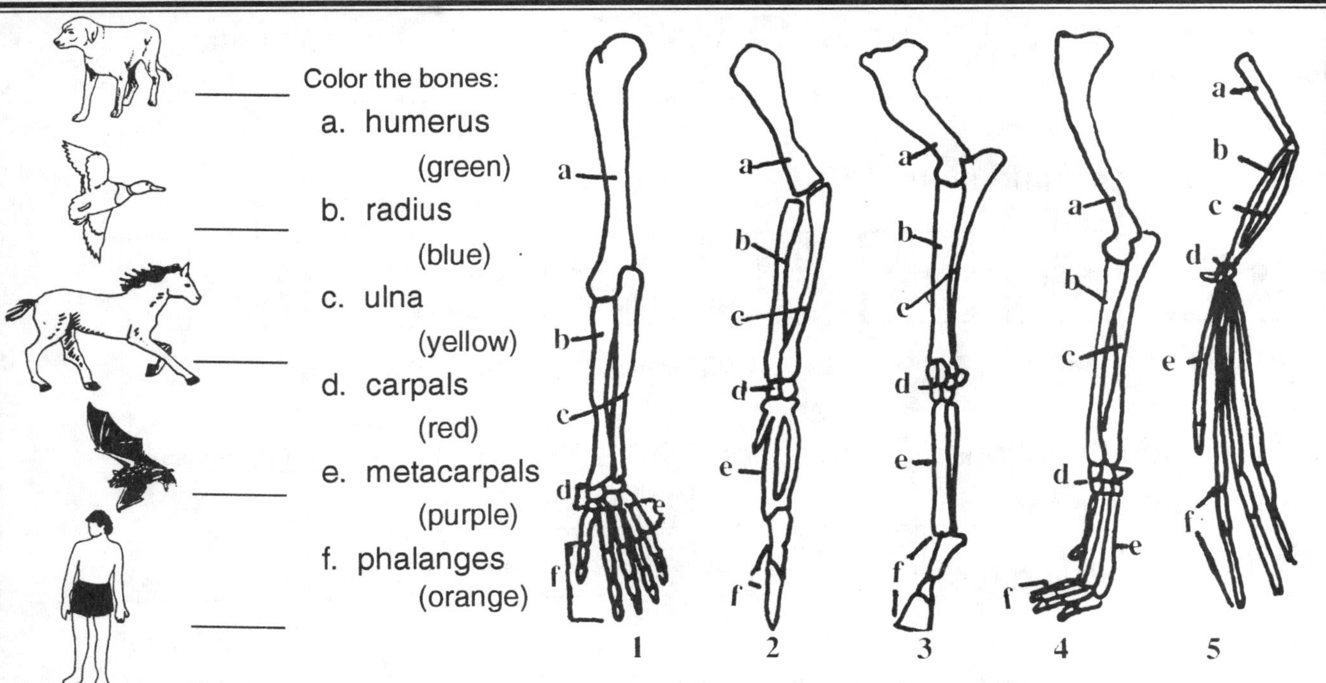
Color the bones:
a. humerus
(green)
b. radius
(blue)
c. ulna
(yellow)
d. carpals
(red)
e. metacarpals
(purple)
f. phalanges
(orange)
1
2
3
4
5

Cut out the bones from A Pile of Bones, p. 2, and carefully glue them on the animal they belong above. In the lower half, color the bones according to the color code. Then number the bones that match each animal.

Scientist Detective

Scientist: ______________________________ Born: ______ Died: ______

BC ——|——|——|——|——|——|——|——|——|——|——|——— AD

200 0 200 400 600 800 1000 1200 1400 1600 1800 2000

Portrait

Background:

Nationality: ____________________

Parents: ____________________

Influence was: ❐ helpful ❐ injuring

Example: ____________________

Schooling: ____________________

Family:

Spouse: ____________________

Number of children: ____________________

Turning point experience that got him/her into field of work:

____

Religion: ❐ There is a personal God. ❐ There is no God.

❐ There are many gods. ❐ Science is 'god'. ❐ Man is 'god'.

Did religion affect work: ❐ a lot? ❐ a little? ❐ none at all?

Example: ____

Field of contribution:

astronomy botany zoology psychology geology medicine physics ____________

Major contributions: ❐ Invention ❐ Theory ❐ Discovery

Best known for: ____

Far-reaching results: ____

Horns and Antlers

Growth of antlers of adult buck in one year.

May

June

July

August

September

December

Horns: Are found on male and female animals and continue to grow throughout the animal's life. Made of keratin (also found in fingernails).

Antlers: Purely bone, shed yearly, mainly for males. No other bone grows this fast. Growing process takes five months and requires high calcium. Starts as bud, and with older animals, are elaborate. While growing are covered with "velvet" (skin).

Horn growth over 16 years.

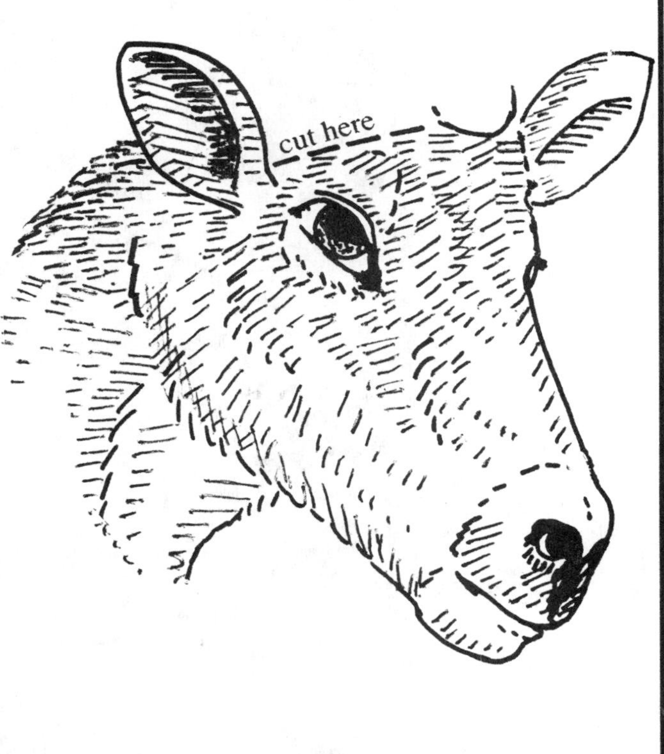
cut here

Flight

Glue or draw a feather.

Only birds have feathers. Each feather has a shaft and hundreds of barbs, which are like little hooks. These and even smaller hooks, hold all the parts of a feather together so that the surface is flat and perfect for flying.

Close-up view of a feather

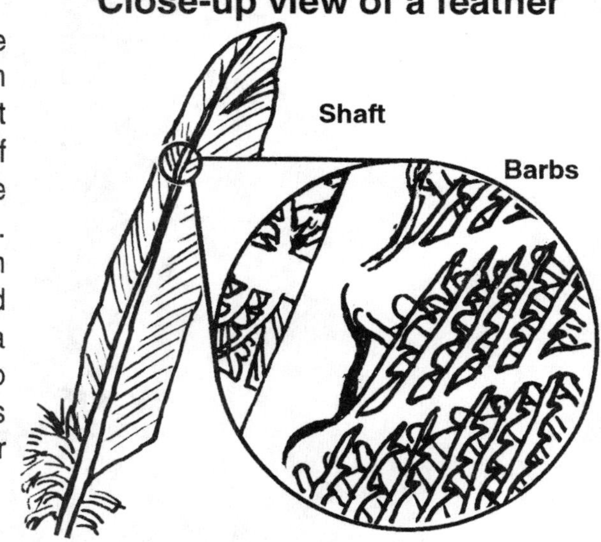

Shaft
Barbs

Birds fly at high altitudes where there is little oxygen with the help of 8 or 9 air sacs and lungs. The air sacs enable them to take more oxygen out of the air than any other animal.

a
b
c
d
e
f
g

Air is first taken in to the rear air sacs. Color in (a), (b), and (c).

a
b
c
d
e
f
g

It then passes to the lungs where the gases are exchanged. Color in (d).

a
b
c
d
e
f
g

The air goes from the lungs to the front air sacs and out. Color in (e), (f), (g) and (a).

Fill in the correct letter:

In order to fly, bird bones are hollow and have braces for strength. _____

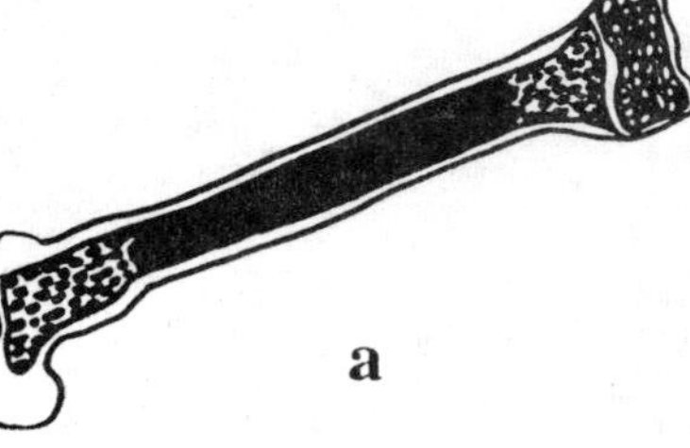

a

Mammal bones are thicker and filled with marrow (to produce red blood cells). _____

b

Hold this booklet with left thumb on left side and flip pages with right thumb.

Glue "Bird in Flight" booklet here from "Flight" (page 2). **Note: Booklet will not flip unless all pages are trimmed to exactly the same length.**

Flight (page 2)

Bird in Flight

Animal Tracks Game

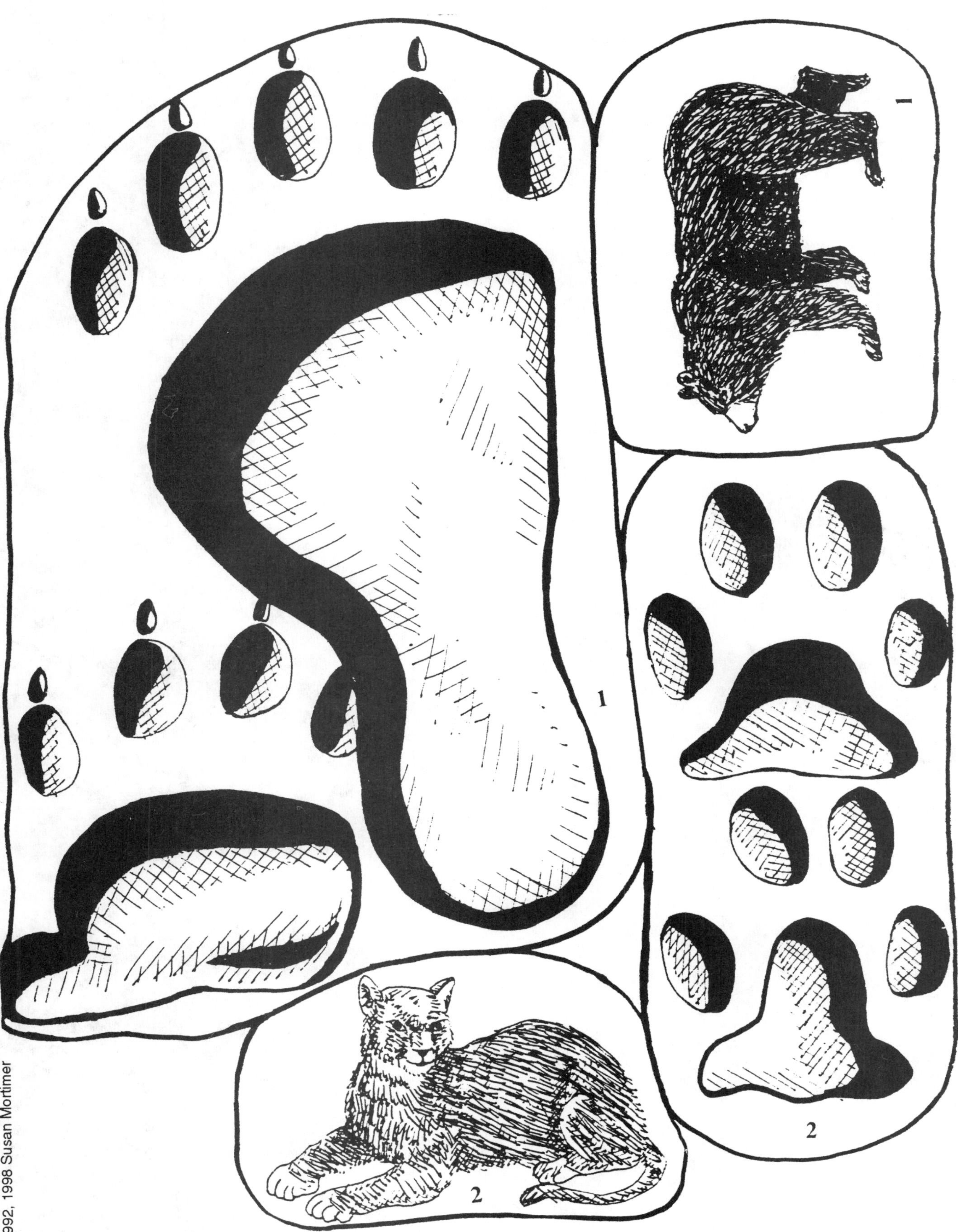
1
2
2

Laminate, then cut out. See directions for game in teacher's manual.

Animal Tracks Game (page 2)

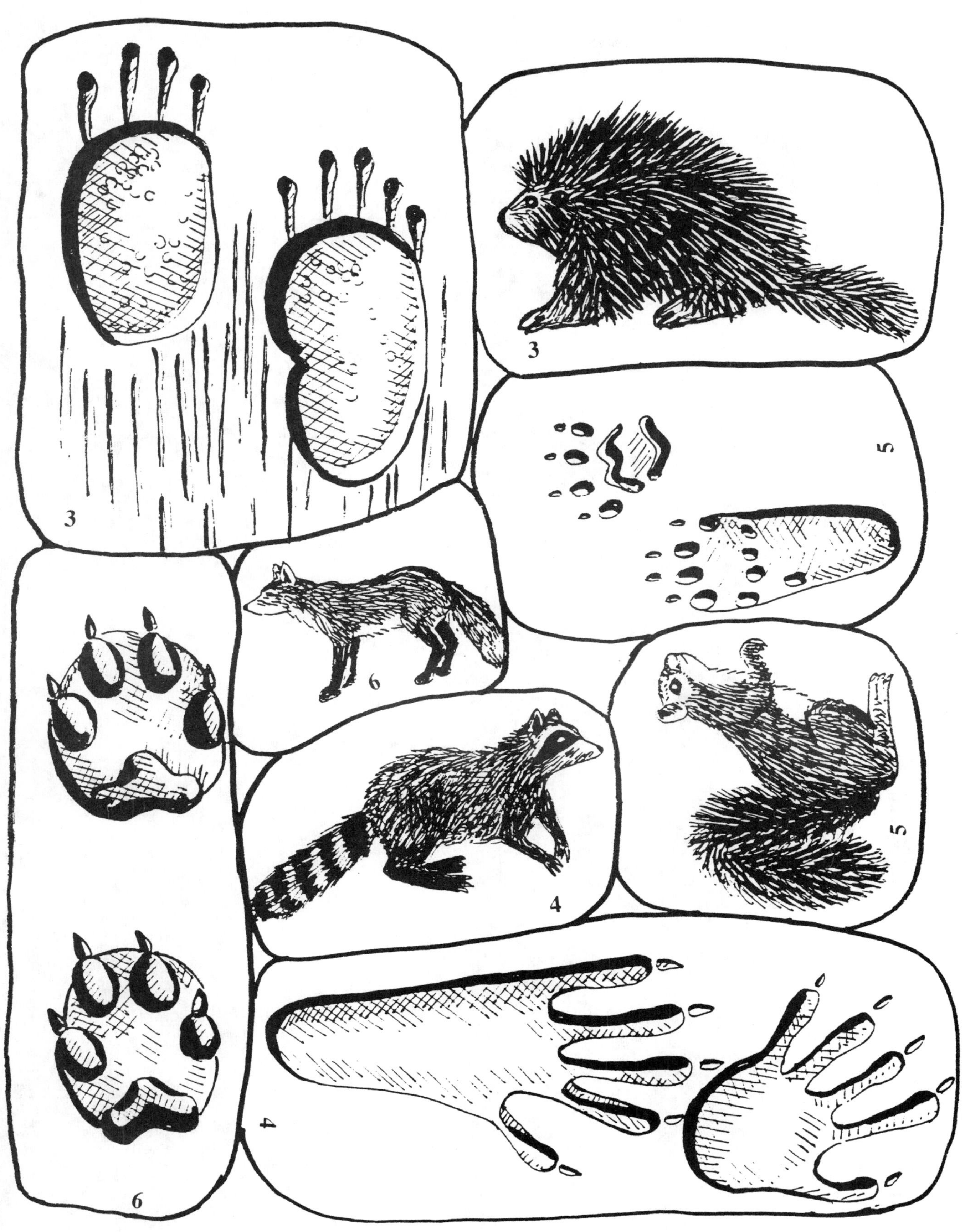
3
3
5
6
5
4
6
4

Animal Tracks Game (page 3)

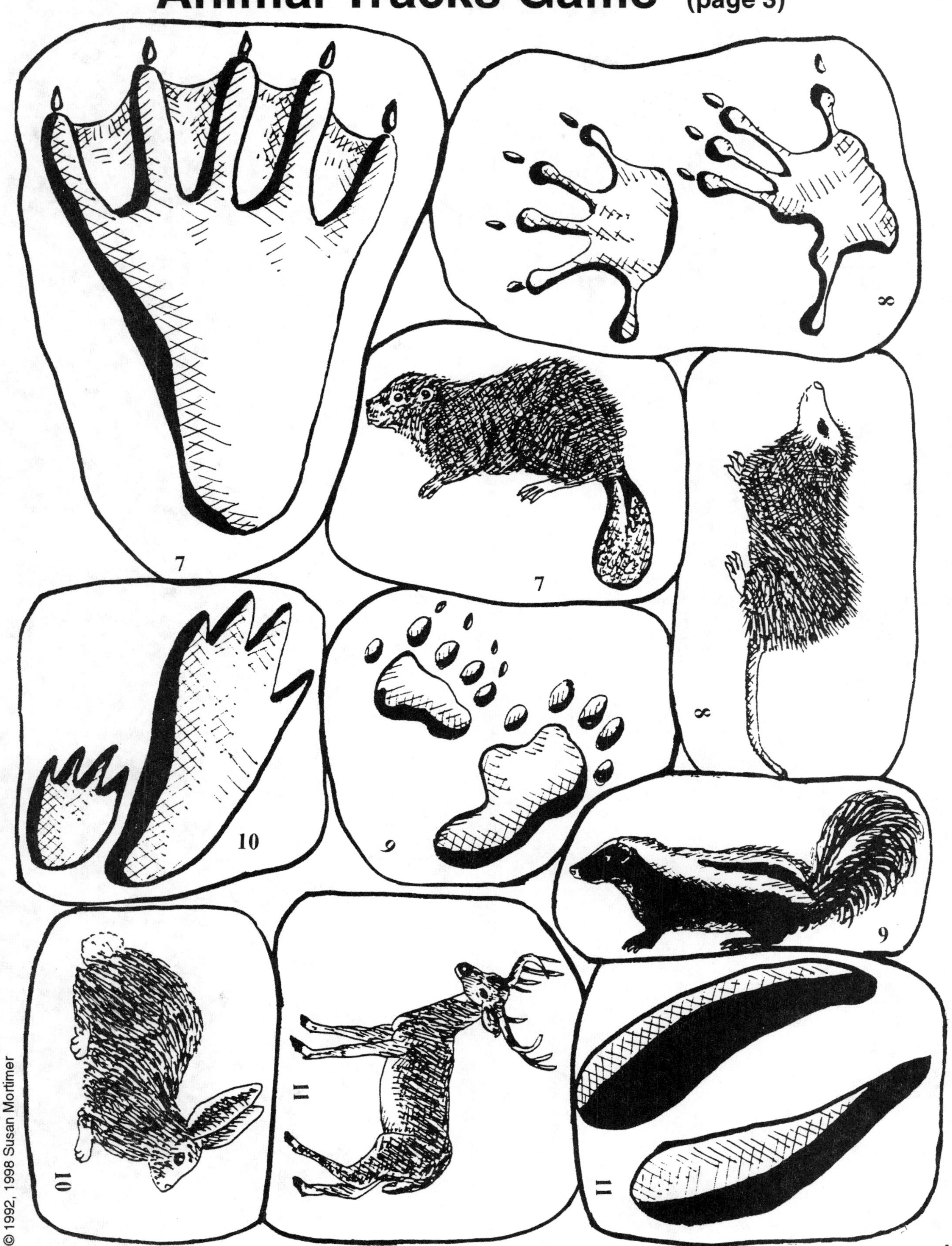

7
8
7
8
10
6
9
10
11
11

My Animal Tracks Book

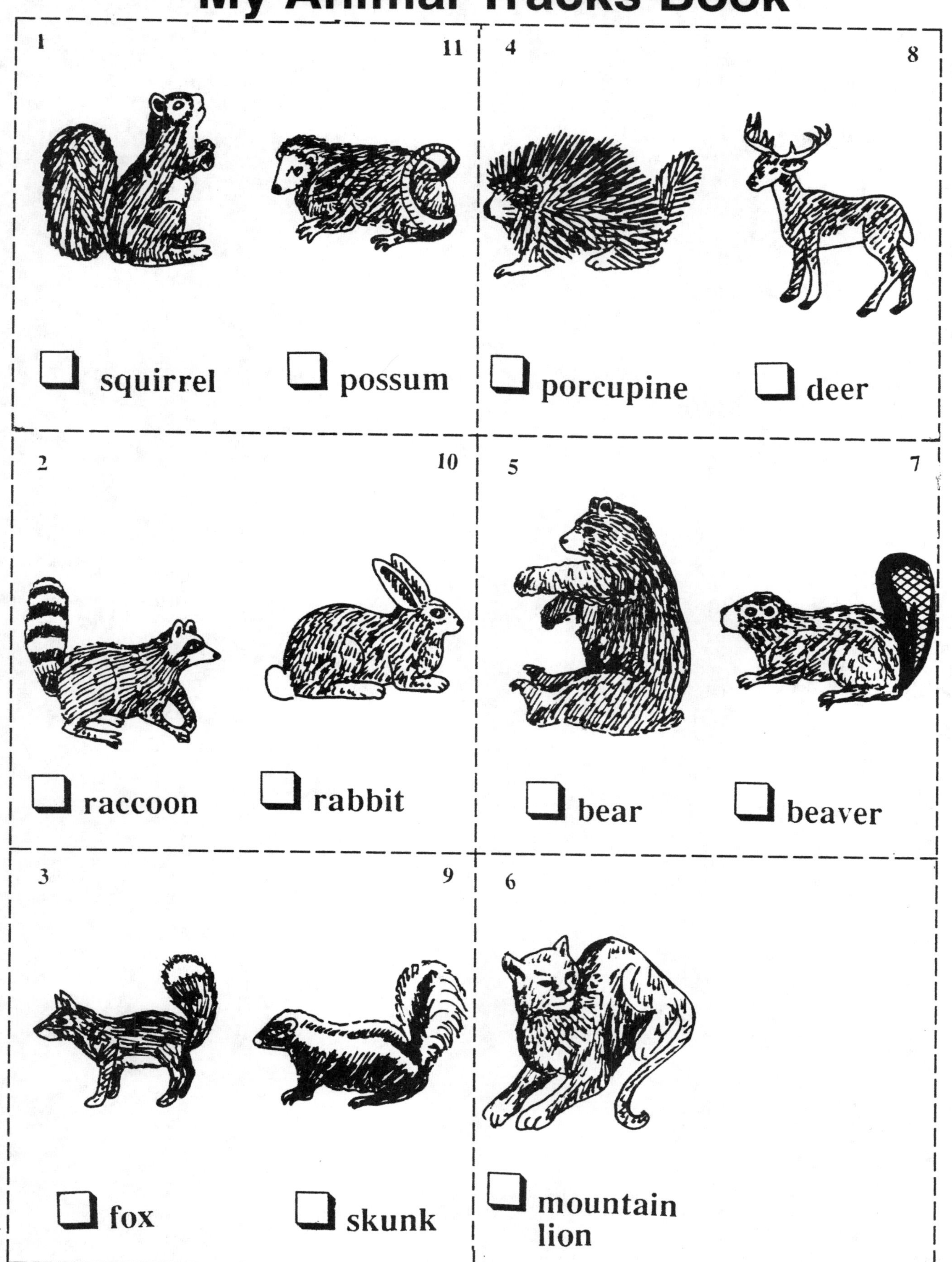
1
11
4
8
squirrel
possum
porcupine
deer
2
10
5
7
raccoon
rabbit
bear
beaver
3
9
6
fox
skunk
mountain
lion

Color and cut on dotted lines. Put the pages in order, fold in half and staple on fold. Draw footprints across from each animal [see "My Animal Tracks Book" (page 2)].

My Animal Tracks Book (page 2)

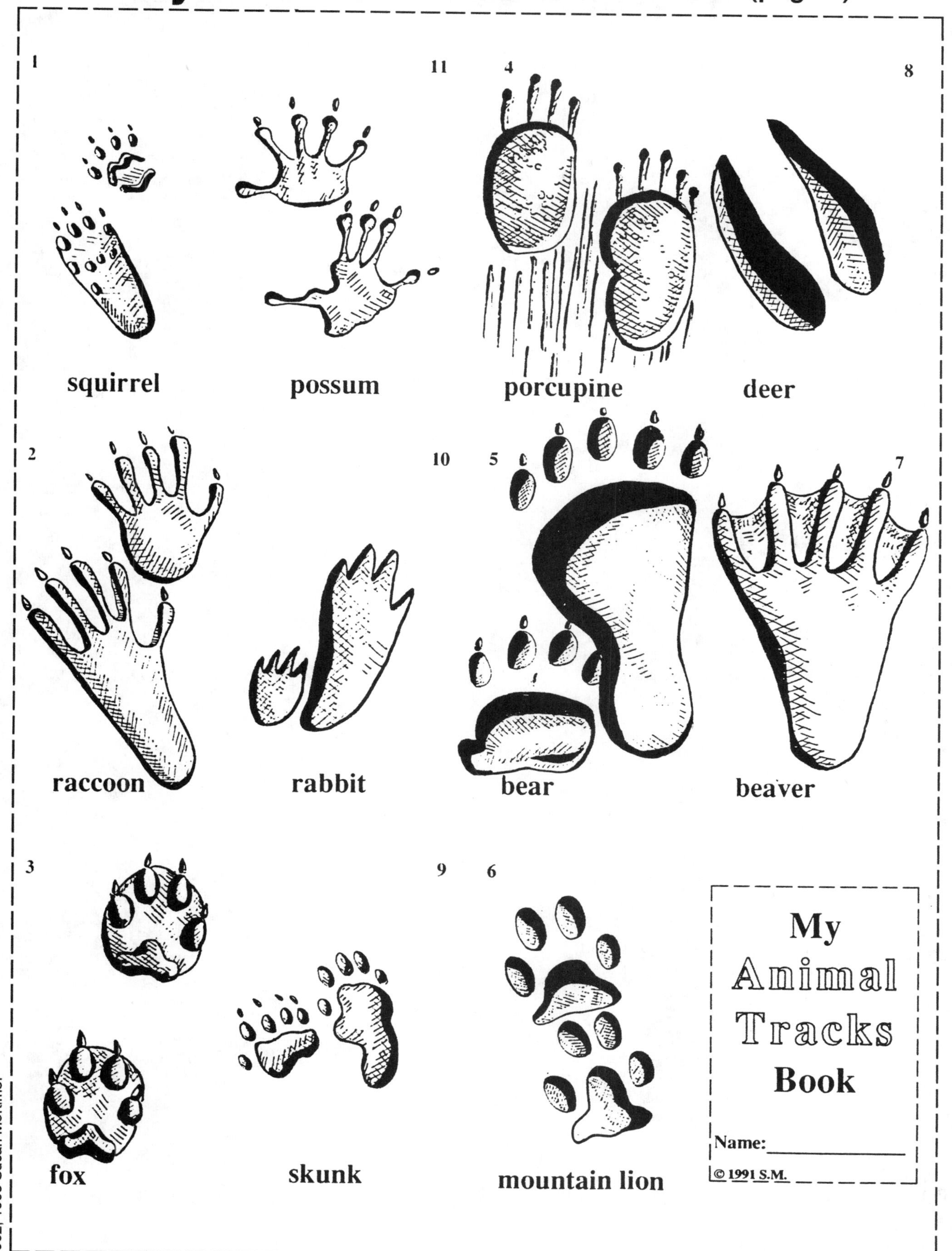
1
11
4
8
squirrel
possum
porcupine
deer
2
10
5
7
raccoon
rabbit
bear
beaver
3
9
6
fox
skunk
mountain lion
My
Animal
Tracks
Book
Name:
© 1991 S.M.

Draw footprints across from each animal on "My Animal Tracks Book". (Younger students may cut and glue footprints in place.)

You'll Know Them by Their Footprints

How can you tell there's a rabbit around,
Just by looking at the ground?
How can you tell that a bird's nearby,
Without even looking at the sky?

You'll know it by their footprints and there's more,
By where they walk and what they live for.
You'll know them by their footprints,
You'll know them by their footprints.

How can you tell that a skunk's been there,
Just by smelling of the air?
How can you tell that a bear was here,
But that he's long gone and there's no need to fear?

You'll know it by their footprints and there's more,
By where they walk and what they live for.
You'll know them by their footprints,
You'll know them by their footprints.

How can they know that a Christian passed by,
Without a word and without a sigh?
How can they know there's a better place,
Before they see Jesus face to face?

They'll know us by our footprints and what's more,
By where we walk and what we live for.
They'll know us by our footprints,
They'll know us by His footprints.

Glue "My Animal Tracks Book" here.

Glue "Horse in Motion" book here.

Horse in Motion

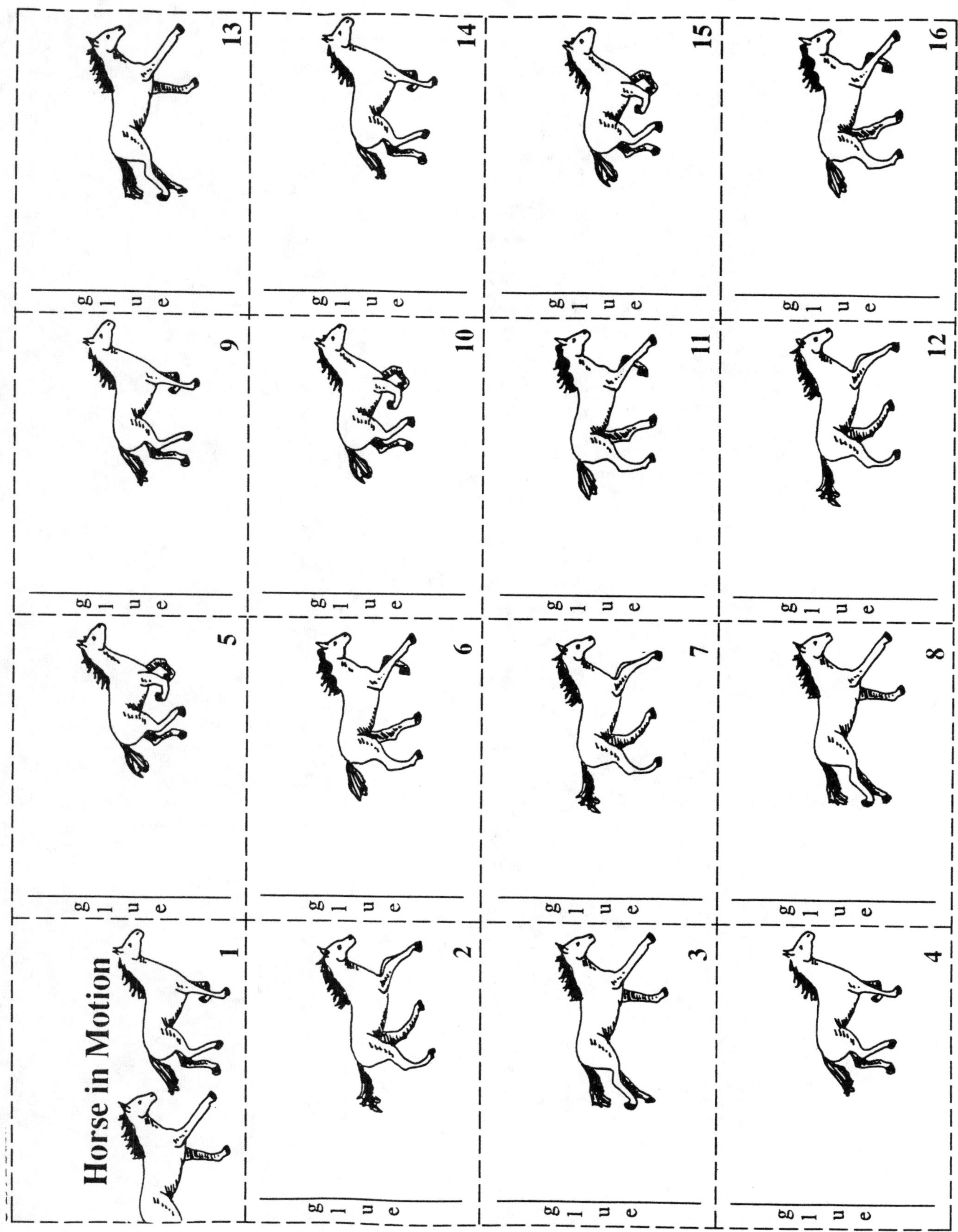

Horse in Motion
1
2
3
4
5
6
7
8
9
10
11
12
13
14
15
16
glue

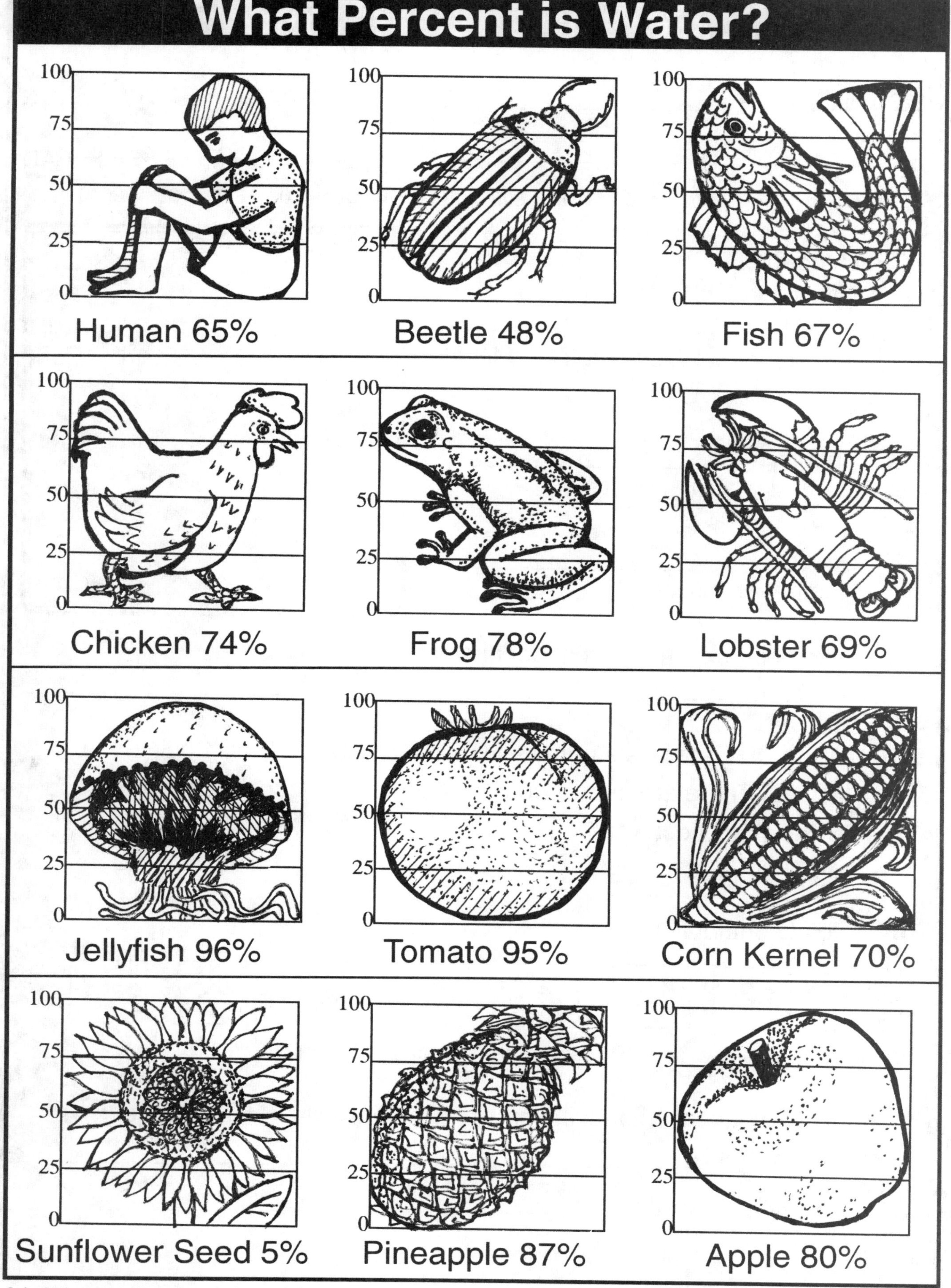
What Percent is Water?
Human 65%
Beetle 48%
Fish 67%
Chicken 74%
Frog 78%
Lobster 69%
Jellyfish 96%
Tomato 95%
Corn Kernel 70%
Sunflower Seed 5%
Pineapple 87%
Apple 80%

Color in the approximate amount of water in each item above.

Scientist Detective

Scientist: ______________________________ Born: ______ Died: ______

BC — 200 — 0 — 200 — 400 — 600 — 800 — 1000 — 1200 — 1400 — 1600 — 1800 — 2000 — AD

Portrait

Background:
Nationality: ____________________
Parents: ____________________
Influence was: ❐ helpful ❐ injuring
Example: ____________________

Schooling: ____________________

Family:
Spouse: ____________________
Number of children: ____________________

Turning point experience that got him/her into field of work:

____

Religion: ❐ There is a personal God. ❐ There is no God.
❐ There are many gods. ❐ Science is 'god'. ❐ Man is 'god'.
Did religion affect work: ❐ a lot? ❐ a little? ❐ none at all?
Example: ______________________________

Field of contribution:

astronomy | botany | zoology | psychology | geology | medicine | physics | ____________

Major contributions: ❐ Invention ❐ Theory ❐ Discovery
Best known for: ______________________________
Far-reaching results: ______________________________

Beaks and Feet Show Where Birds Live and What They Eat

Beaks made to:
Feet made to:
Beaks made to:
Feet made to:
Beaks made to:
Feet made to:
Beaks made to:
Feet made to:
Beaks made to:
Feet made to:
Beaks made to:
Feet made to:
Beaks made to:
Feet made to:
Beaks made to:
Feet made to:
Beaks made to:
Feet made to:
Beaks made to:
Feet made to:

Glue "Beaks and Feet Show Where Birds Live and What They Eat" (page 2) here.

Beaks and Feet Show Where Birds Live and What They Eat (page 2)

Beaks made to:

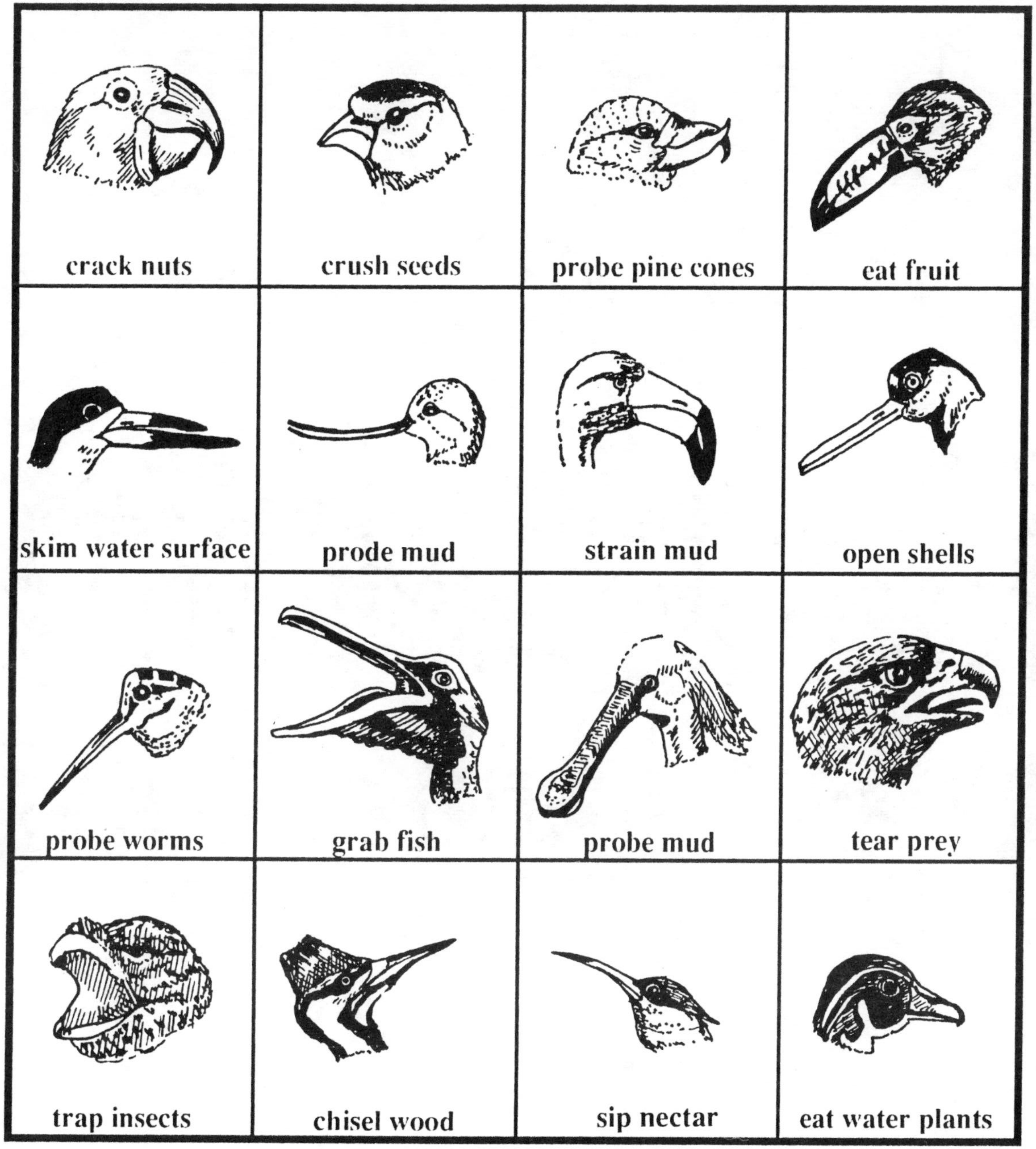

crack nuts	crush seeds	probe pine cones	eat fruit
skim water surface	prode mud	strain mud	open shells
probe worms	grab fish	probe mud	tear prey
trap insects	chisel wood	sip nectar	eat water plants

Feet made to:

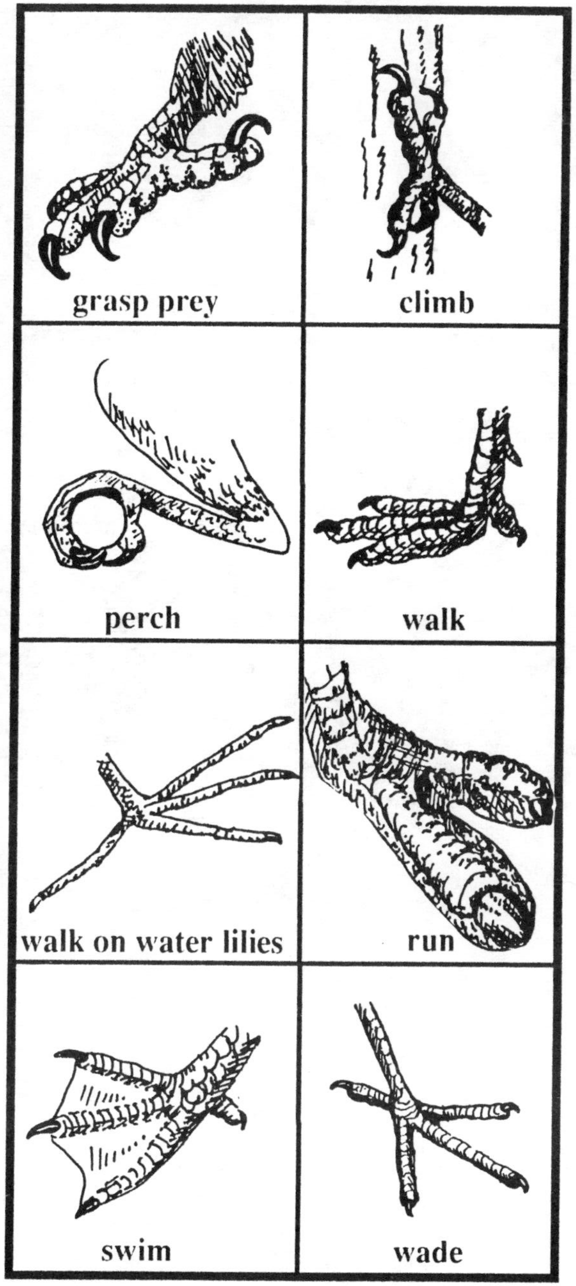

grasp prey	climb
perch	walk
walk on water lilies	run
swim	wade

Cud Chewers and Meat Eaters

glue step 3 here

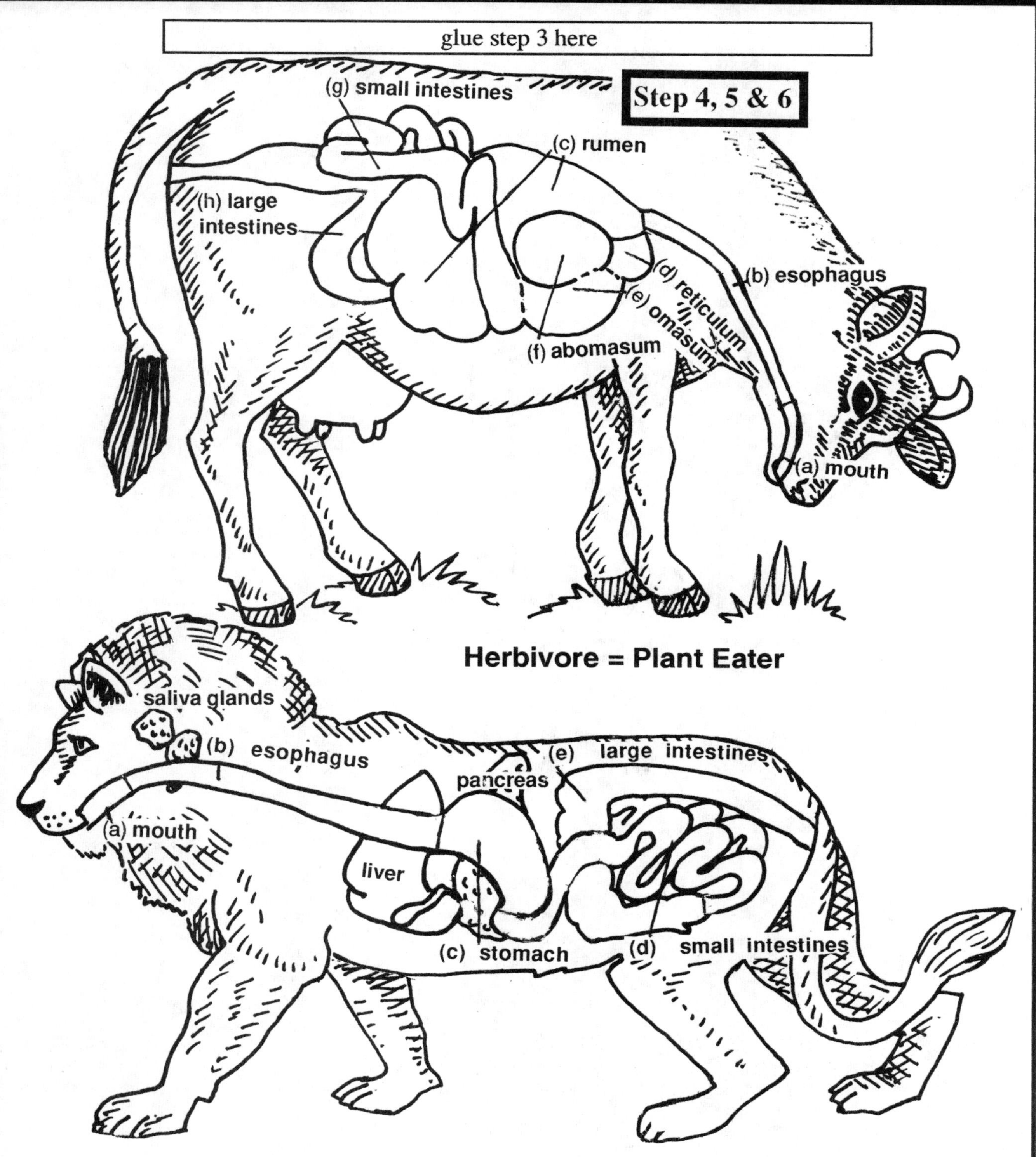
Step 4, 5 & 6
(g) small intestines
(c) rumen
(h) large intestines
(b) esophagus
(d) reticulum
(e) omasum
(f) abomasum
(a) mouth
Herbivore = Plant Eater
saliva glands
(b) esophagus
(e) large intestines
pancreas
(a) mouth
liver
(c) stomach
(d) small intestines
Carnivore = Meat Eater

The meat-eating lion's (a) sharp **teeth** tear up its food. It passes down the (b) **esophagus** into the (c) **stomach**, where pepsin and hydrochloric acid begin digesting the protein in the meat. The food goes into the (d) **small intestines** where most of digestion occurs. Unusable food moves to the (e) **large intestines** and then out of the body. [Color (a) blue; (b) purple; (c) yellow; (d) red; (e) brown.]

Glue page 2 here.

Cut and glue "Cud Chewers and Meat Eaters" (page 2) as directed. Follow the directions from the Herbivore column to complete the corresponding 'lift-up' page. Directions for the lion are below it.

Cud Chewers and Meat Eaters (page 2)

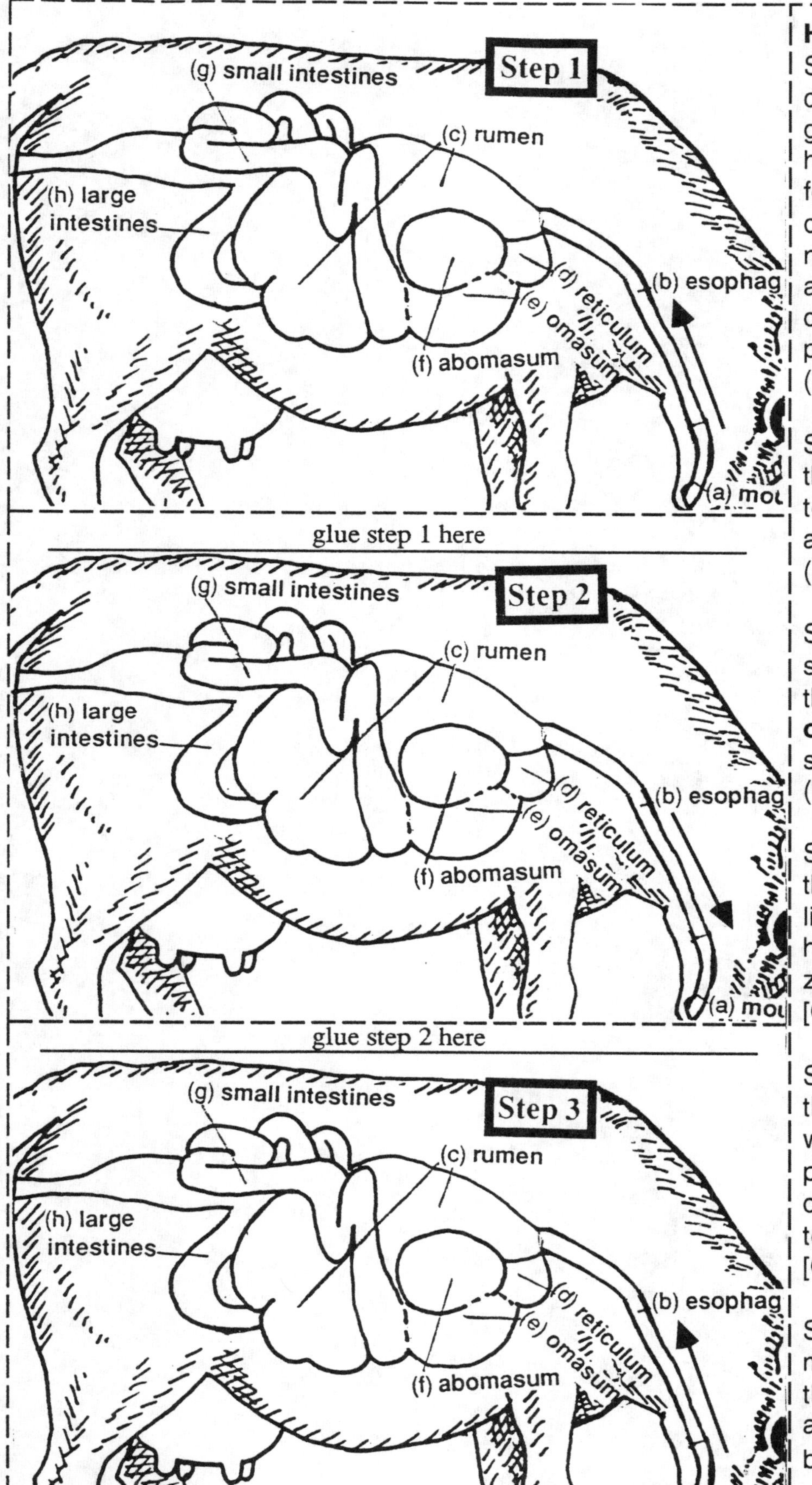
Step 1
(g) small intestines
(c) rumen
(h) large intestines
(b) esophag
(d) reticulum
(e) omasum
(f) abomasum
(a) mou
glue step 1 here
Step 2
(g) small intestines
(c) rumen
(h) large intestines
(b) esophag
(d) reticulum
(e) omasum
(f) abomasum
(a) mou
glue step 2 here
Step 3
(g) small intestines
(c) rumen
(h) large intestines
(b) esophag
(d) reticulum
(e) omasum
(f) abomasum
(a) mou

Herbivore = Plant Eater

Step 1. The plant-eating cow chews its food, then it goes to the (c)**rumen** which holds up to sixty gallons of food. The cow could not digest plant fibers if it were not for the microorganism and bacteria that break down tough cellulose in the plants. [Color (a), (b) and (c) yellow.]

Step 2. Now the cow returns the food (now called 'cud') to its (a) **mouth** to chew again. [Color (a), (b) and (c) purple.]

Step 3. The cud is re-swallowed and goes into the (d) **reticulum** and (e) **omasum** where water is squeezed out. [Color (a), (b), (d) and (e) blue.]

Step 4. It now goes to (f) the **abomasum** (which is like our stomachs) where hydrochloric acid and enzymes digest the protein. [Color (f) orange.]

Step 5. It then moves into the (g) **small intestines** where enzymes from the pancreas finish breaking down the food into nutrients to be used by the body. [Color (g) green.]

Step 6. The undigested material passes through the (h) **large intestines** and out the anus. [Color (h) brown.]

Forest Food Chain

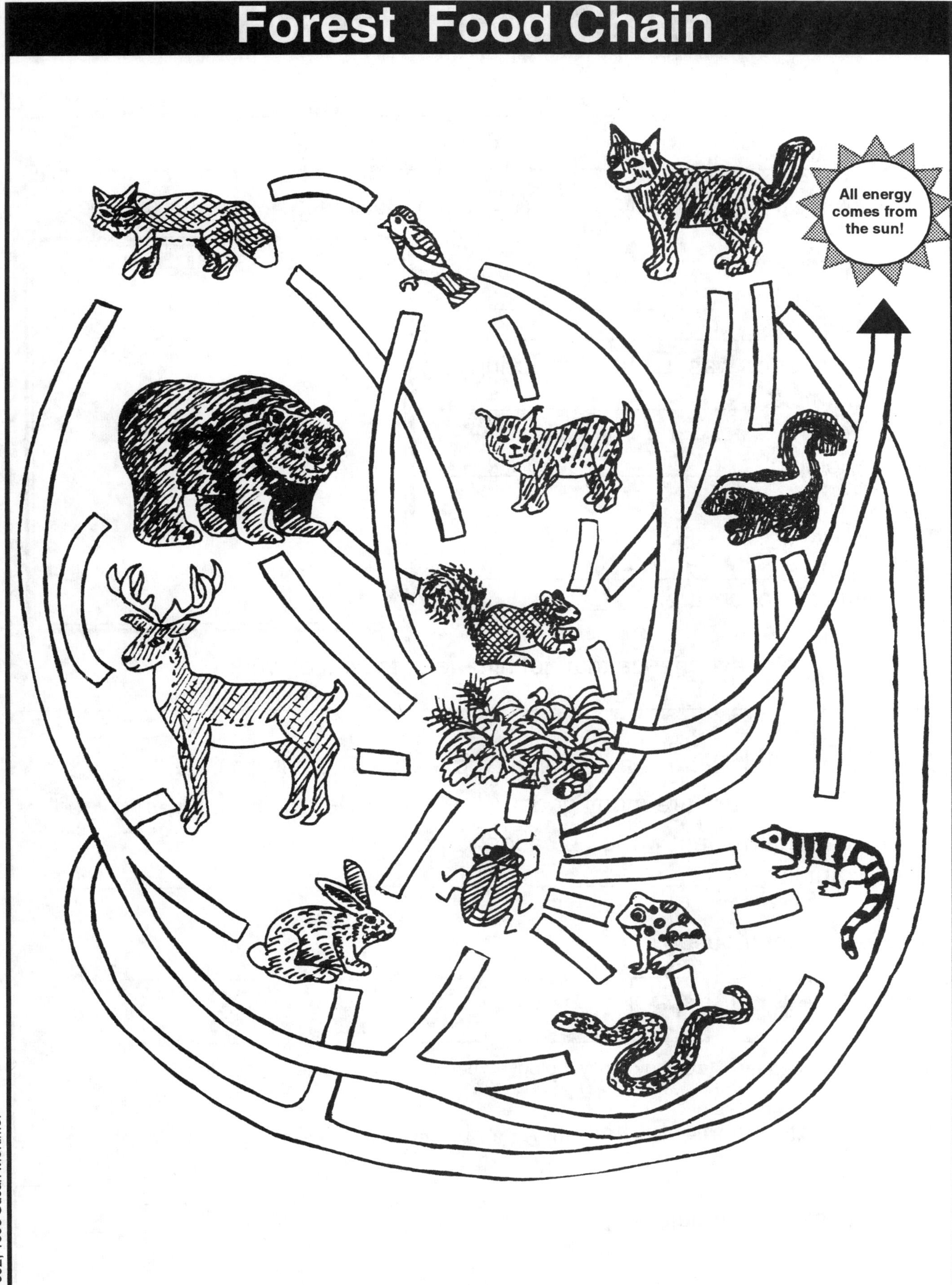
All energy comes from the sun!

Draw arrows connecting forest food chain.

Scientist Detective

Scientist: ______________________ Born: _______ Died: _______

BC —|—|—|—|—|—|—|—|—|—|—|—|— AD

200 0 200 400 600 800 1000 1200 1400 1600 1800 2000

Background:

Nationality: ______________________

Parents: ______________________

Influence was: ❐ helpful ❐ injuring

Example: ______________________

Portrait

Schooling: ______________________

Family:

Spouse: ______________________

Number of children: ______________________

Turning point experience that got him/her into field of work:

____

Religion: ❐ There is a personal God. ❐ There is no God.

❐ There are many gods. ❐ Science is 'god'. ❐ Man is 'god'.

Did religion affect work: ❐ a lot? ❐ a little? ❐ none at all?

Example: ______________________

Field of contribution:

astronomy botany zoology psychology geology medicine physics ____________

Major contributions: ❐ Invention ❐ Theory ❐ Discovery

Best known for: ______________________

Far-reaching results: ______________________

Prey for a Year

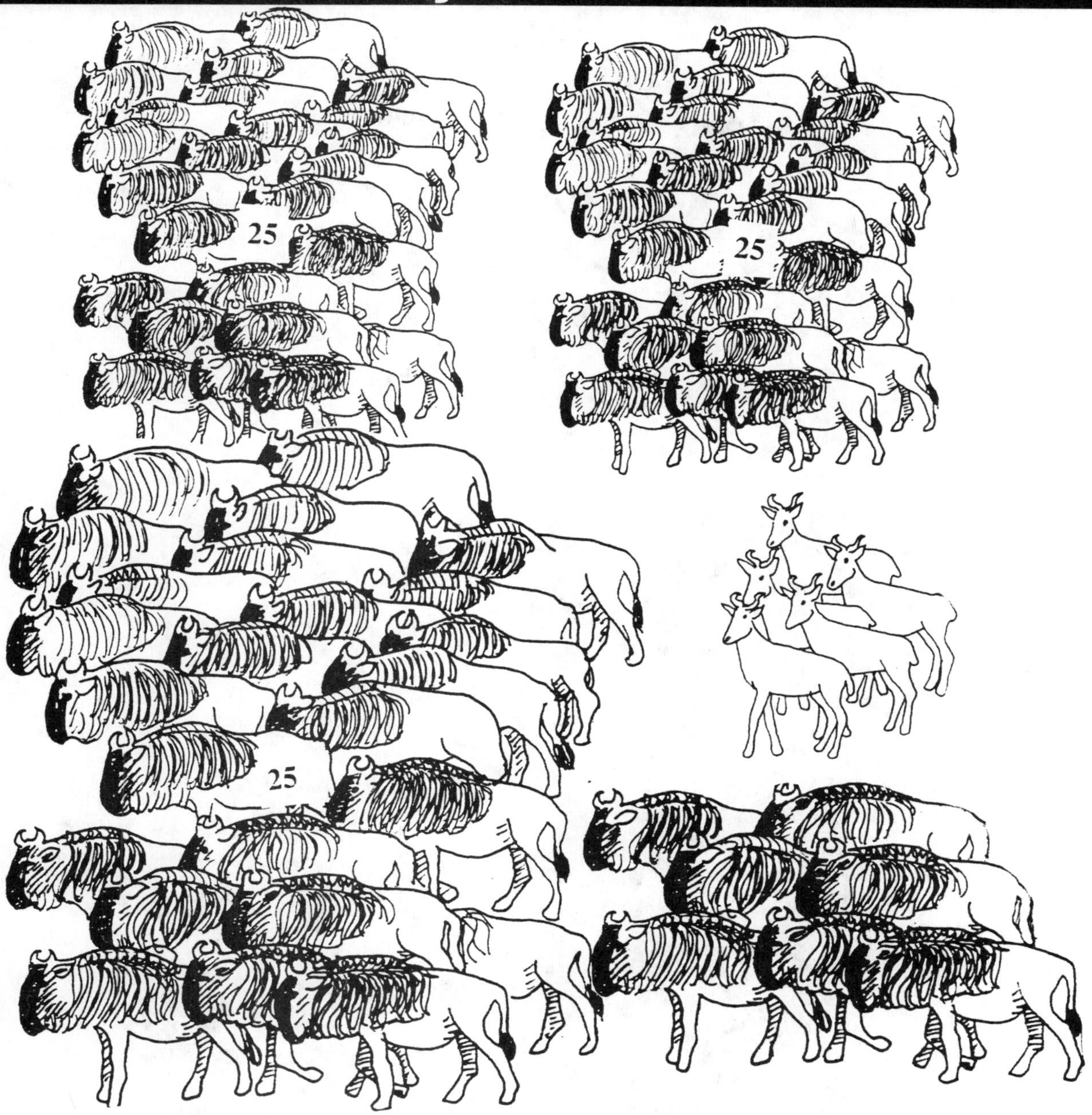

Glue "Prey for a Year" (page 2 here

Wildebeests _______ + Zebras _______ + Thomson's Gazelles _______ + Buffaloes _______ + Giraffes _______ +

Hartebeests _______ + Impalas_______ + Elands_______ + Other___14___ = Total: _______

How many lions does this feed for a year? _________

Color, cut, fold and glue "Prey for a Year" (page 2) above. Then count each kind of animal and write in totals.

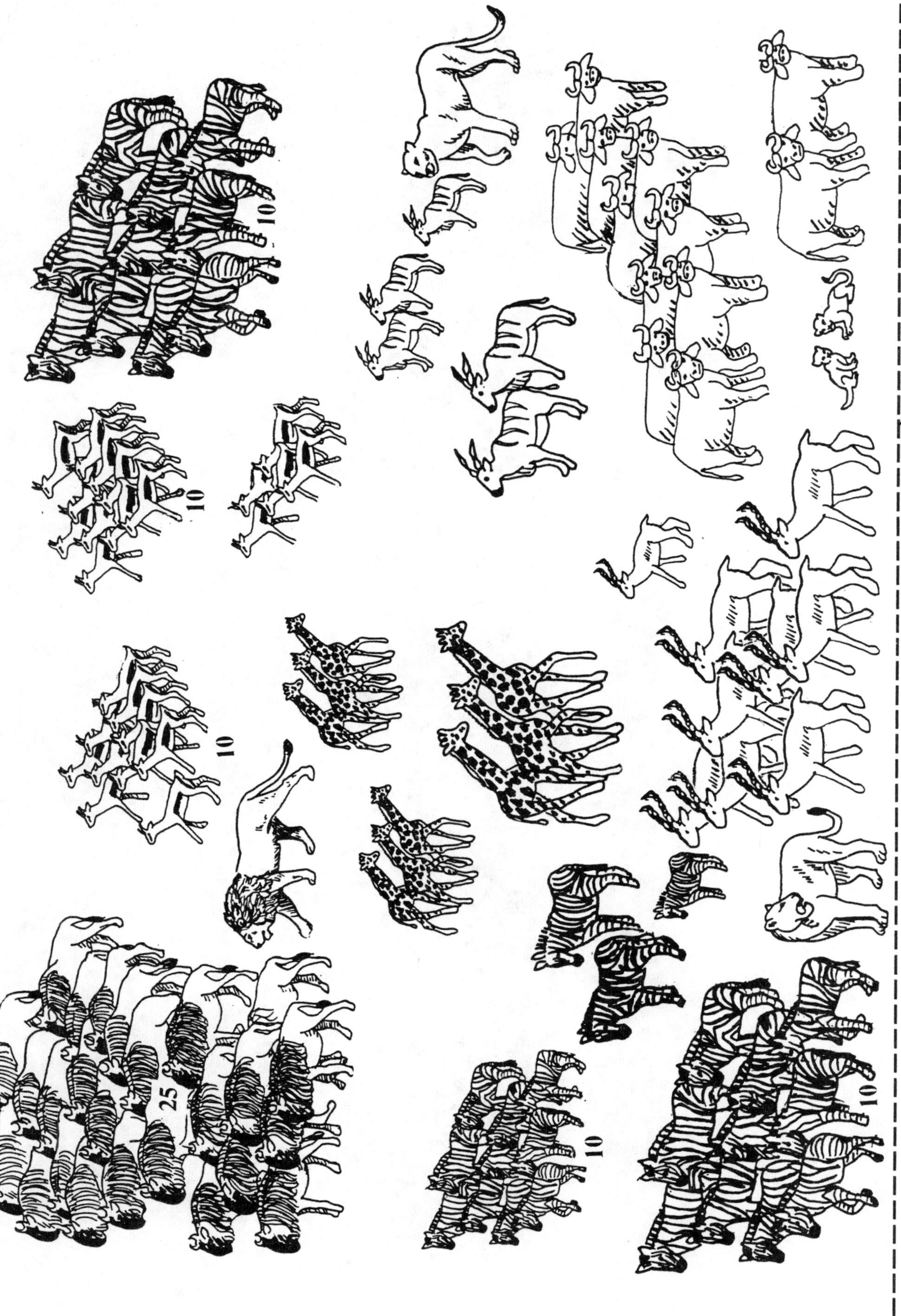
Fold here
10
10
10
10
10
10
25
Fold here

Feeding the Multitudes

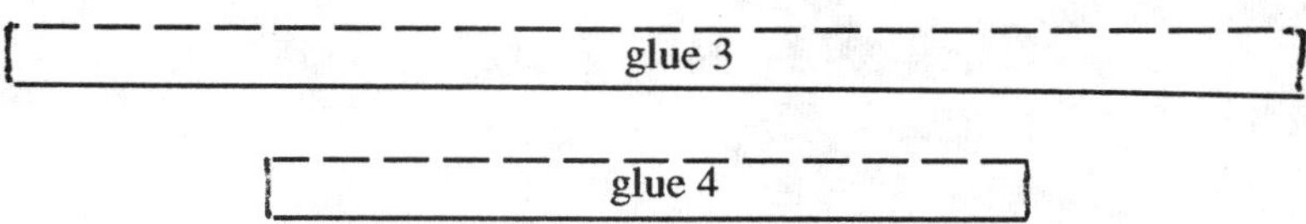
glue 3
glue 4

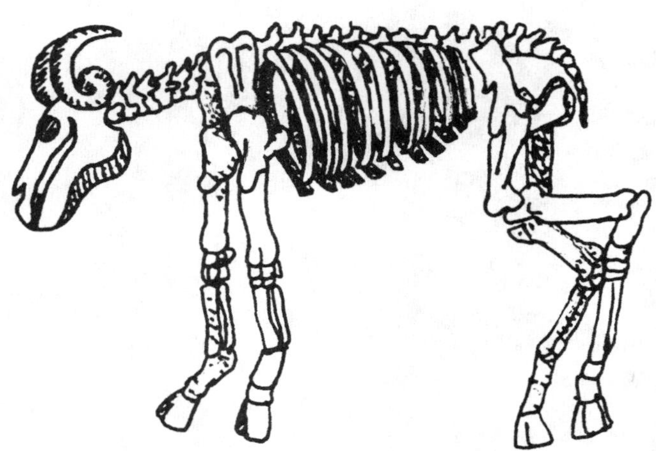

The lioness kills the Wildebeest to provide the pride with enough food for a couple of days. Next to arrive for a meal are the scavengers; the hyenas and jackals. Carrion (meat-eating) birds such as vultures and ravens then eat their fill. Lastly, carrion flies and beetles clean up the carcass.

All in a Lion's Day

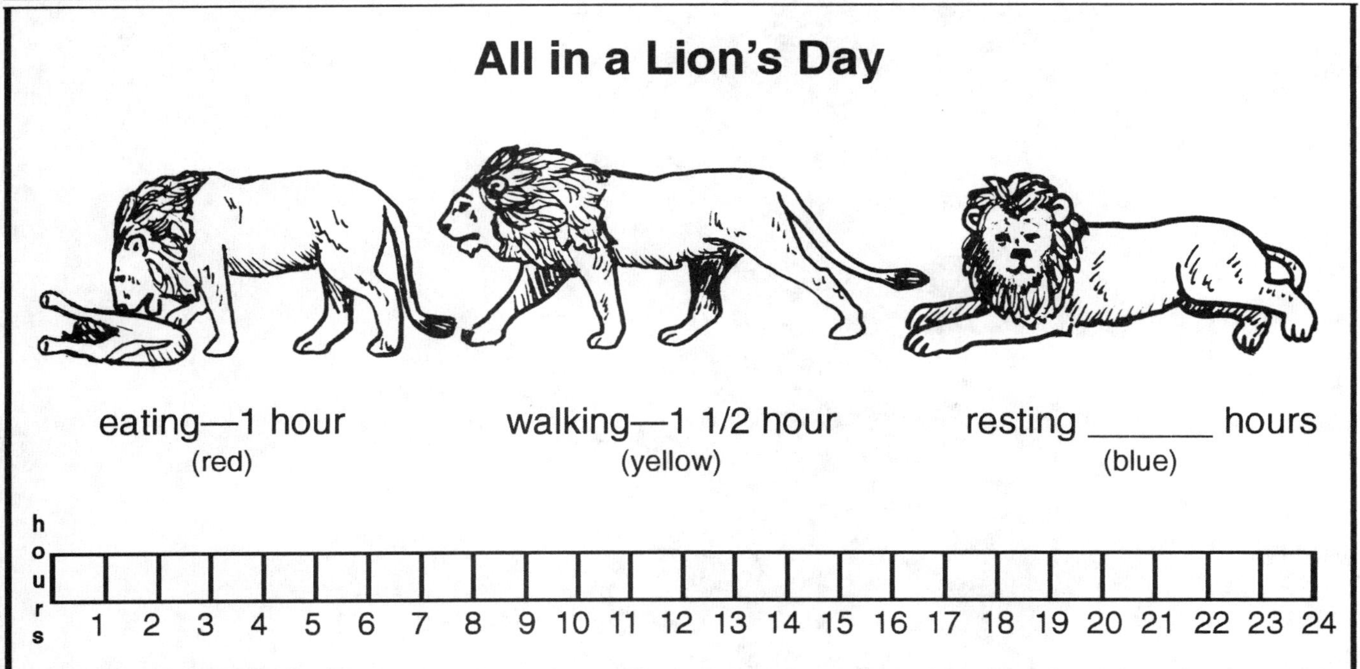

eating—1 hour (red)

walking—1 1/2 hour (yellow)

resting ______ hours (blue)

hours

1	2	3	4	5	6	7	8	9	10	11	12	13	14	15	16	17	18	19	20	21	22	23	24

Cut out figures on dotted lines on "Feeding the Multitudes" (page 2) and glue in reverse order above. Then write in how many hours of the lion's day remain for resting. On the bar graph, color the eating hours "red", the walking hours "yellow", and the resting hours "blue".

Feeding the Multitudes (page 2)

1
2
3
4
glue 2
glue 1

Each After Its Own Kind

Glue "Birth of a Zebra" Booklet here.

Armadillos have four identical offspring attached to one placenta.

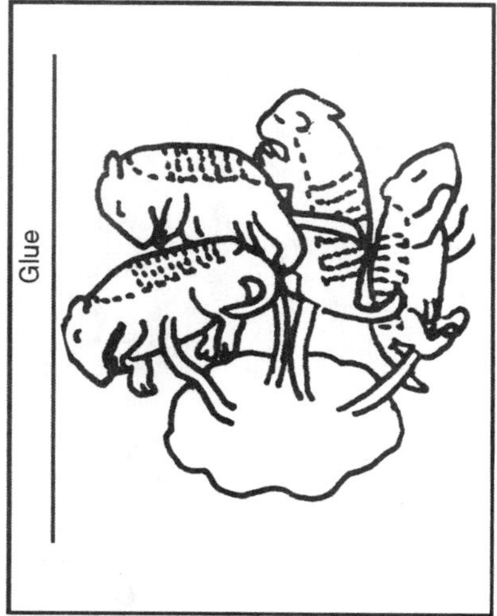
Glue

Rabbit babies grow like peas in a pod.
c
Glue b

Color, cut, fold and glue booklet from "Each After its Own Kind" (page 2) on top left corner of page. Do the same with booklet from "Each After Its Own Kind" (page 3) on bottom half of page.

Each After Its Own Kind (page 2)

Birth
of
a
Zebra
© 1992 Susan Mortimer
1
glue
2
glue
3
glue
4
glue
5
Cut and glue into booklet like this. Glue in reverse order, with page 7 first.
glue
6
glue
7

Each After Its Own Kind (page 3)

Kangaroos can have three offspring at different stages. a

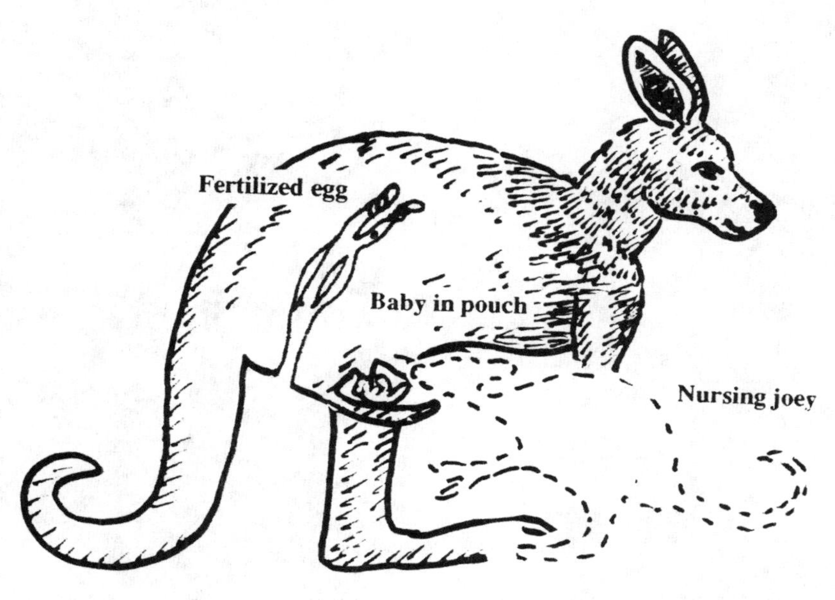
Fertilized egg
Baby in pouch
Nursing joey

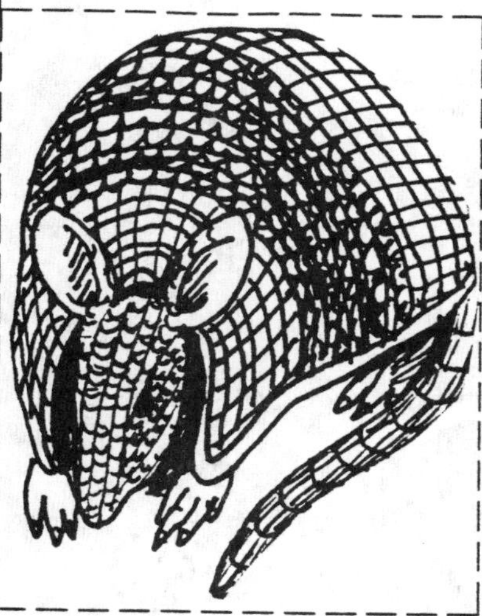

Platypus
lays 3 eggs and incubates them for 14 days.

Echidna
lays an egg and carries it around in a pouch. b

glue a

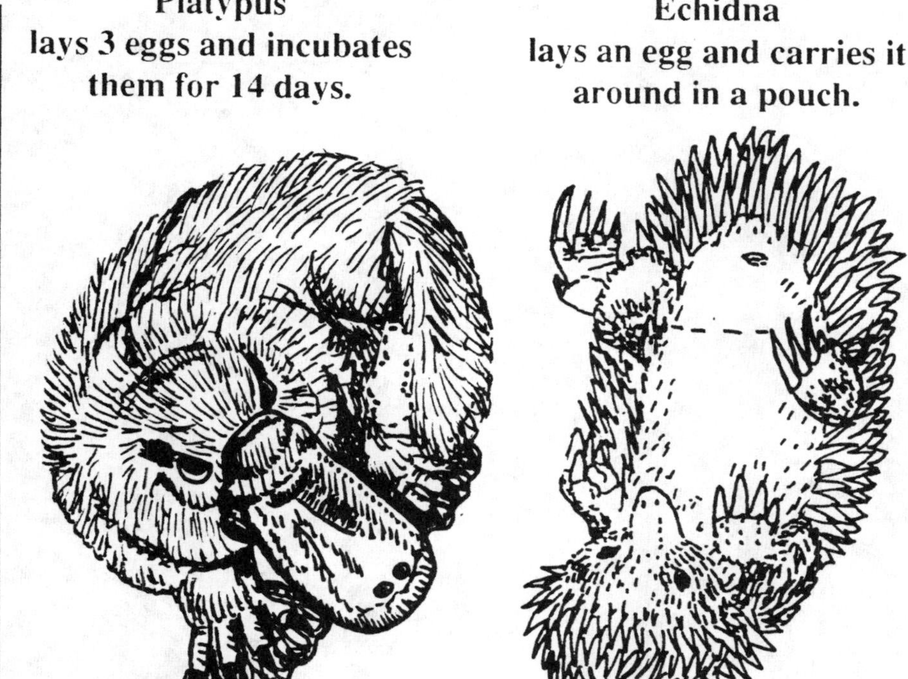

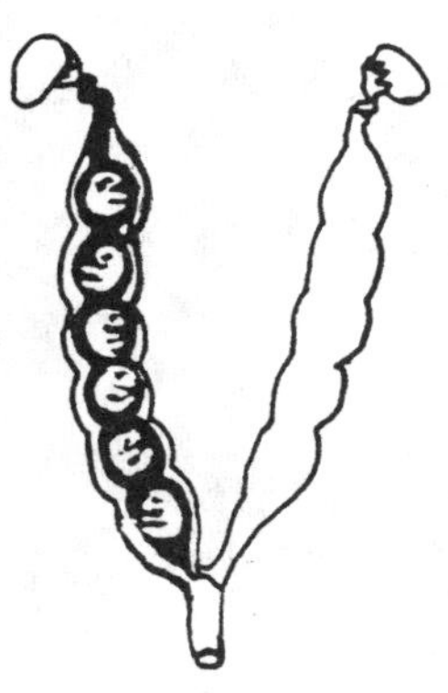

Color, cut, and glue

Egg Factory

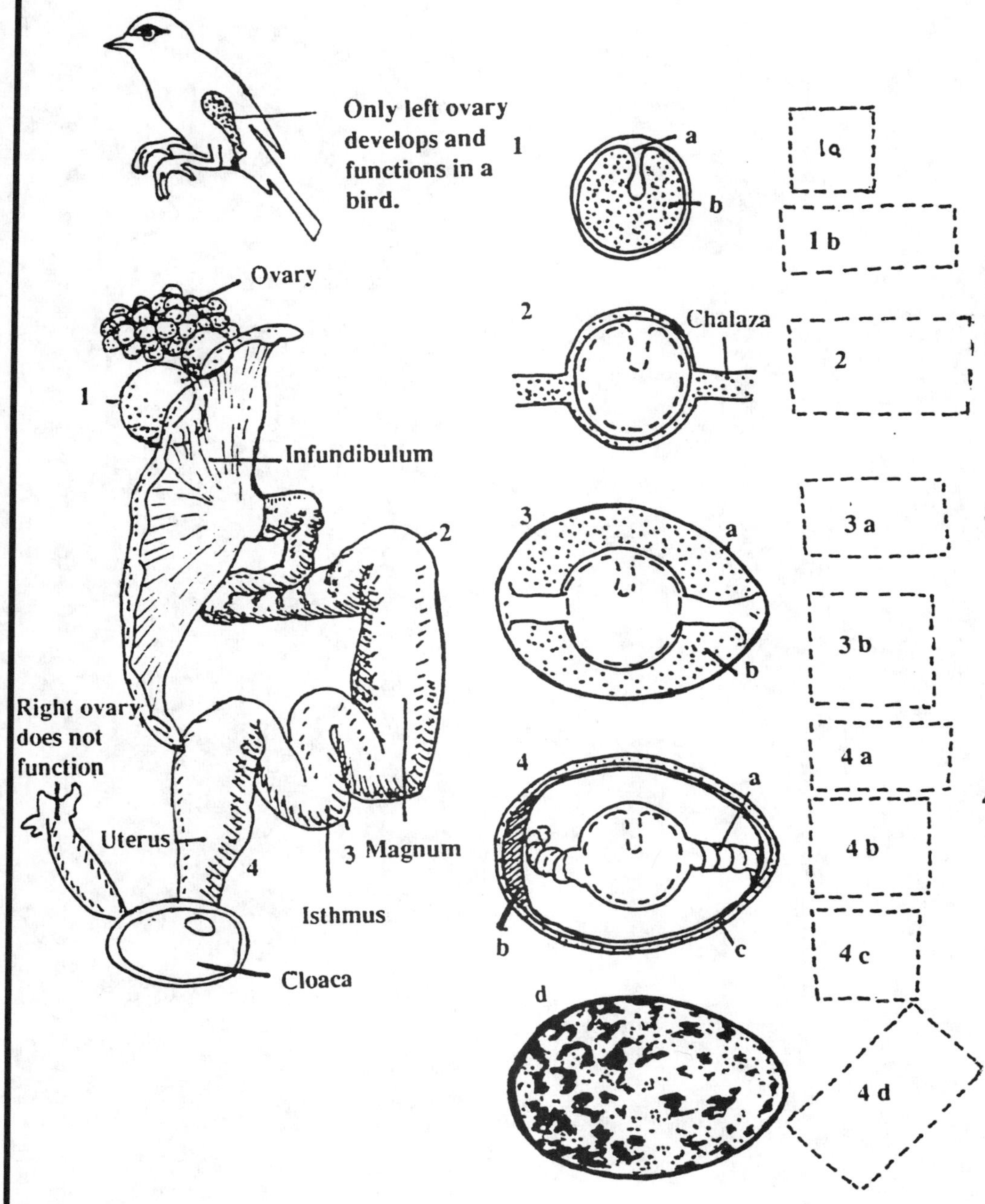

Only left ovary develops and functions in a bird.

Ovary

1

Infundibulum

2

Right ovary does not function

Uterus

4

3 Magnum

Isthmus

Cloaca

1 a b

1a

1 b

2 Chalaza

2

3 a b

3 a

3 b

4 a b c

4 a

4 b

4 c

d

4 d

1. In the **Ovary**:
   a. LIFE
      (embryonic growth region)
   b. FOOD
      (yolk)
2. Yolk moves down **Infundibulum** to **Magnum**.
   STABILIZER
      (chalaza holds yolk in the middle)
3. In the **Isthmus**:
   a. MEMBRANE
      (three layers)
   b. WATER
      (penetrates the membrane forming the egg white and doubling weight)
4. In the **Uterus**:
   a. ROTATION
      (coils the chalaza)
   b. AIR
      (pocket of air between membrane and shell)
   c. SHELL
      (secreted on egg)
   d. COLOR
      (added in the last few hours before being laid through the cloaca)

h
21 days

Watch an egg develop

Color, cut and glue pictures from "Egg Factory" (page 2). For "Hatch a Chick", first color and glue embryos into shell, then glue shells in reverse order on "Egg Factory " page.

Egg Factory (page 2)

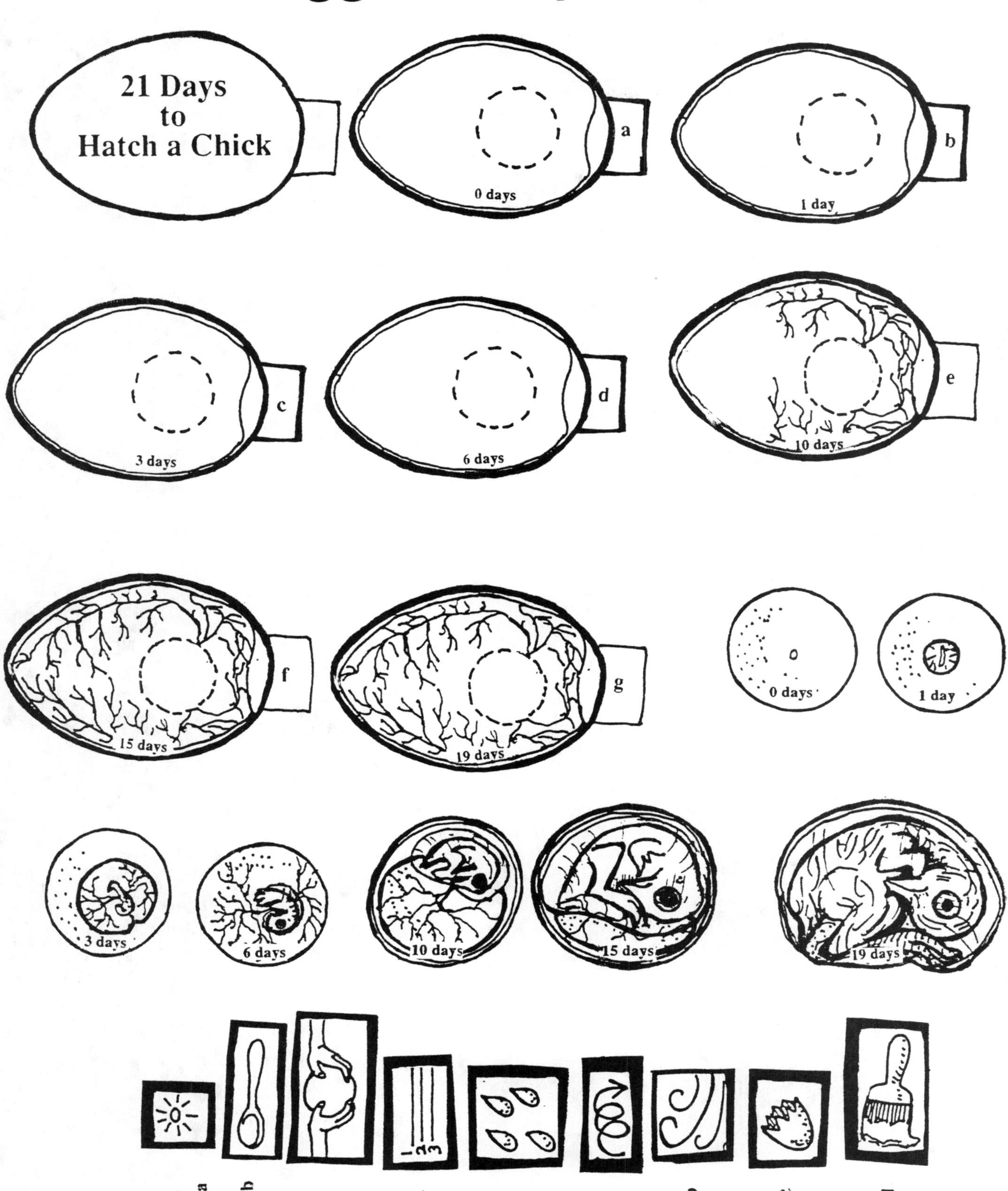
21 Days
to
Hatch a Chick
a
0 days
b
1 day
c
3 days
d
6 days
e
10 days
f
15 days
g
19 days
0 days
1 day
3 days
6 days
10 days
15 days
19 days
1 a
1 b
2
3 a
3 b
4 a
4 b
4 c
4 d

The Orders of Class Mammalia

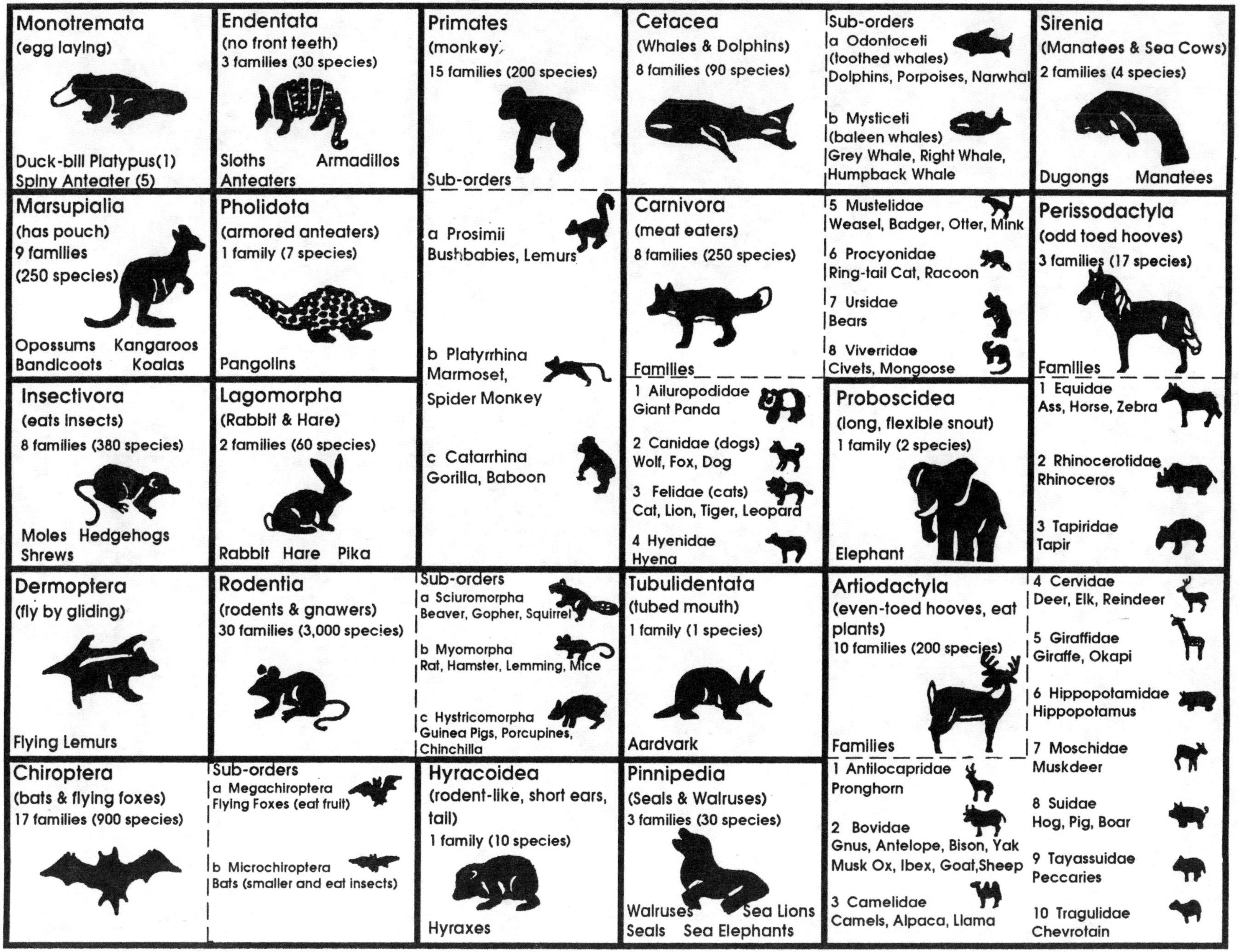

Monotremata
(egg laying)
Duck-bill Platypus(1)
Spiny Anteater (5)

Endentata
(no front teeth)
3 families (30 species)
Sloths Armadillos
Anteaters

Primates
(monkey)
15 families (200 species)
Sub-orders
a Prosimii
Bushbabies, Lemurs
b Platyrrhina
Marmoset,
Spider Monkey
c Catarrhina
Gorilla, Baboon

Cetacea
(Whales & Dolphins)
8 families (90 species)
Sub-orders
a Odontoceti
(toothed whales)
Dolphins, Porpoises, Narwhal
b Mysticeti
(baleen whales)
Grey Whale, Right Whale,
Humpback Whale

Sirenia
(Manatees & Sea Cows)
2 families (4 species)
Dugongs Manatees

Marsupialia
(has pouch)
9 families
(250 species)
Opossums Kangaroos
Bandicoots Koalas

Pholidota
(armored anteaters)
1 family (7 species)
Pangolins

Carnivora
(meat eaters)
8 families (250 species)
Families
1 Ailuropodidae
Giant Panda
2 Canidae (dogs)
Wolf, Fox, Dog
3 Felidae (cats)
Cat, Lion, Tiger, Leopard
4 Hyenidae
Hyena
5 Mustelidae
Weasel, Badger, Otter, Mink
6 Procyonidae
Ring-tail Cat, Racoon
7 Ursidae
Bears
8 Viverridae
Civets, Mongoose

Perissodactyla
(odd toed hooves)
3 families (17 species)
Families
1 Equidae
Ass, Horse, Zebra
2 Rhinocerotidae
Rhinoceros
3 Tapiridae
Tapir

Insectivora
(eats insects)
8 families (380 species)
Moles Hedgehogs
Shrews

Lagomorpha
(Rabbit & Hare)
2 families (60 species)
Rabbit Hare Pika

Proboscidea
(long, flexible snout)
1 family (2 species)
Elephant

Dermoptera
(fly by gliding)
Flying Lemurs

Rodentia
(rodents & gnawers)
30 families (3,000 species)
Sub-orders
a Sciuromorpha
Beaver, Gopher, Squirrel
b Myomorpha
Rat, Hamster, Lemming, Mice
c Hystricomorpha
Guinea Pigs, Porcupines,
Chinchilla

Tubulidentata
(tubed mouth)
1 family (1 species)
Aardvark

Artiodactyla
(even-toed hooves, eat plants)
10 families (200 species)
Families
1 Antilocapridae
Pronghorn
2 Bovidae
Gnus, Antelope, Bison, Yak
Musk Ox, Ibex, Goat,Sheep
3 Camelidae
Camels, Alpaca, Llama
4 Cervidae
Deer, Elk, Reindeer
5 Giraffidae
Giraffe, Okapi
6 Hippopotamidae
Hippopotamus
7 Moschidae
Muskdeer
8 Suidae
Hog, Pig, Boar
9 Tayassuidae
Peccaries
10 Tragulidae
Chevrotain

Chiroptera
(bats & flying foxes)
17 families (900 species)
Sub-orders
a Megachiroptera
Flying Foxes (eat fruit)
b Microchiroptera
Bats (smaller and eat insects)

Hyracoidea
(rodent-like, short ears, tail)
1 family (10 species)
Hyraxes

Pinnipedia
(Seals & Walruses)
3 families (30 species)
Walruses Sea Lions
Seals Sea Elephants

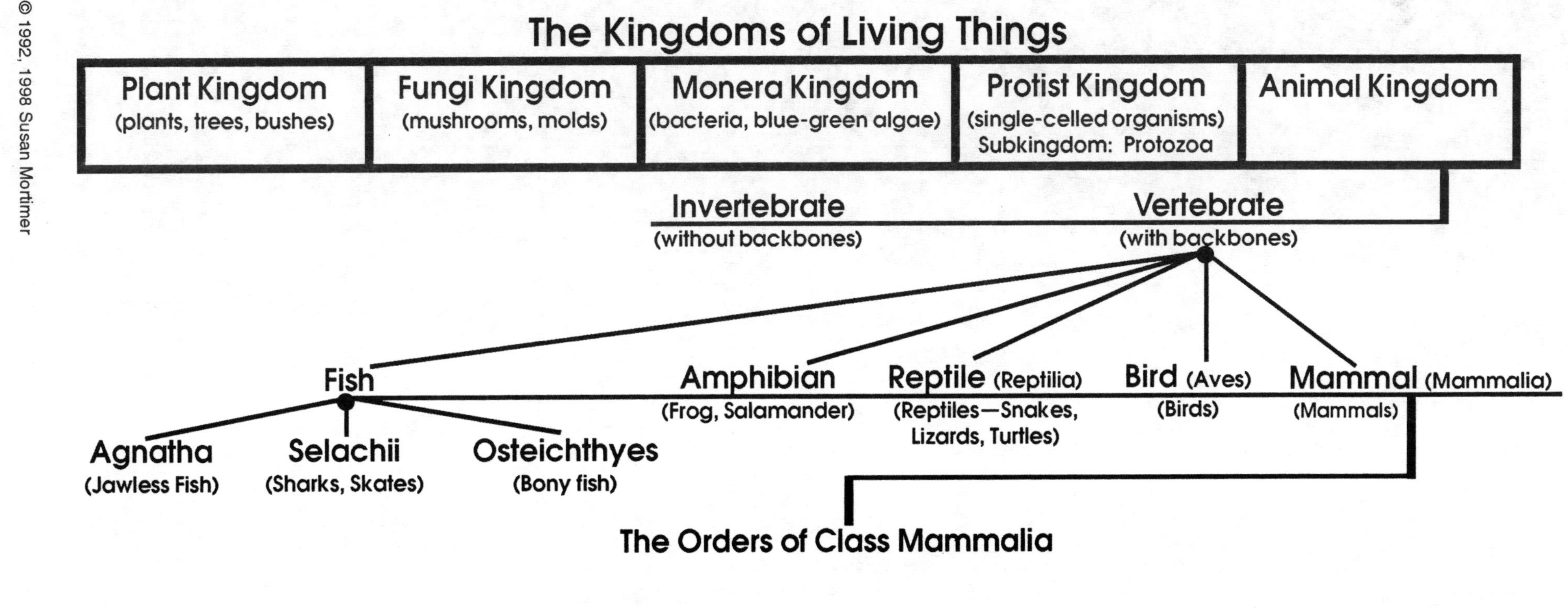
The Kingdoms of Living Things
Plant Kingdom
(plants, trees, bushes)
Fungi Kingdom
(mushrooms, molds)
Monera Kingdom
(bacteria, blue-green algae)
Protist Kingdom
(single-celled organisms)
Subkingdom: Protozoa
Animal Kingdom
Invertebrate
(without backbones)
Vertebrate
(with backbones)
Fish
Agnatha
(Jawless Fish)
Selachii
(Sharks, Skates)
Osteichthyes
(Bony fish)
Amphibian
(Frog, Salamander)
Reptile (Reptilia)
(Reptiles—Snakes, Lizards, Turtles)
Bird (Aves)
(Birds)
Mammal (Mammalia)
(Mammals)
The Orders of Class Mammalia

Glue "The Orders of Class Mammalia" here.

Classifying Animals

Kingdom: ❐ plant ❐ animal
Phylum: ❐ invertebrate
❐ vertebrate
Class: ❐ fish ❐ amphibian
❐ reptile ❐ bird ❐ mammal
Order: ____________
Family: ____________
Name: Deer

Kingdom: ❐ plant ❐ animal
Phylum: ❐ invertebrate
❐ vertebrate
Class: ❐ fish ❐ amphibian
❐ reptile ❐ bird ❐ mammal
Order: ____________
Family: ____________
Name: Right Whale

Kingdom: ❐ plant ❐ animal
Phylum: ❐ invertebrate
❐ vertebrate
Class: ❐ fish ❐ amphibian
❐ reptile ❐ bird ❐ mammal
Order: ____________
Family: ____________
Name: Zebra

Kingdom: ❐ plant ❐ animal
Phylum: ❐ invertebrate
❐ vertebrate
Class: ❐ fish ❐ amphibian
❐ reptile ❐ bird ❐ mammal
Order: ____________
Family: ____________
Name: Camel

Kingdom: ❐ plant ❐ animal
Phylum: ❐ invertebrate
❐ vertebrate
Class: ❐ fish ❐ amphibian
❐ reptile ❐ bird ❐ mammal
Order: ____________
Family: ____________
Name: Armadillo

Kingdom: ❐ plant ❐ animal
Phylum: ❐ invertebrate
❐ vertebrate
Class: ❐ fish ❐ amphibian
❐ reptile ❐ bird ❐ mammal
Order: ____________
Family: ____________
Name: Giant Panda

Kingdom: ❐ plant ❐ animal
Phylum: ❐ invertebrate
❐ vertebrate
Class: ❐ fish ❐ amphibian
❐ reptile ❐ bird ❐ mammal
Order: ____________
Family: ____________
Name: Giraffe

Kingdom: ❐ plant ❐ animal
Phylum: ❐ invertebrate
❐ vertebrate
Class: ❐ fish ❐ amphibian
❐ reptile ❐ bird ❐ mammal
Order: ____________
Family: ____________
Name: Flying Fox

Kingdom: ❐ plant ❐ animal
Phylum: ❐ invertebrate
❐ vertebrate
Class: ❐ fish ❐ amphibian
❐ reptile ❐ bird ❐ mammal
Order: ____________
Family: ____________
Name: Wolf

Classifying Animals (page 2)

Kingdom: ❒ plant ❒ animal
Phylum: ❒ invertebrate ❒ vertebrate
Class: ❒ fish ❒ amphibian ❒ reptile ❒ bird ❒ mammal
Order: ____________
Family: ____________
Name: Bear

Kingdom: ❒ plant ❒ animal
Phylum: ❒ invertebrate ❒ vertebrate
Class: ❒ fish ❒ amphibian ❒ reptile ❒ bird ❒ mammal
Order: ____________
Family: ____________
Name: Elephant

Kingdom: ❒ plant ❒ animal
Phylum: ❒ invertebrate ❒ vertebrate
Class: ❒ fish ❒ amphibian ❒ reptile ❒ bird ❒ mammal
Order: ____________
Family: ____________
Name: Rhinoceros

Kingdom: ❒ plant ❒ animal
Phylum: ❒ invertebrate ❒ vertebrate
Class: ❒ fish ❒ amphibian ❒ reptile ❒ bird ❒ mammal
Order: ____________
Family: ____________
Name: Mouse

Kingdom: ❒ plant ❒ animal
Phylum: ❒ invertebrate ❒ vertebrate
Class: ❒ fish ❒ amphibian ❒ reptile ❒ bird ❒ mammal
Order: ____________
Family: ____________
Name: Racoon

Kingdom: ❒ plant ❒ animal
Phylum: ❒ invertebrate ❒ vertebrate
Class: ❒ fish ❒ amphibian ❒ reptile ❒ bird ❒ mammal
Order: ____________
Family: ____________
Name: Rabbit

Kingdom: ❒ plant ❒ animal
Phylum: ❒ invertebrate ❒ vertebrate
Class: ❒ fish ❒ amphibian ❒ reptile ❒ bird ❒ mammal
Order: ____________
Family: ____________
Name: Bison

Kingdom: ❒ plant ❒ animal
Phylum: ❒ invertebrate ❒ vertebrate
Class: ❒ fish ❒ amphibian ❒ reptile ❒ bird ❒ mammal
Order: ____________
Family: ____________
Name: Kangaroo

Kingdom: ❒ plant ❒ animal
Phylum: ❒ invertebrate ❒ vertebrate
Class: ❒ fish ❒ amphibian ❒ reptile ❒ bird ❒ mammal
Order: ____________
Family: ____________
Name: Lion

Guess Genes for Guinea Pigs

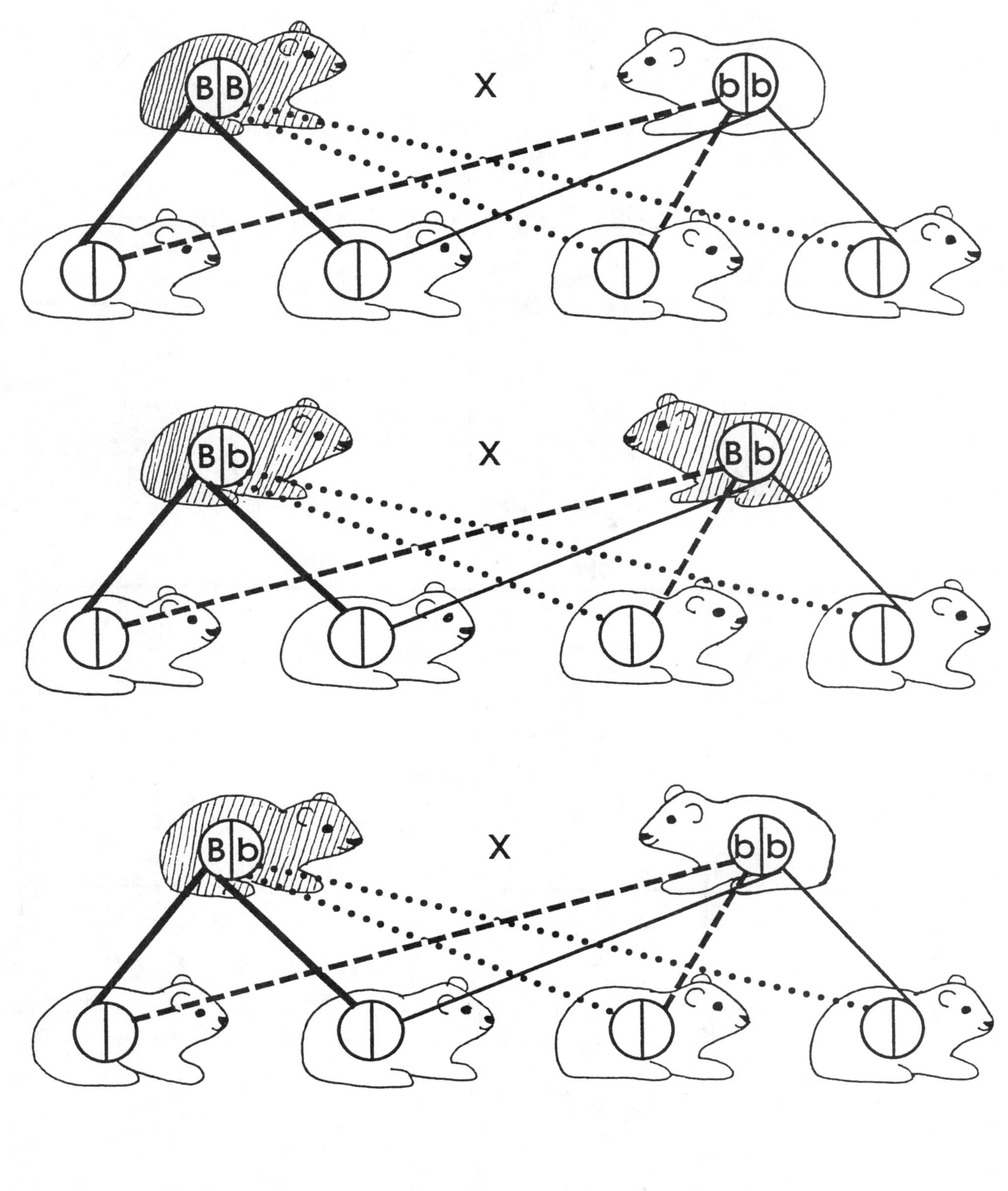
B B
X
b b
B b
X
B b
B b
X
b b

Write in the letter of the gene that is inherited from each parent. Then color the babies brown if a 'B' gene is present and white if it is not.

Breeding Domestic Chickens

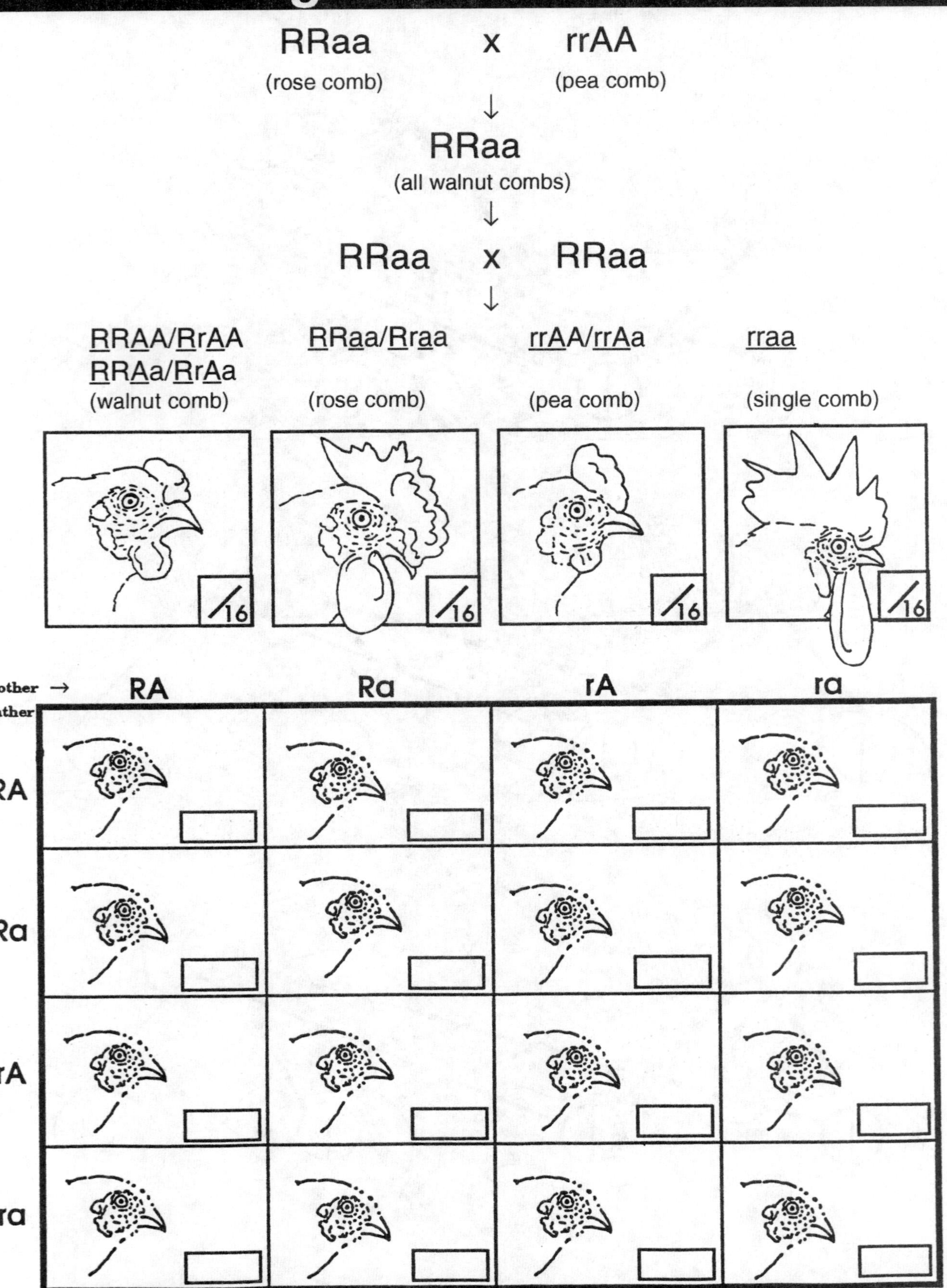
RRaa x rrAA
(rose comb) (pea comb)
RRaa
(all walnut combs)
RRaa x RRaa
RRAA/RrAA
RRAa/RrAa
(walnut comb)
RRaa/Rraa
(rose comb)
rrAA/rrAa
(pea comb)
rraa
(single comb)
/16
/16
/16
/16
Mother →
Father ↓
RA
Ra
rA
ra
RA
Ra
rA
ra

 Write in the letters of the genes that are inherited from each parent. Then draw in the correct comb.

Migration

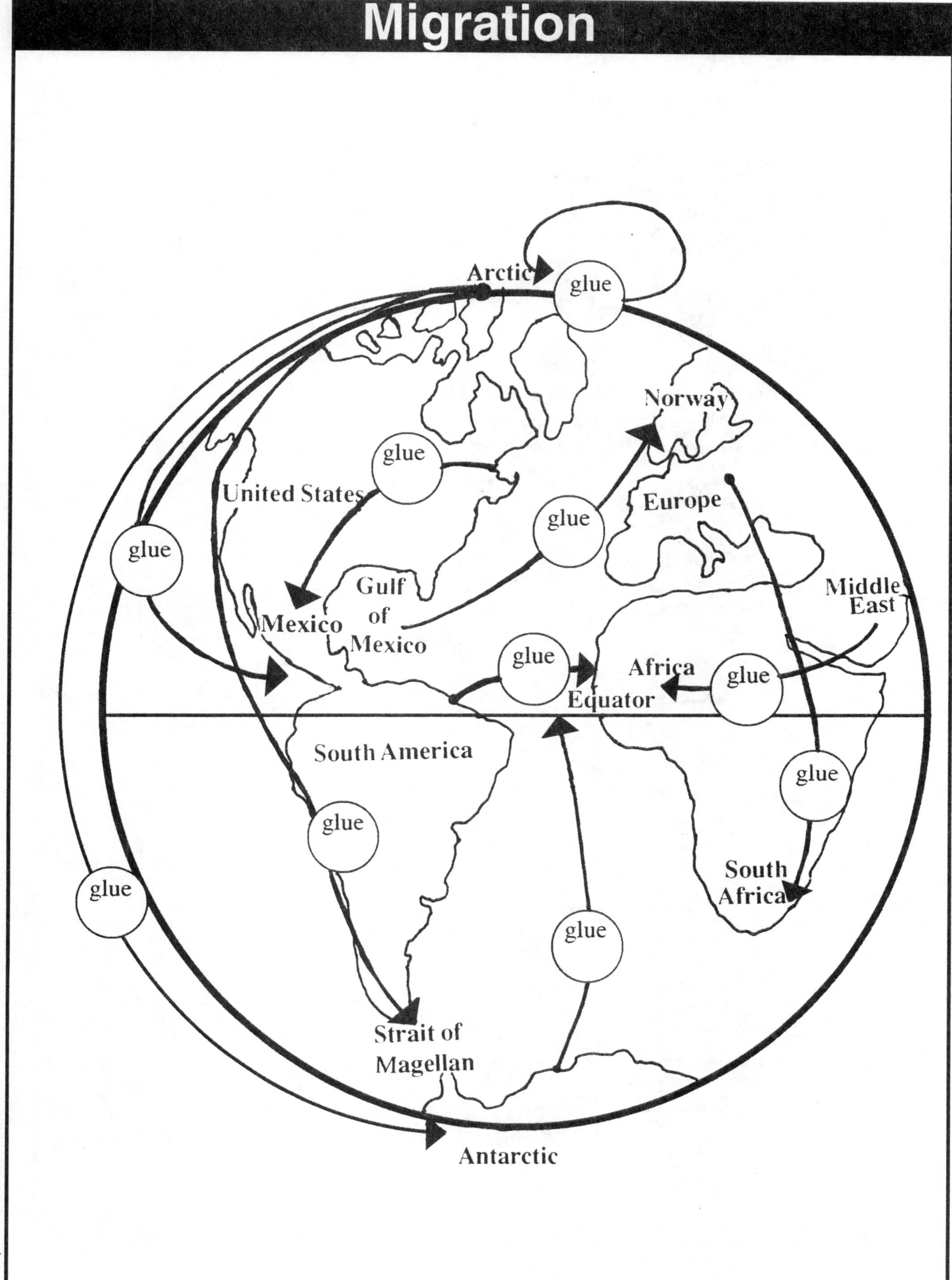

Arctic
glue
Norway
glue
United States
Europe
glue
glue
glue
Gulf of Mexico
Middle East
Mexico
glue
Africa
glue
Equator
South America
glue
glue
glue
South Africa
glue
glue
Strait of Magellan
Antarctic

Glue "Migration" page 2 here.

Cut and glue "Migration Routes" from "Migration" (page 2) on the side of this page. Cut out the animals with their names, and from the clues under the Migration Routes, figure out each migration path and glue the animal on the correct circle.

Migration (page 2)

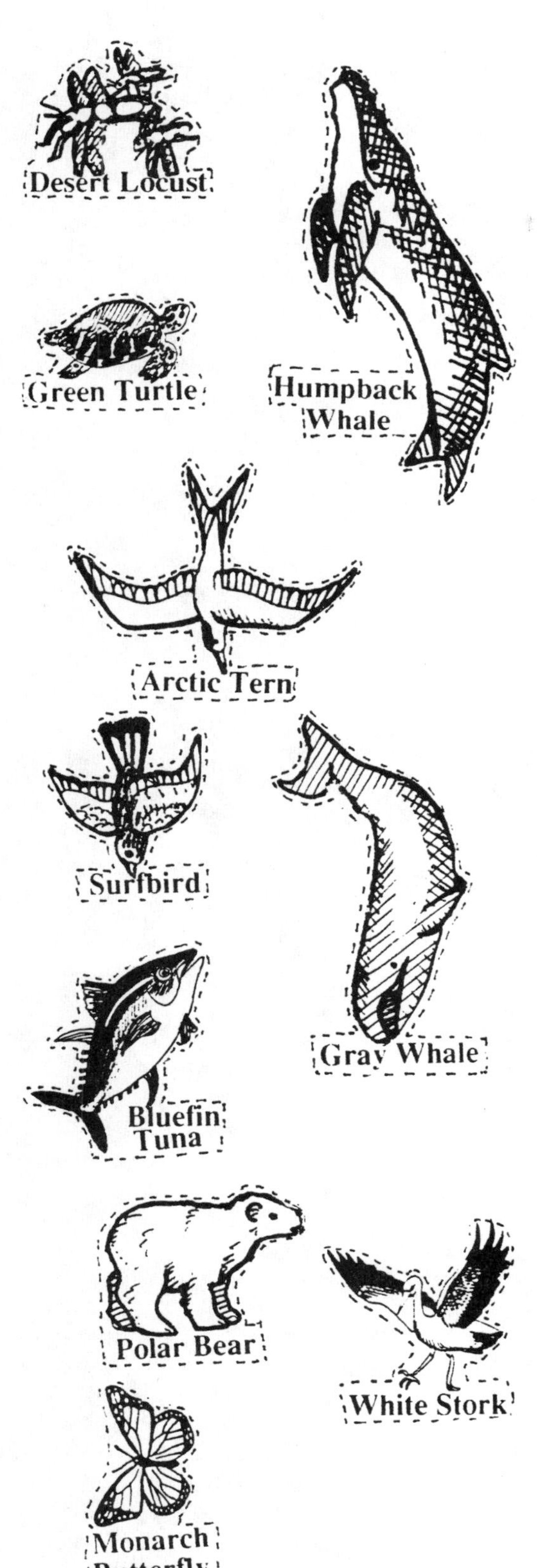
Desert Locust
Green Turtle
Humpback Whale
Arctic Tern
Surfbird
Gray Whale
Bluefin Tuna
Polar Bear
White Stork
Monarch Butterfly

Migration Routes

1. The arctic tern flies from the Arctic to the Antarctic to enjoy the summers of both places.

2. The white stork spends summers in Europe and then flies to South Africa.

3. The green turtle swims from the coast of South America to the coast of Africa.

4. The humpback whale spends summers in the Antarctic and goes to breed at the equator.

5. The Monarch butterfly flies from the northeastern United States to Mexico to spend the winter.

6. The gray whale travels from the Arctic Sea to breeding grounds off the coast of Mexico, a total of 16,000 miles round trip.

7. The surfbird flies 9,900 miles from the Arctic to the Strait of Magellan.

8. Polar bears live on ice packs in the Arctic Sea. Ocean currents pull these in a circle over a period of 5-6 years.

9. Millions of desert locust swarm across the Middle East to Africa, eating everything as they go.

10. Bluefin tuna swim 4,200 miles from the Gulf of Mexico to off the coast of Norway.

The Eyes Have It

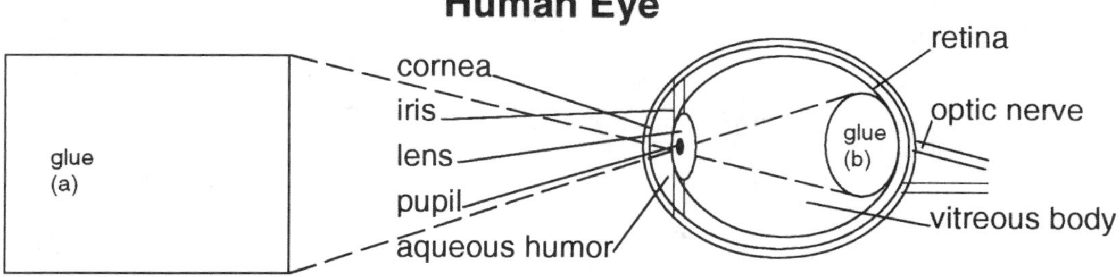
Human Eye
glue
(a)
cornea
iris
lens
pupil
aqueous humor
retina
glue
(b)
optic nerve
vitreous body

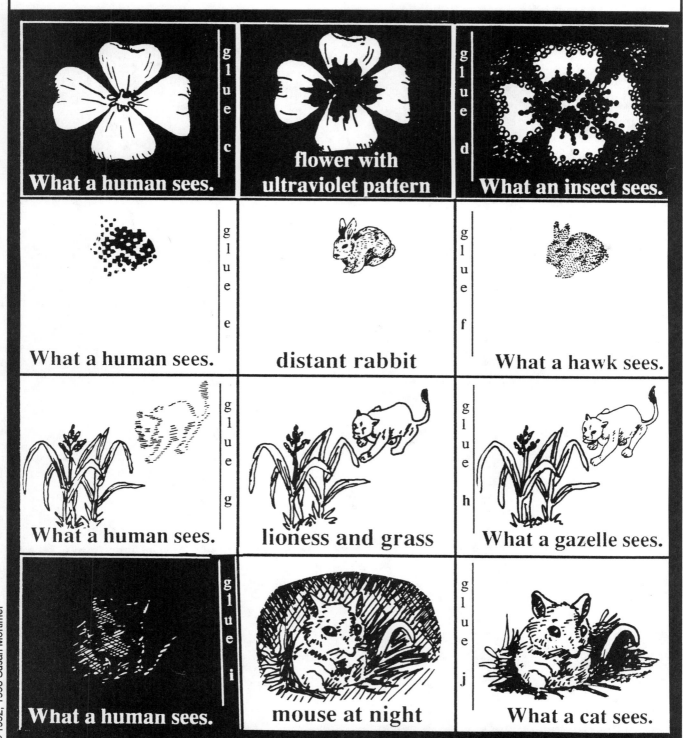

What a human sees. (glue c)	flower with ultraviolet pattern	(glue d) What an insect sees.
What a human sees. (glue e)	distant rabbit	(glue f) What a hawk sees.
What a human sees. (glue g)	lioness and grass	(glue h) What a gazelle sees.
What a human sees. (glue i)	mouse at night	(glue j) What a cat sees.

Color and cut "The Eyes Have It" (page 2) and glue to corresponding letters.

The Eyes Have It (page 2)

a

b

(c) Eyes can only detect certain light waves. Many insects, in order to survive, rely on ultraviolet patterns in flowers and other insects that humans can not even see.

glue k

insect's eye (d)

compound eye: each eye has its own lens.

insect (k)

(e) A hawk's eye has eight times as many visual cells as a human's eye. This means a hawk can easily recognize a distant rabbit that appears as only a blur to a human.

glue l

hawk's eye (f)

pecten: pleats that carry extra blood to the eye

hawk (l)

(g) Unlike the human eye, which can focus on only one thing at a time, a grazing animal can see what it is eating while at the same time watch out for predators.

glue m

gazelle's eye (h)

eye can focus near and far

gazelle (m)

(i) The cat can see easily in the dark because its eyes, like a mirror, reflect the light that enters the eye, thus doubling the available light.

glue n

cat's eye (j)

tapetum: mirror that reflects light

cat (n)

Color and cut along the dotted lines and glue to corresponding letters on "The Eyes Have It" page.

Brains

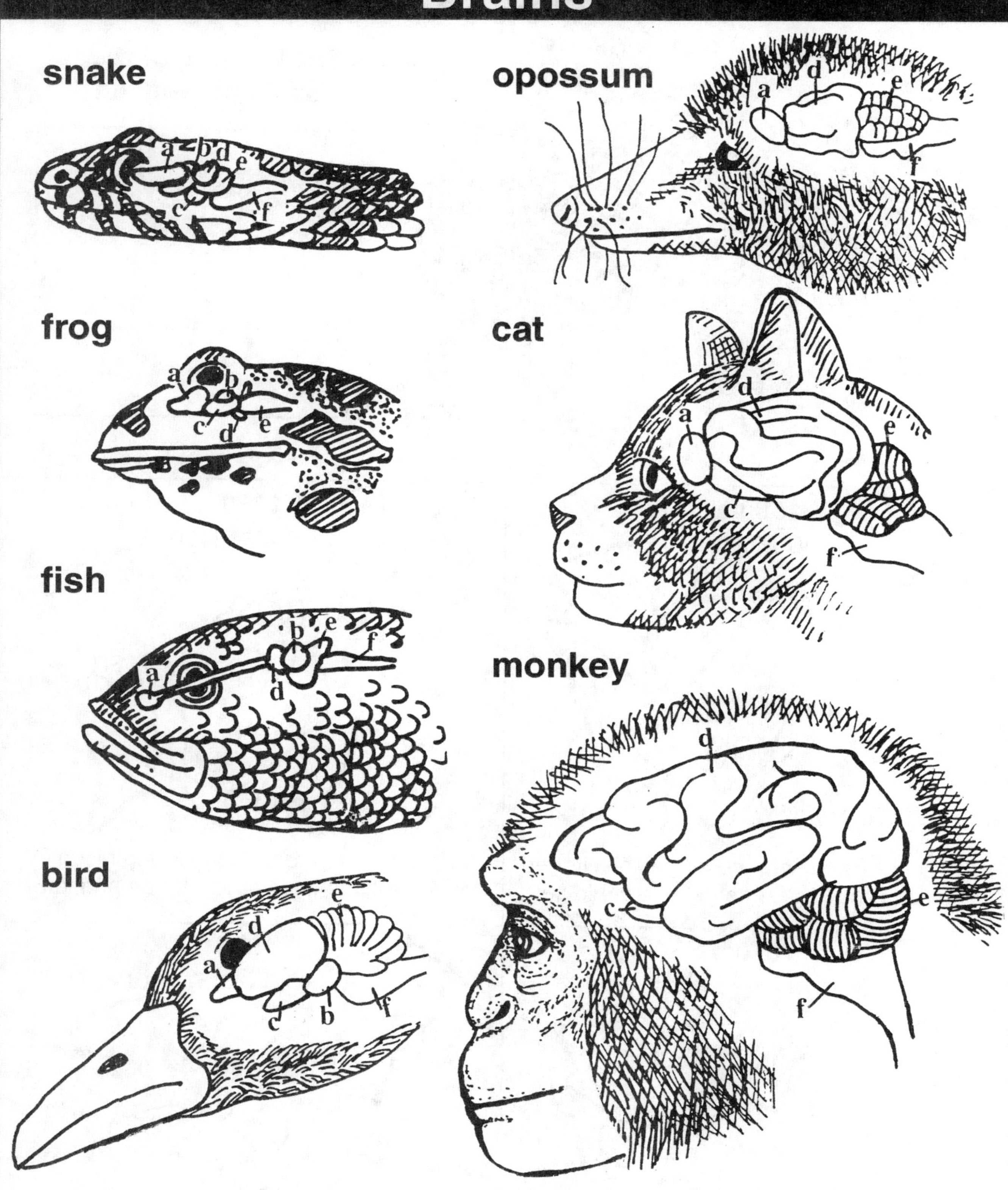
snake
opossum
frog
cat
fish
monkey
bird

Color code: (a) **olfactory bulb** (smell) — red (b) **optic lobes** (sight) — blue
(c) **pituitary** (growth) — green (d) **cerebrum** (intelligence, movement) — gray
(e) **cerebellum** (voluntary muscles) — purple (f) **medulla** (involuntary muscles) — orange

Color each part of the brain according to the corresponding color code.

Extinct is Forever

Bison (buffalo) on the Range

The Passing of the Passenger Pigeon

Glue "Passenger Pigeon" booklet here.

1500's
60 Million

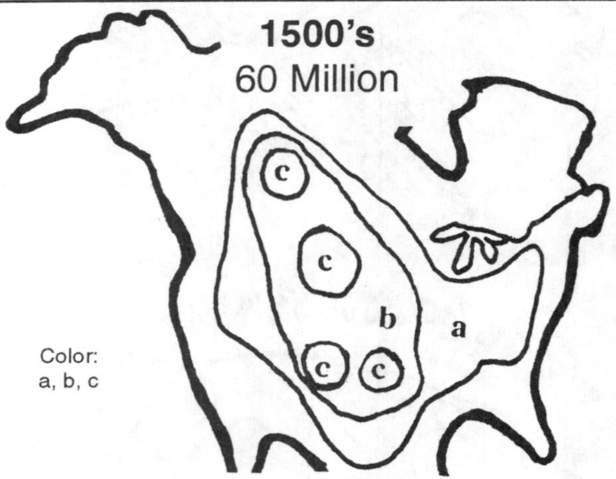

c
c
b
a
c
c

Color:
a, b, c

The countryside seemed almost blackened by bison herds as far as the eye could see.

1850
Millions killed

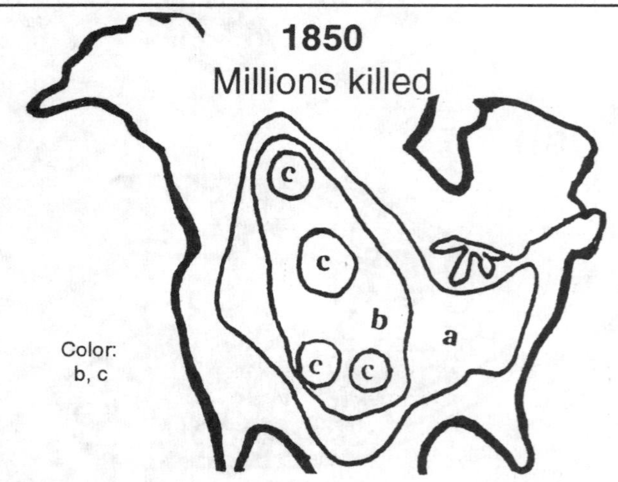

c
c
b
a
c
c

Color:
b, c

Professional hunters began killing bison in 1825. Millions were shot for hide and left.

1870's
2 1/2 Million killed each year.

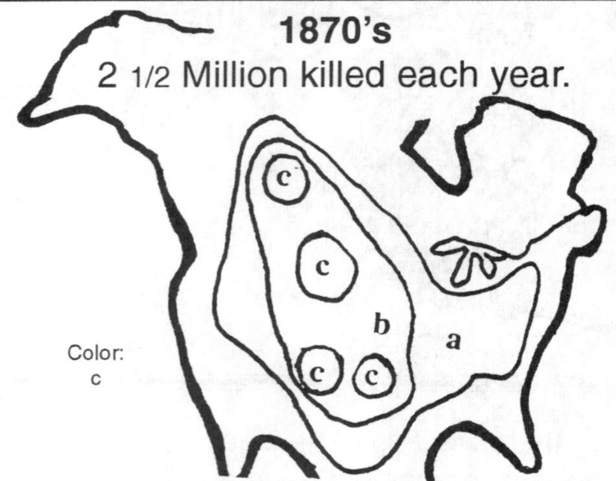

c
c
b
a
c
c

Color:
c

To subdue the Plains Indians, the Government killed their food supply, which was bison.

1894
Last wild bison shot.

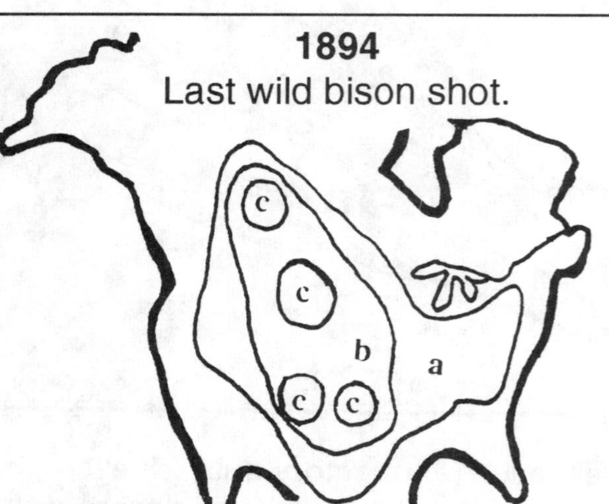

c
c
b
a
c
c

Only 250 bison remained in captivity. They have now increased to several thousand.

Color, cut, fold and glue booklet "Extinct is Forever (page 2) on top left corner of page.

Extinct is Forever (page 2)

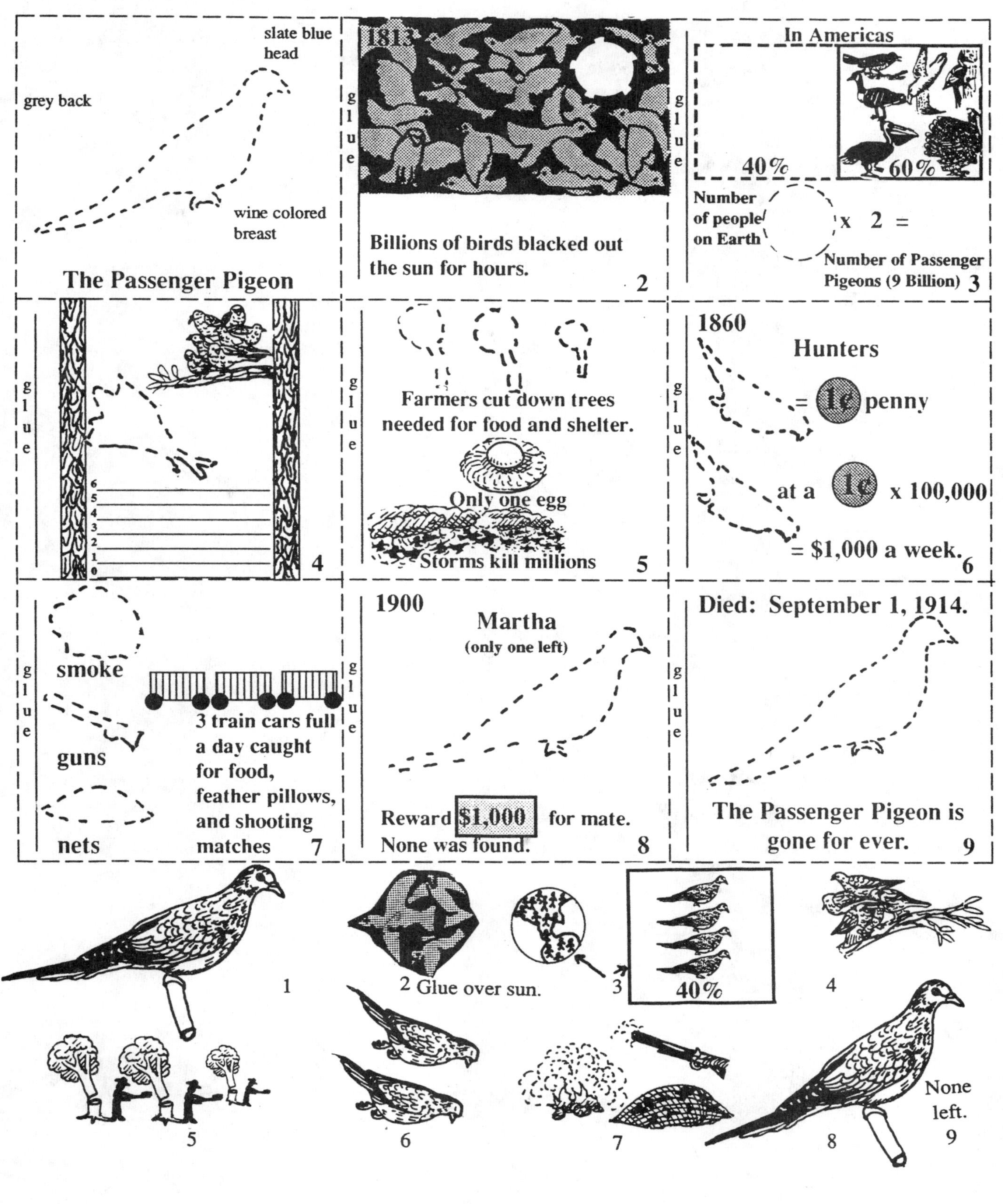

slate blue head
grey back
wine colored breast
The Passenger Pigeon
1813
glue
Billions of birds blacked out the sun for hours.
2
In Americas
40%
60%
Number of people on Earth
x 2 =
Number of Passenger Pigeons (9 Billion) 3
glue
6
5
4
3
2
1
0
4
glue
Farmers cut down trees needed for food and shelter.
Only one egg
Storms kill millions
5
1860
Hunters
glue
= 1¢ penny
at a 1¢ x 100,000
= $1,000 a week.
6
glue
smoke
guns
nets
3 train cars full a day caught for food, feather pillows, and shooting matches
7
1900
Martha
(only one left)
glue
Reward $1,000 for mate.
None was found.
8
Died: September 1, 1914.
glue
The Passenger Pigeon is gone for ever.
9
1
2 Glue over sun.
3
40%
4
5
6
7
8
None left.
9

Cut out pictures from lower half of page and glue on corresponding page above. Then color, cut out and make into a booklet. Glue booklet on "Extinct is Forever" page.

A Whale of Information

Humpback

(black) (white)

then now

148,000 142,000 136,000 130,000 126,000 120,000 114,000 108,000 102,000 96,000 90,000 84,000 78,000 72,000 66,000 60,000 54,000 48,000 42,000 36,000 30,000 24,000 18,000 12,000 6,000 0

Whale Count

❑Baleen ❑Toothed
Endangered ❑Yes ❑No
Protected__________
Length__________
Weight__________
Facts__________

Fin

(gray) (white)

then now

1,250,000 1,200,000 1,150,000 1,100,000 1,050,000 1,000,000 950,000 900,000 850,000 800,000 750,000 700,000 650,000 600,000 550,000 500,000 450,000 400,000 350,000 300,000 250,000 200,000 150,000 100,000 50,000 0

Whale Count

❑Baleen ❑Toothed
Endangered ❑Yes ❑No
Protected__________
Length__________
Weight__________
Facts__________

Orca
(killer whale)

(black) (white)

❑Baleen ❑Toothed
Endangered ❑Yes ❑No
Protected__________
Length__________
Weight__________
Facts__________

Blue

(blue)

then now

1,250,000 1,200,000 1,150,000 1,100,000 1,050,000 1,000,000 950,000 900,000 850,000 800,000 750,000 700,000 650,000 600,000 550,000 500,000 450,000 400,000 350,000 300,000 250,000 200,000 150,000 100,000 50,000 0

Whale Count

❑Baleen ❑Toothed
Endangered ❑Yes ❑No
Protected__________
Length__________
Weight__________
Facts__________

Right

(black) (white)

then now

50,000 48,000 46,000 44,000 42,000 40,000 38,000 36,000 34,000 32,000 30,000 28,000 26,000 24,000 22,000 20,000 18,000 16,000 14,000 12,000 10,000 8,000 6,000 4,000 2,000 0

Whale Count

❑Baleen ❑Toothed
Endangered ❑Yes ❑No
Protected__________
Length__________
Weight__________
Facts__________

Bowhead

(black) (white)

then now

50,000 48,000 46,000 44,000 42,000 40,000 38,000 36,000 34,000 32,000 30,000 28,000 26,000 24,000 22,000 20,000 18,000 16,000 14,000 12,000 10,000 8,000 6,000 4,000 2,000 0

Whale Count

❑Baleen ❑Toothed
Endangered ❑Yes ❑No
Protected__________
Length__________
Weight__________
Facts__________

Sperm

(black)

then now

3,000,000 2,880,000 2,760,000 2,640,000 2,520,000 2,400,000 2,280,000 2,160,000 2,040,000 1,920,000 1,800,000 1,680,000 1,560,000 1,440,000 1,320,000 1,200,000 1,080,000 960,000 840,000 720,000 600,000 480,000 360,000 240,000 120,000 0

Whale Count

❑Baleen ❑Toothed
Endangered ❑Yes ❑No
Protected__________
Length__________
Weight__________
Facts__________

Gray

(gray)

1947 now

25,000 24,000 23,000 22,000 21,000 20,000 19,000 18,000 17,000 16,000 15,000 14,000 13,000 12,000 11,000 10,000 9,000 8,000 7,000 6,000 5,000 4,000 3,000 2,000 1,000 0

Whale Count

❑Baleen ❑Toothed
Endangered ❑Yes ❑No
Protected__________
Length__________
Weight__________
Facts__________

Fill in the information as the teacher reads about each whale.

Wonderfully Made

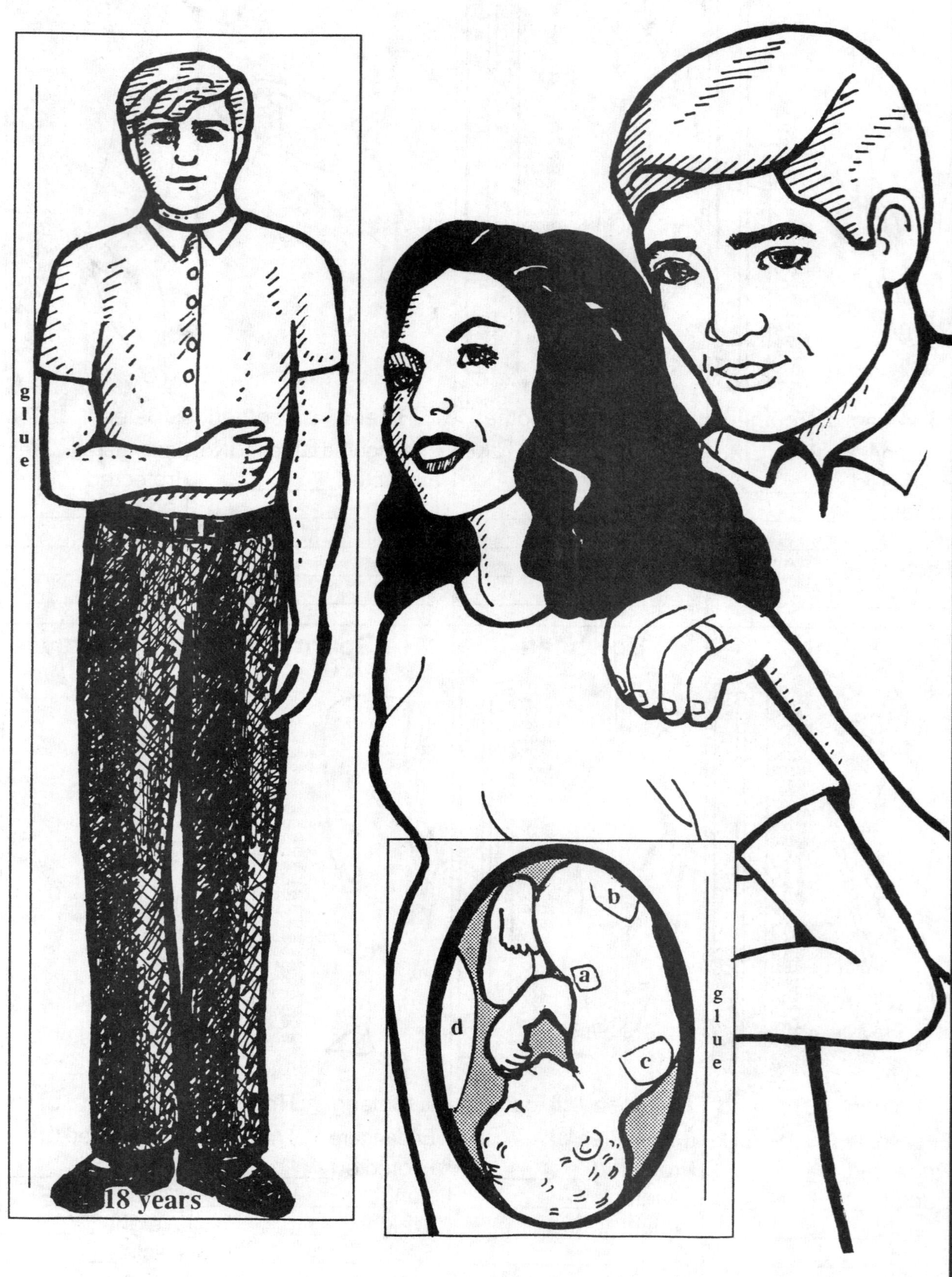

glue
18 years
b
a
d
c
glue

 Cut out and glue the different age pictures of the boy (from "Wonderfully Made" page 2). Start with the oldest to youngest. Then cut and glue leg, arm, placenta and mother's blouse on baby.

Wonderfully Made (page 2)

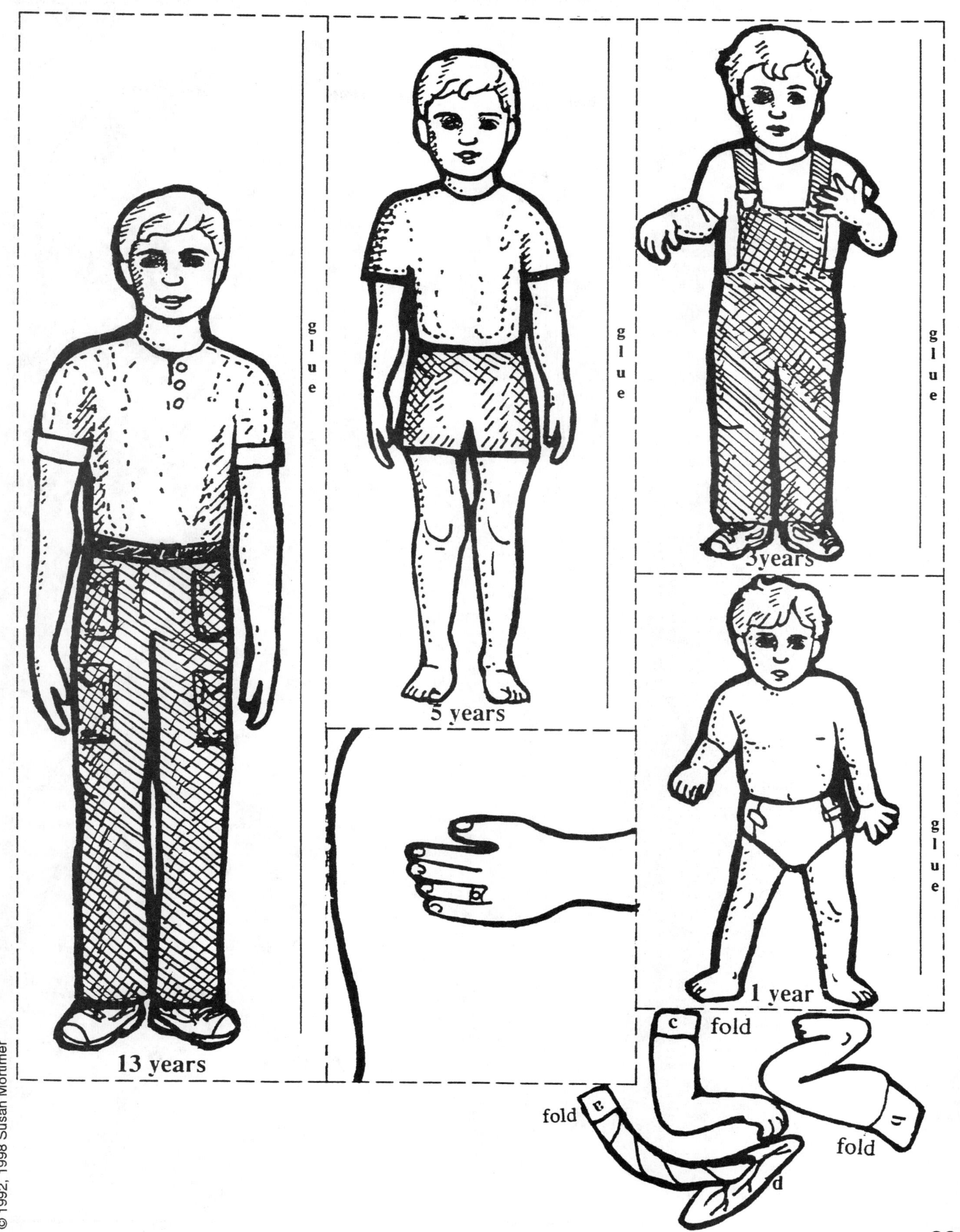
glue
glue
glue
glue
13 years
5 years
3years
1 year
c
fold
fold
fold
d

Cell City

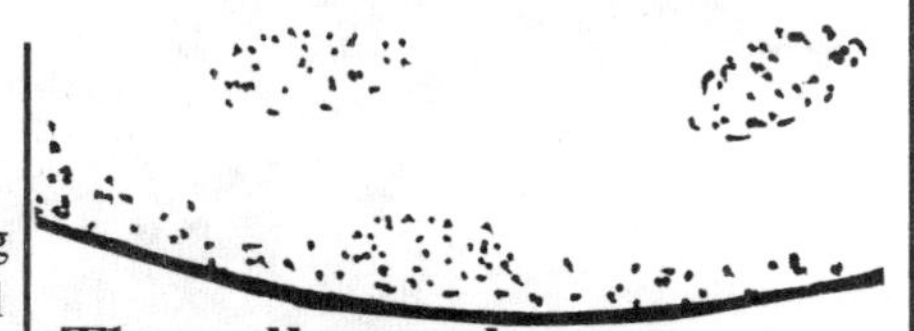

glue

The **cell membrane** acts like a "guarded wall" that controls what can enter or leave the cell. It does not let protein, fat, or starch through, but water, oxygen, and carbon dioxide can easily pass.

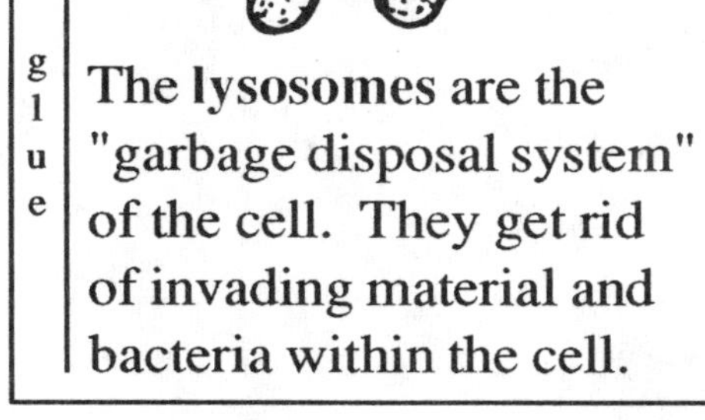

glue

The **lysosomes** are the "garbage disposal system" of the cell. They get rid of invading material and bacteria within the cell.

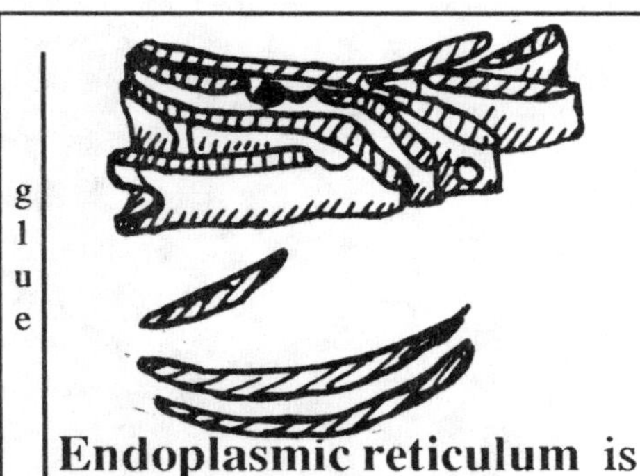

glue

Endoplasmic reticulum is an inter-locking maze of "transportation", carrying protein throughout the cell.

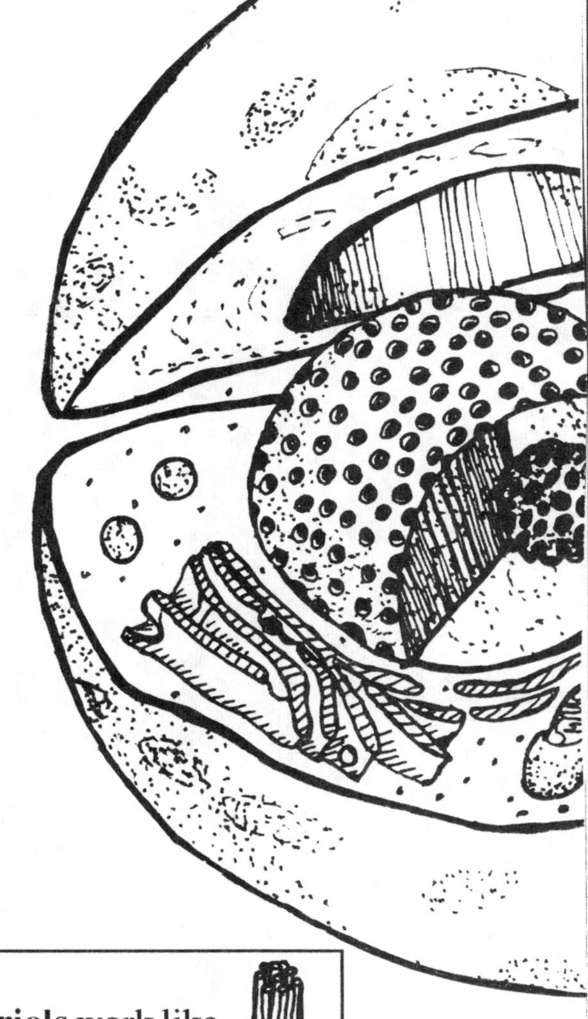

Glue "Cell City" page 2 here.

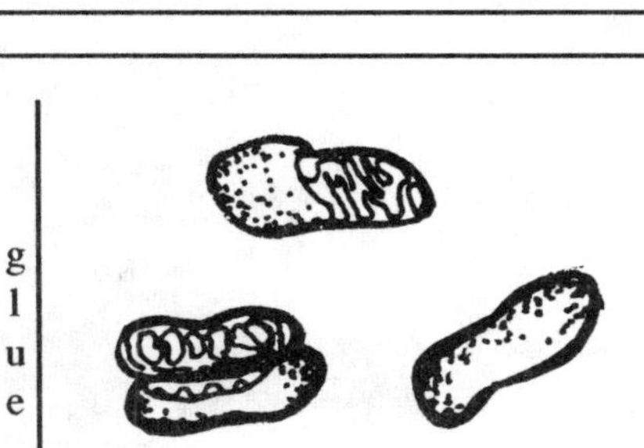

glue

The **mitochondria** are the "power plant" of the cell. They make energy for the cell to function.

glue

Centriols work like "magnets." During cell division, they get on opposite sides of the cell and each pull half of the chromosomes to their side.

This is a diagram of a cell. There are over 100 trillion cells in your body!

Cell City (page 2)

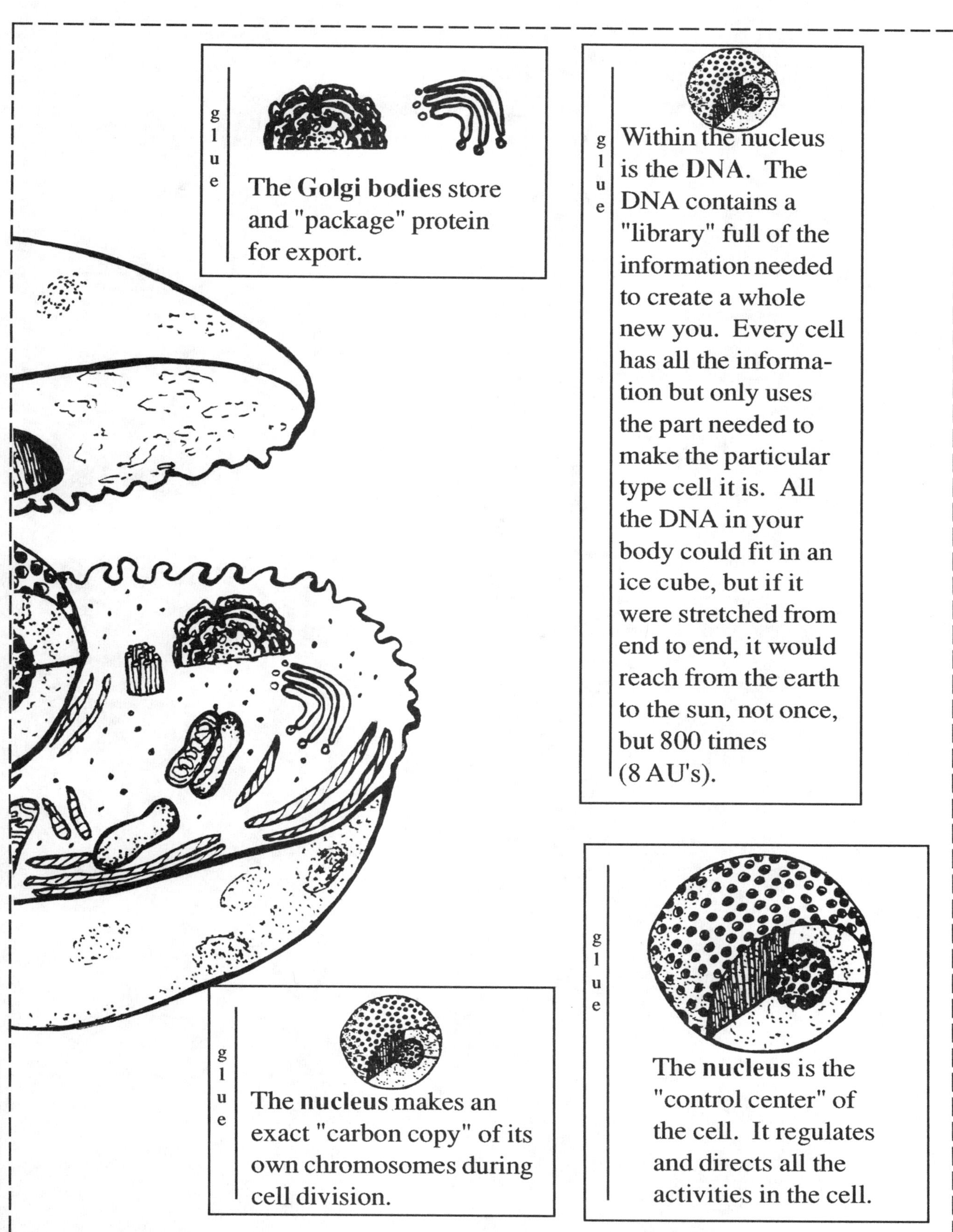
glue
The **Golgi bodies** store and "package" protein for export.
glue
Within the nucleus is the **DNA**. The DNA contains a "library" full of the information needed to create a whole new you. Every cell has all the information but only uses the part needed to make the particular type cell it is. All the DNA in your body could fit in an ice cube, but if it were stretched from end to end, it would reach from the earth to the sun, not once, but 800 times (8 AU's).
glue
The **nucleus** makes an exact "carbon copy" of its own chromosomes during cell division.
glue
The **nucleus** is the "control center" of the cell. It regulates and directs all the activities in the cell.

Cell City (page 3)

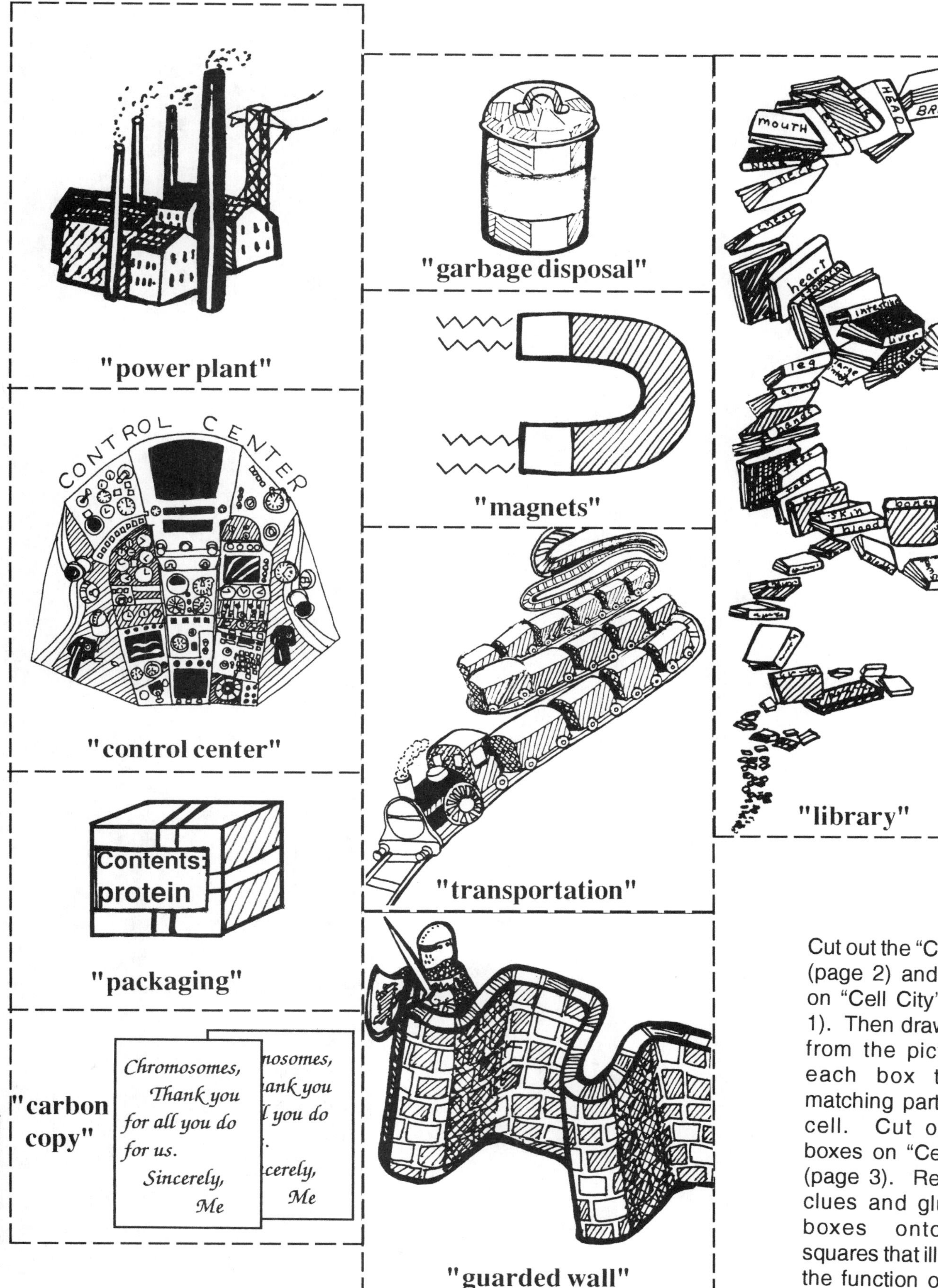
"power plant"
CONTROL CENTER
"control center"
Contents:
protein
"packaging"
"carbon copy"
Chromosomes,
Thank you
for all you do
for us.
Sincerely,
Me
"garbage disposal"
"magnets"
"transportation"
"guarded wall"
BRAIN
HEAD
mouth
heart
intestine
liver
leg
skin
blood
spine
"library"

Cut out the "Cell City" (page 2) and glue it on "Cell City" (page 1). Then draw a line from the picture in each box to the matching part in the cell. Cut out the boxes on "Cell City' (page 3). Read the clues and glue the boxes onto the squares that illustrate the function of each cell structure.

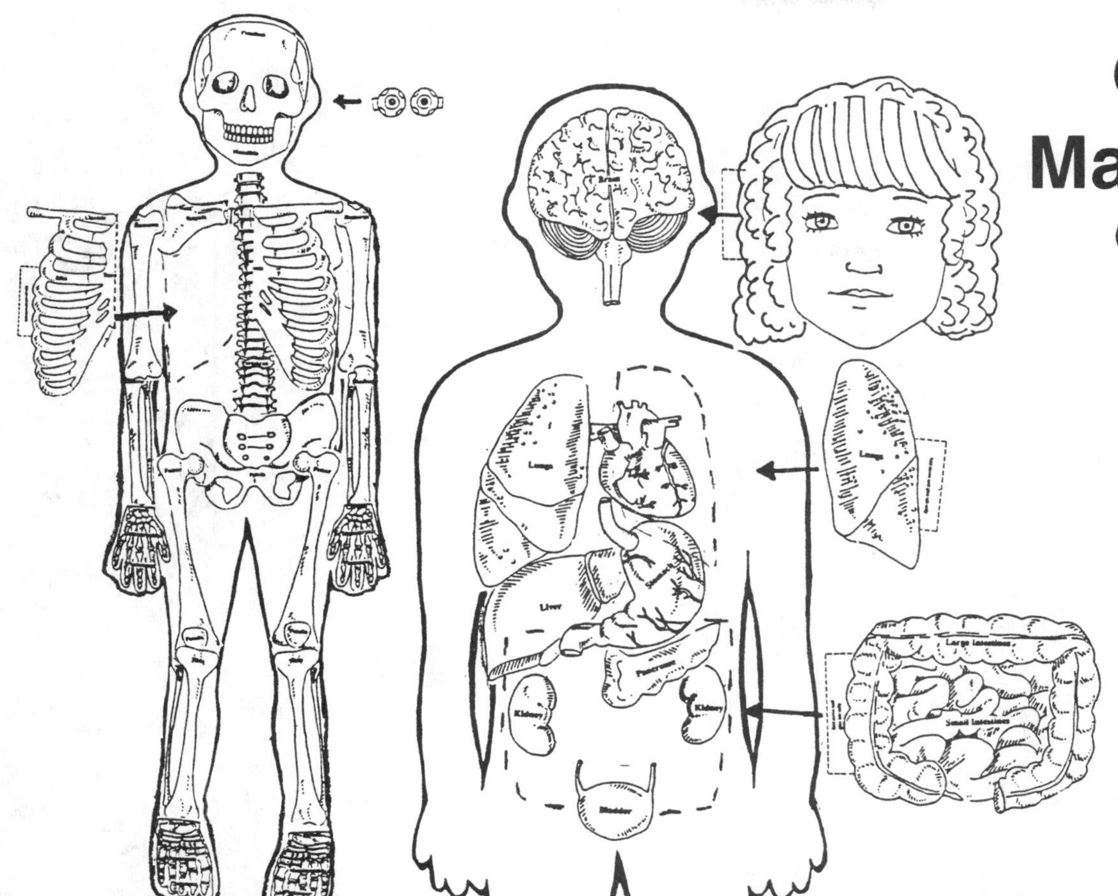

God Made Me

(page 1)

Cut out the "God Made Me" pages (1) and (3) and glue on "God Made Me" (page 2) to form the body outline needed for the rest of the "God Made Me" pages. See instructions in the teacher's manual for assembly.

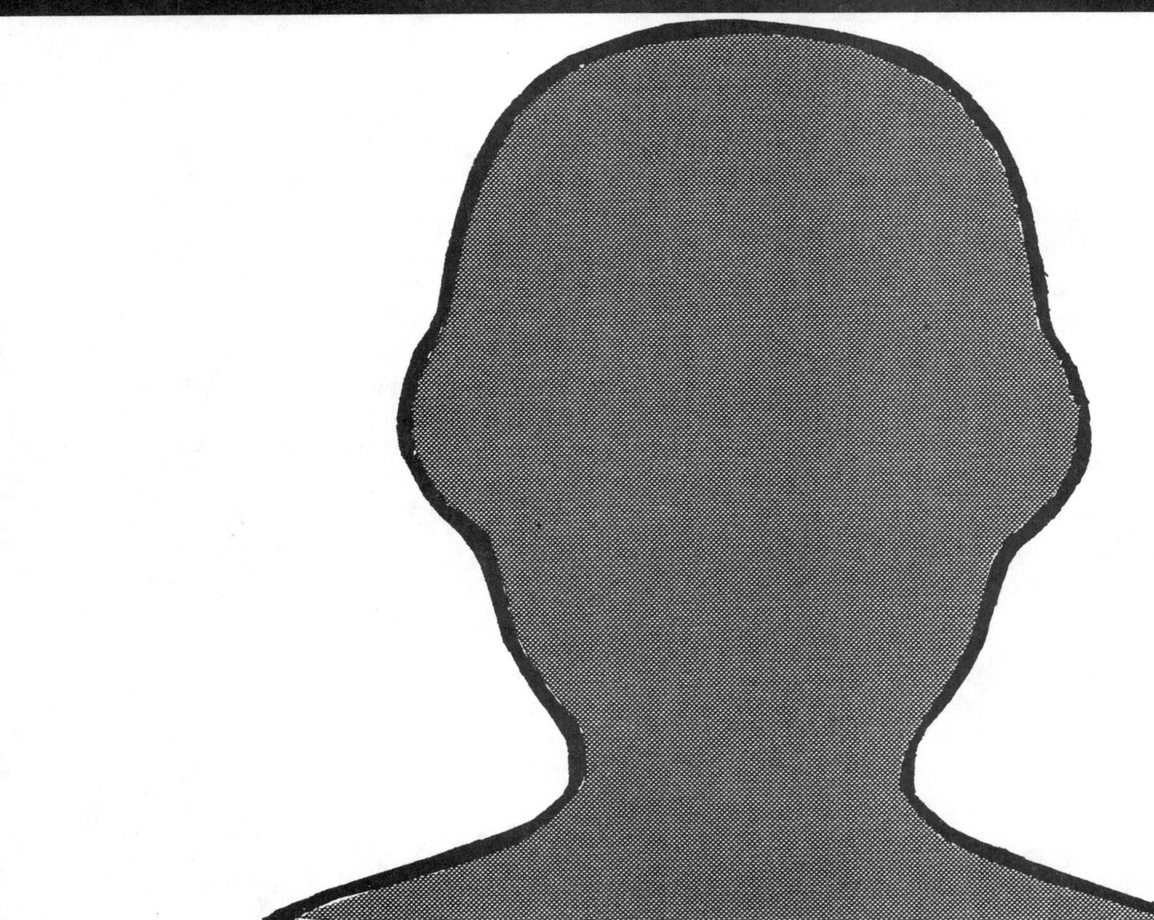
GOD Made ME

God Made Me (page 2) Glue head here ("God Made Me" page 1).

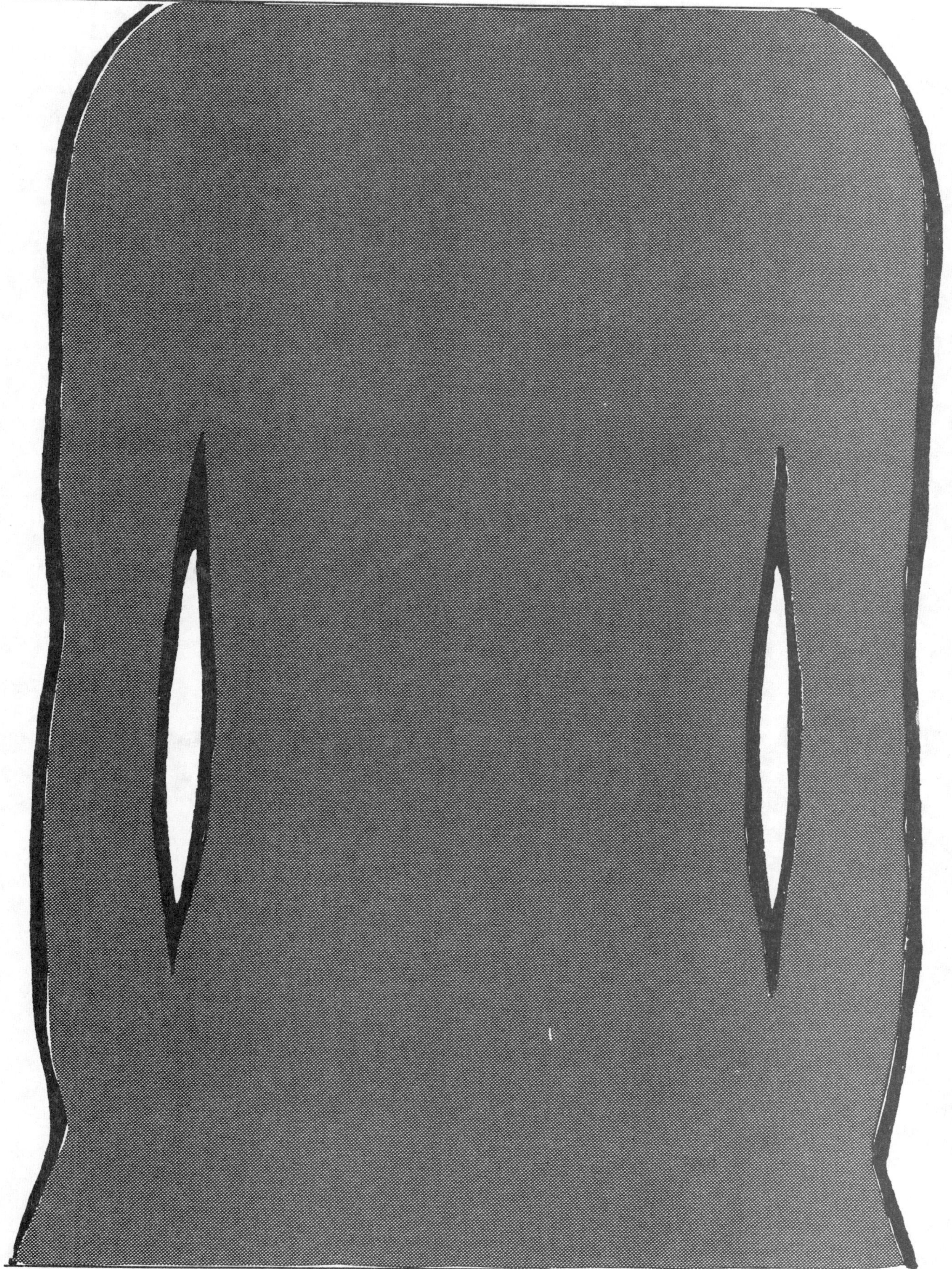

Glue legs here ("God Made Me" page 3).

God Made Me (page 3)

God Made Me (page 4)

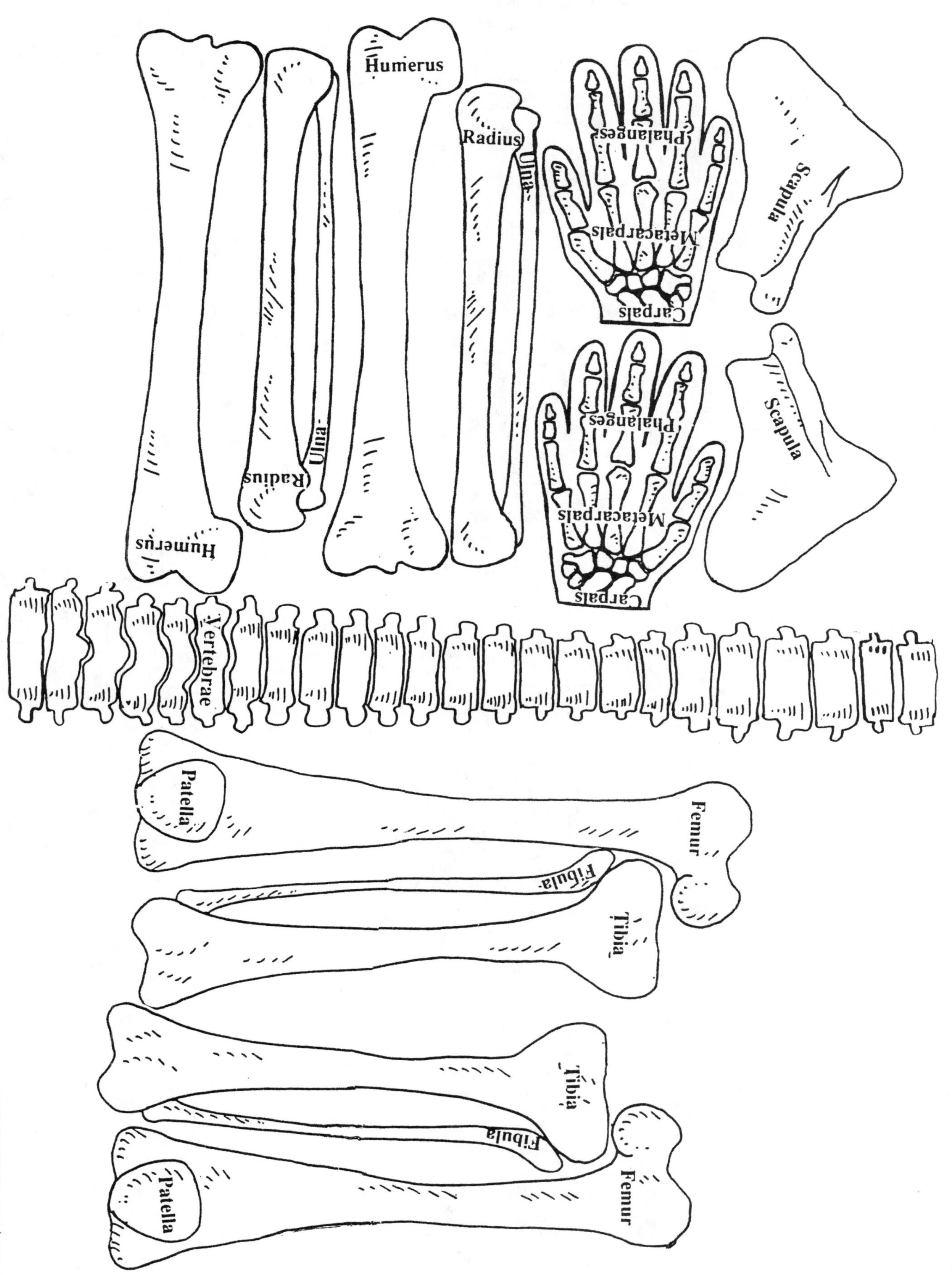

Humerus
Radius
Ulna
Humerus
Radius
Ulna
Phalanges
Metacarpals
Carpals
Scapula
Phalanges
Metacarpals
Carpals
Scapula
Vertebrae
Patella
Femur
Fibula
Tibia
Tibia
Fibula
Patella
Femur

God Made Me (page 5)

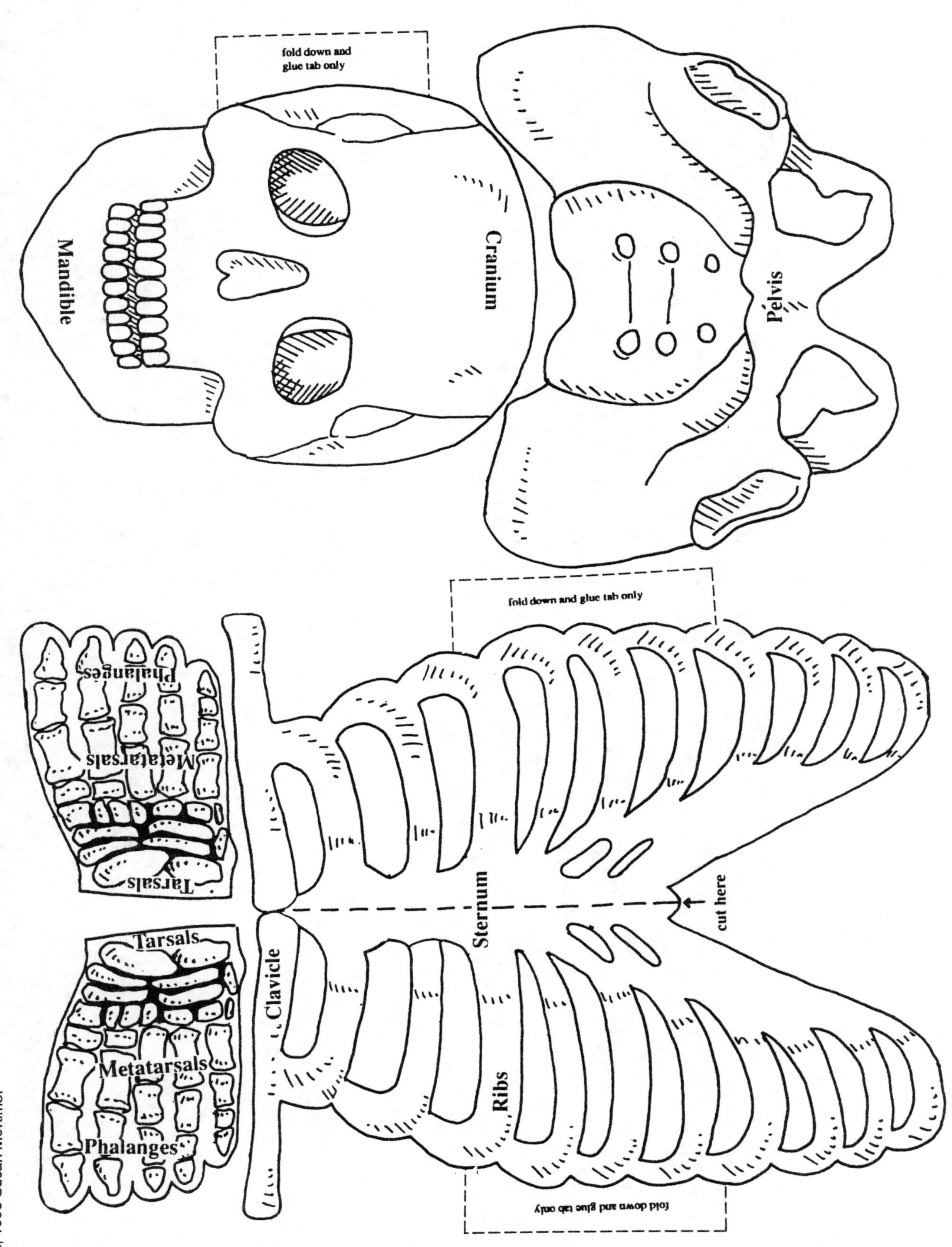
fold down and glue tab only
Mandible
Cranium
Pelvis
fold down and glue tab only
Phalanges
Metatarsals
Tarsals
Tarsals
Metatarsals
Phalanges
Clavicle
Sternum
Ribs
cut here
fold down and glue tab only

God Made Me (page 6)

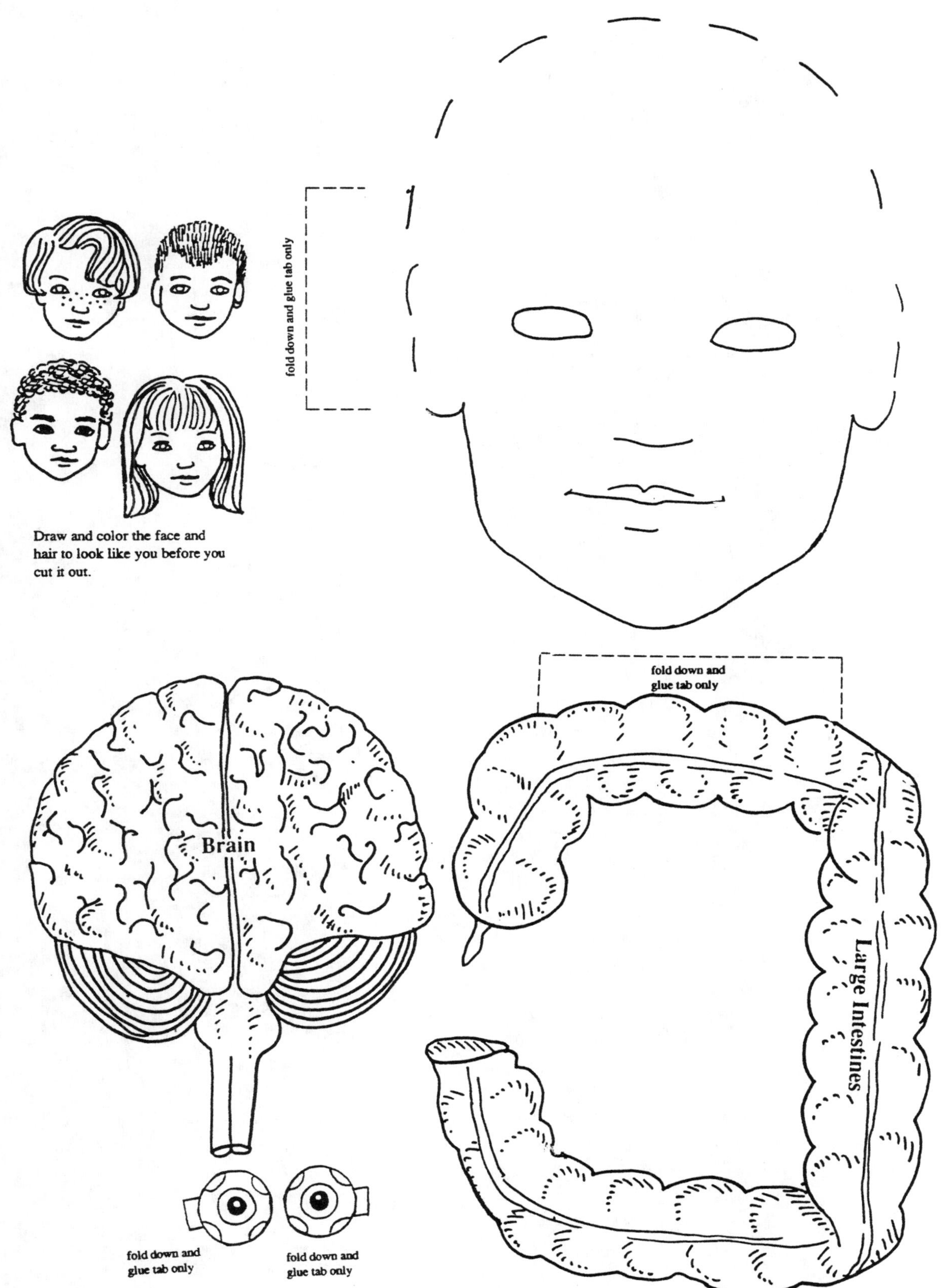
fold down and glue tab only
Draw and color the face and hair to look like you before you cut it out.
fold down and glue tab only
Brain
Large Intestines
fold down and glue tab only
fold down and glue tab only

God Made Me (page 7)

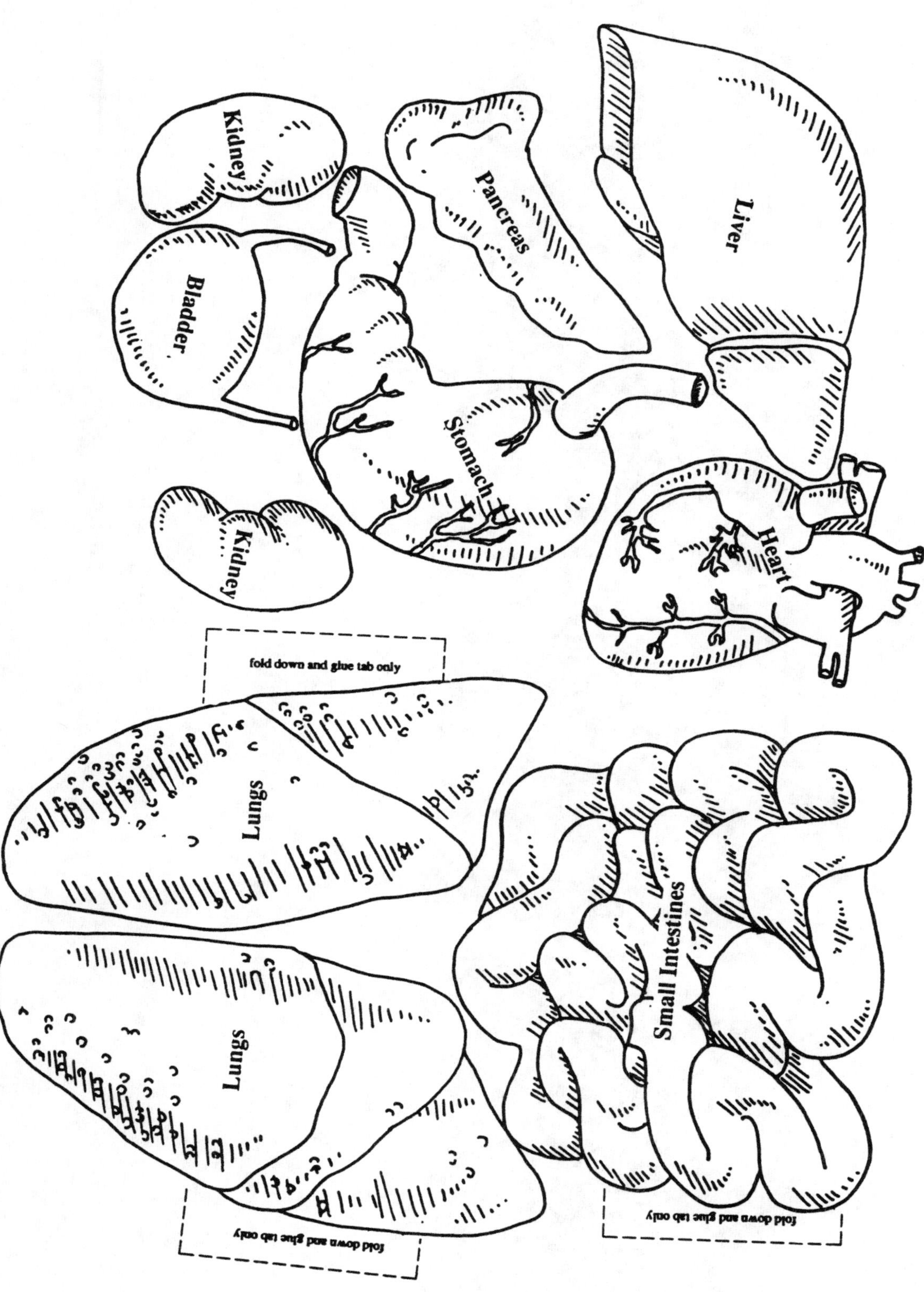
Kidney
Pancreas
Liver
Bladder
Stomach
Heart
Kidney
fold down and glue tab only
Lungs
Lungs
Small Intestines
fold down and glue tab only
fold down and glue tab only

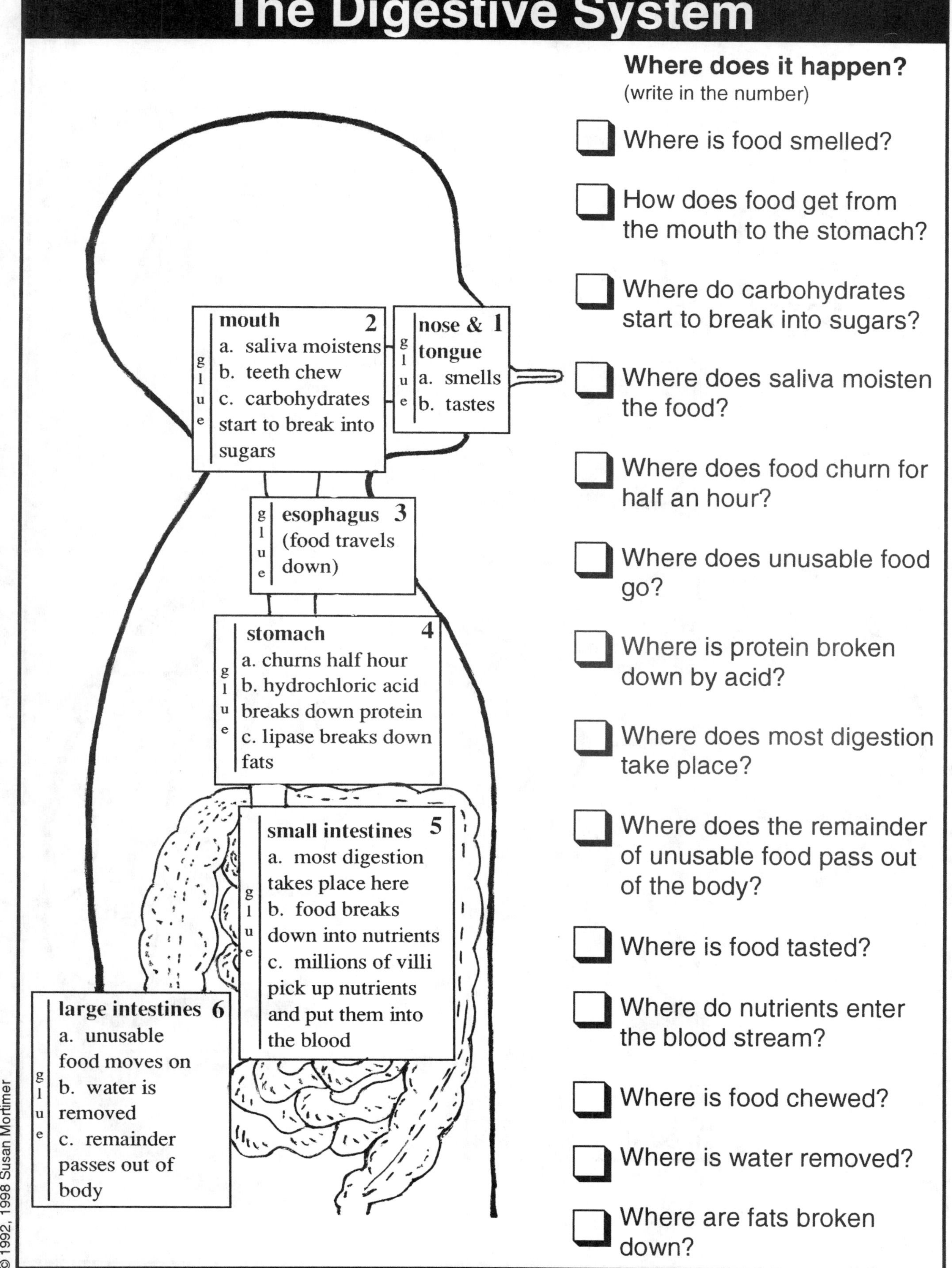
The Digestive System
Where does it happen?
(write in the number)
Where is food smelled?
How does food get from the mouth to the stomach?
Where do carbohydrates start to break into sugars?
Where does saliva moisten the food?
Where does food churn for half an hour?
Where does unusable food go?
Where is protein broken down by acid?
Where does most digestion take place?
Where does the remainder of unusable food pass out of the body?
Where is food tasted?
Where do nutrients enter the blood stream?
Where is food chewed?
Where is water removed?
Where are fats broken down?
mouth 2
a. saliva moistens
b. teeth chew
c. carbohydrates start to break into sugars
glue
nose & 1 tongue
a. smells
b. tastes
glue
esophagus 3
(food travels down)
glue
stomach 4
a. churns half hour
b. hydrochloric acid breaks down protein
c. lipase breaks down fats
glue
small intestines 5
a. most digestion takes place here
b. food breaks down into nutrients
c. millions of villi pick up nutrients and put them into the blood
glue
large intestines 6
a. unusable food moves on
b. water is removed
c. remainder passes out of body
glue

Cut and glue pieces from "The Digestive System" (page 2) to corresponding numbers above. Then answer the questions by writing in the correct number in the boxes.

The Human Brain

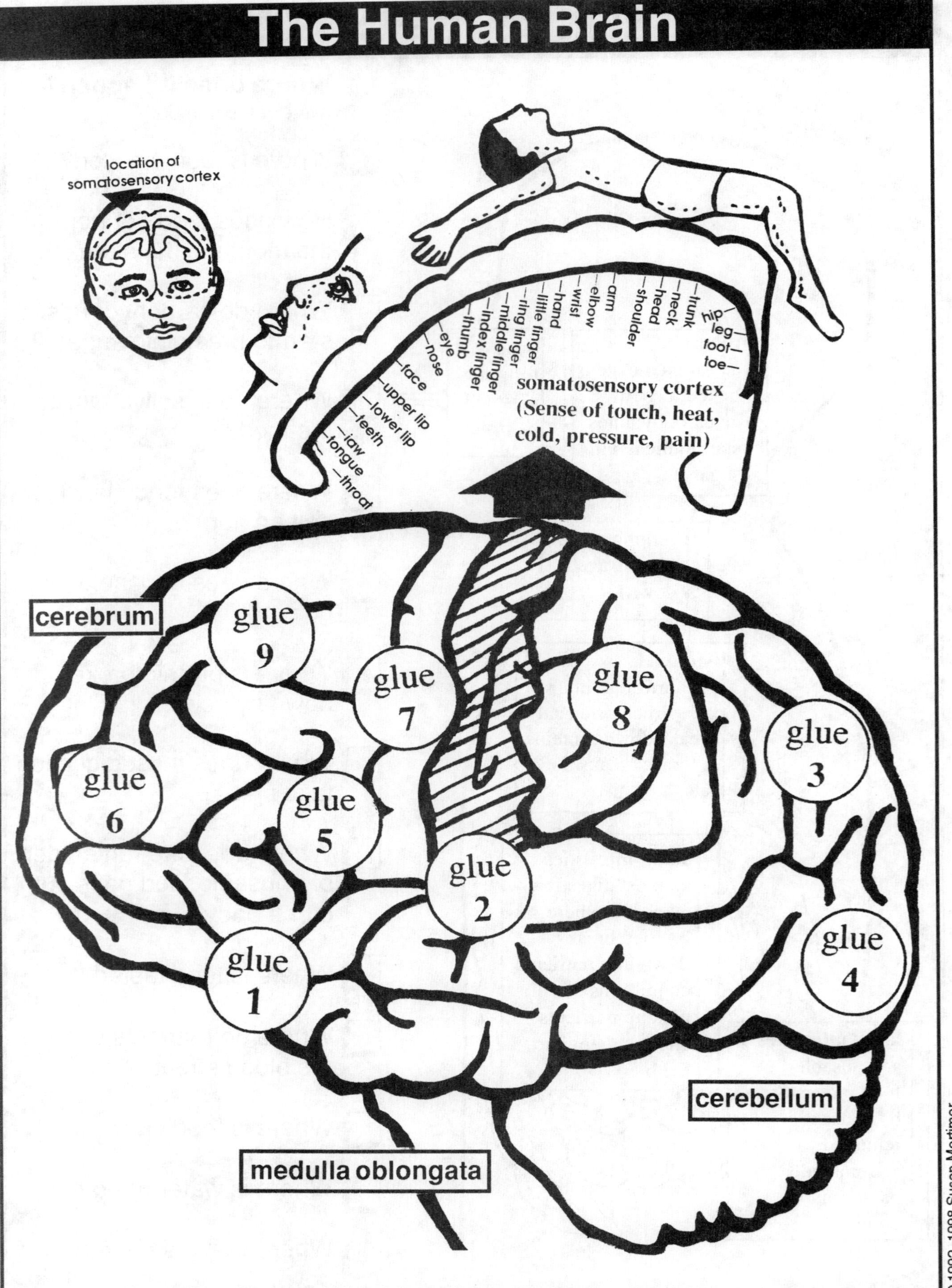

location of
somatosensory cortex
trunk
neck
head
shoulder
arm
elbow
wrist
hand
little finger
ring finger
middle finger
index finger
thumb
eye
nose
face
upper lip
lower lip
teeth
jaw
tongue
throat
hip
leg
foot
toe
somatosensory cortex
(Sense of touch, heat,
cold, pressure, pain)
cerebrum
glue 9
glue 7
glue 8
glue 3
glue 6
glue 5
glue 2
glue 1
glue 4
cerebellum
medulla oblongata

 Cut and glue pictures from "The Human Brain" (page 2) to the corresponding number above. Then draw lines to connect where the particular area of the body is controlled by each area of the somatosensory cortex. (Draw a line from the toe to the word 'toe', and so forth.)

The Digestive System (page 2)

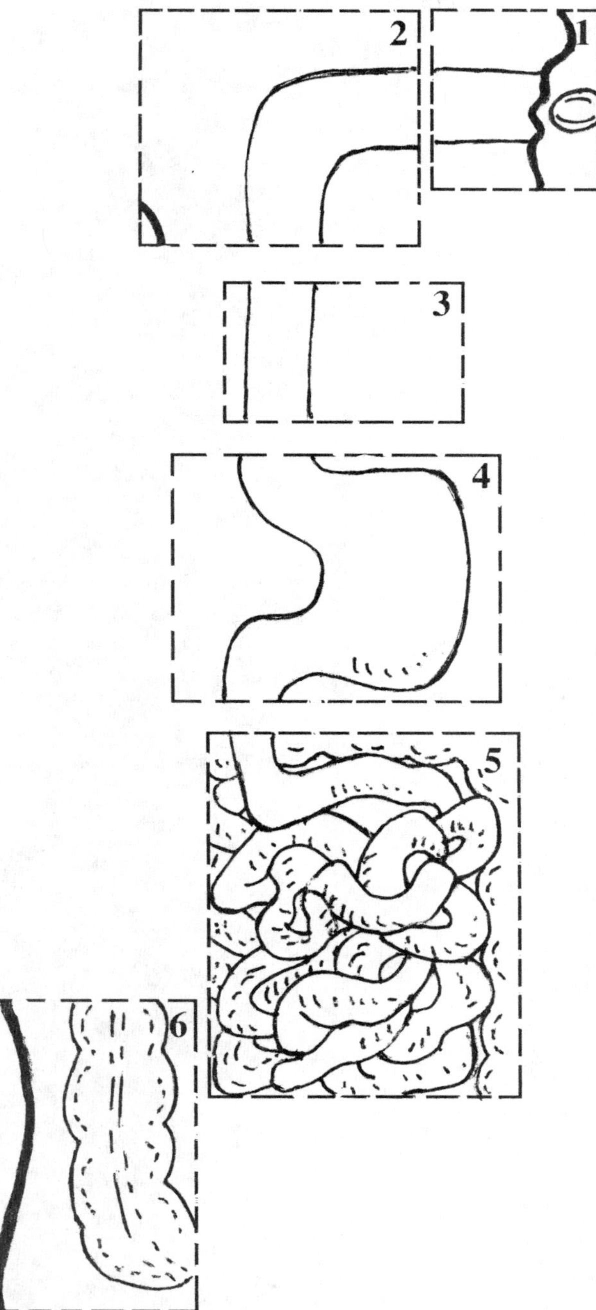

2
1
3
4
5
6

The Human Brain (page 2)

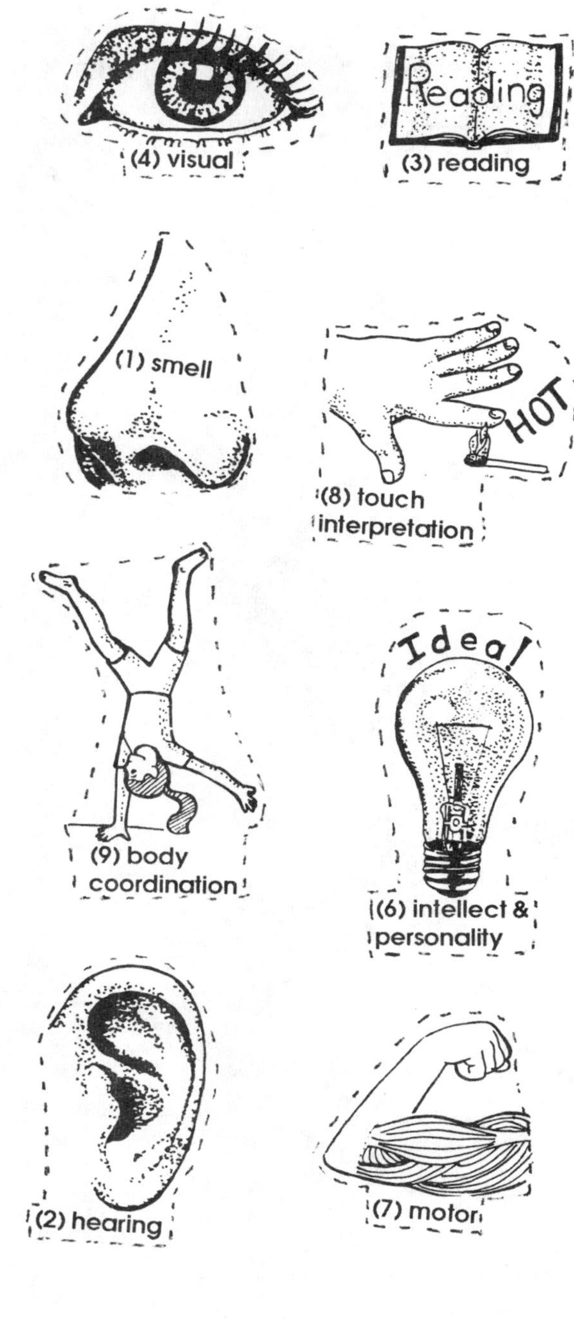

Reading
(4) visual
(3) reading
(1) smell
HOT
(8) touch interpretation
Idea!
(9) body coordination
(6) intellect & personality
(2) hearing
(7) motor

TALK
(5) speech

Automatic Pilot

pupils get smaller ●
pupils open wide ●

saliva produced ●

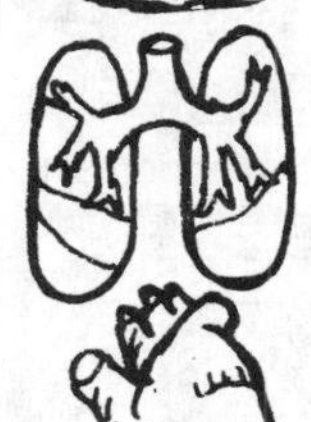

bronchi tighten ●

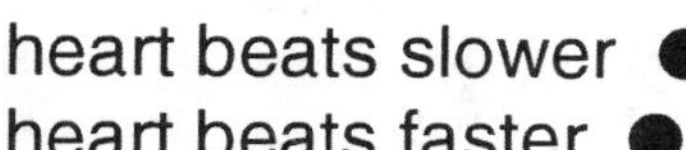

heart beats slower ●
heart beats faster ●

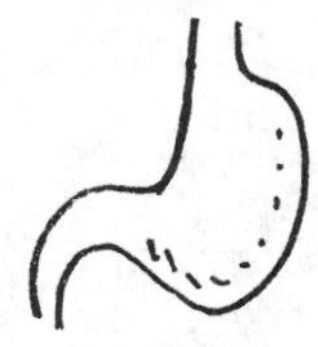

stomach churns ●
stomach stops churning ●

adrenal gland secretes ●
(epinephrin)

small intestines—moves through faster ●
small intestines—slows movement ●

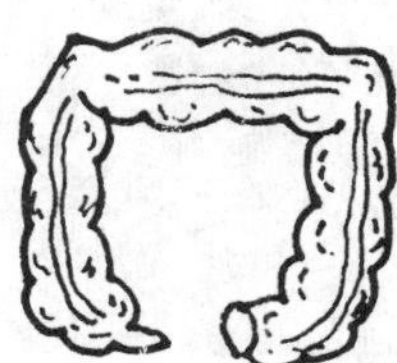

large intestines—moves through faster ●
large intestines—slows movement ●

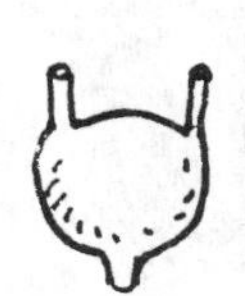

bladder empties fluid ●
bladder holds back fluid ●

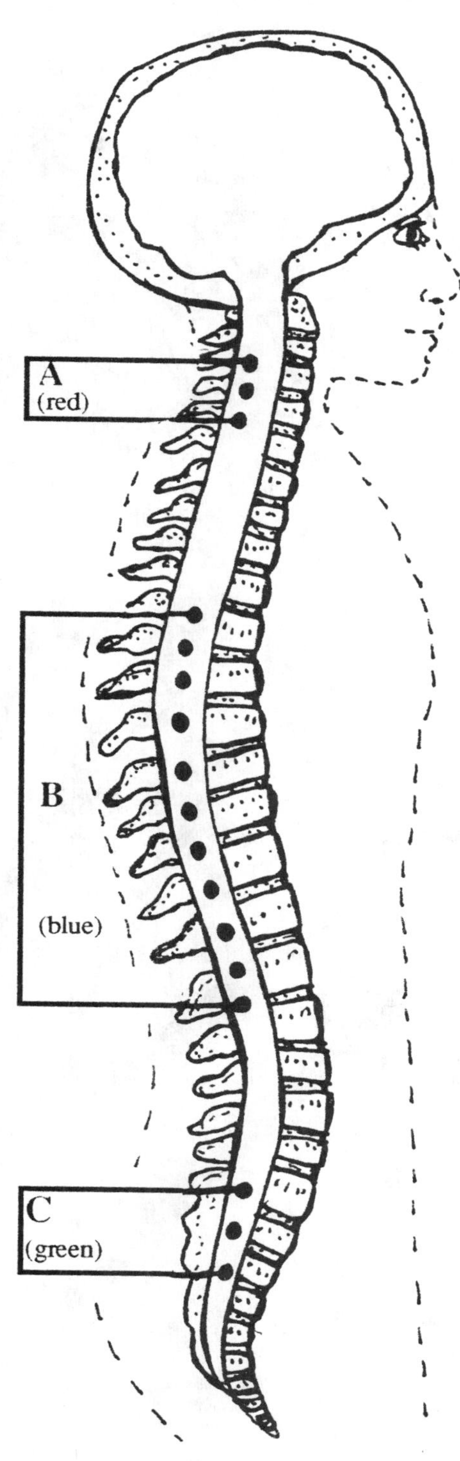
A
(red)
B
(blue)
C
(green)

A. **Parasympathetic nerves**: ✦pupils get smaller ✦saliva produced ✦bronchi tighten ✦heart beats slower ✦stomach churns ✦small intestines—moves through faster ✦large intestines—moves through faster

B. **Sympathetic nerves**: ✦pupils open wide ✦saliva produced ✦bronchi tighten ✦heart beats faster ✦stomach stops churning ✦adrenal gland secretes ✦small intestines—slows movement ✦large intestines—slows movement ✦bladder holds back fluid

C. **Parasympathetic nerves**: ✦bladder empties fluid ✦bladder holds back fluid

Draw a line from each automatic body function to where the message originates in the spine, using the information at the bottom of the page. Use a red line for (A), blue for (B) and green for (C).

Skin Deep

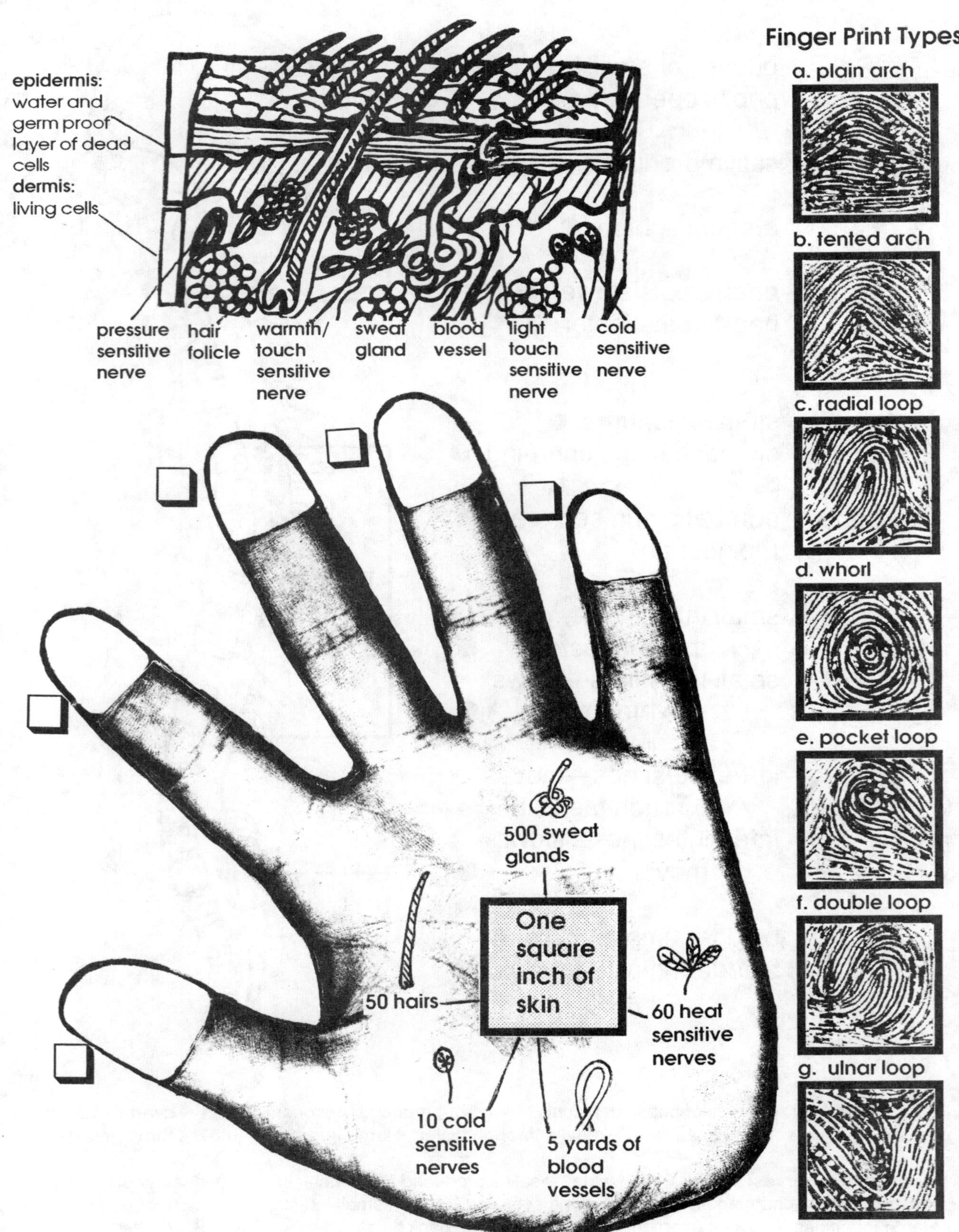

epidermis:
water and germ proof layer of dead cells
dermis:
living cells
pressure sensitive nerve
hair folicle
warmth/ touch sensitive nerve
sweat gland
blood vessel
light touch sensitive nerve
cold sensitive nerve
Finger Print Types
a. plain arch
b. tented arch
c. radial loop
d. whorl
e. pocket loop
f. double loop
g. ulnar loop
500 sweat glands
One square inch of skin
50 hairs
60 heat sensitive nerves
10 cold sensitive nerves
5 yards of blood vessels

 Put the fingerprint of each of your right-hand fingers and thumb in the matching space above. Then figure out which type each is most like. Write the letter of the finger type in the box by each print.

Fingerprint Detective Game

Scenario A: In a small hospital room, you see four objects. The doctor had listened to the patient with the stethoscope. The patient had taken the plastic wrap off a glass and poured in some water. The housekeeper had cleaned the side table. And there was a get-well card from a friend, still unopened. From the fingerprints left on the objects, figure out who each person was.

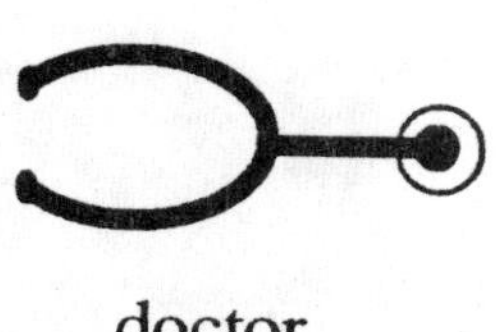

doctor ______________

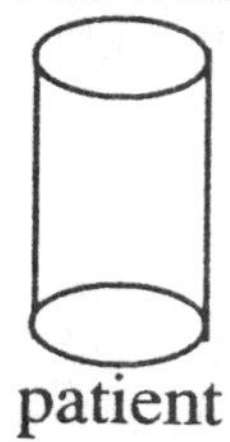

patient ______________

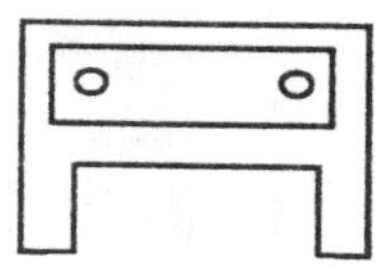

housekeeper ______________

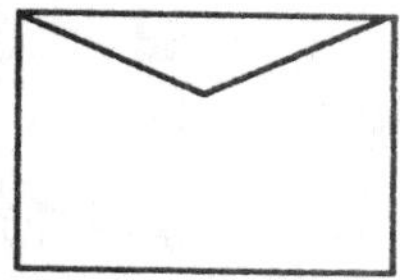

friend ______________

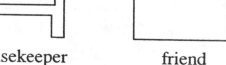

Scenario B: Four people came into a brand new hat store. Each picked up a different hat and tried it on. Which hat did each one try on?

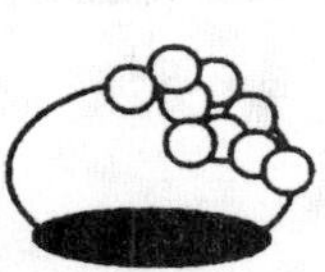

red ______________

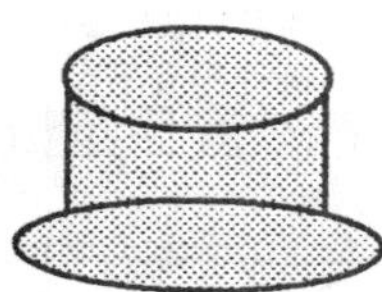

blue ______________

green ______________

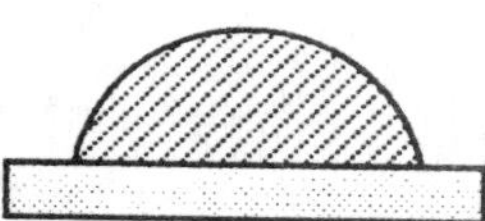

yellow ______________

Scenario C: Four famous artists had an exhibit of their best finger paintings. None of the artists had signed their work. Can you figure out which artist painted each painting?

heart ______________

arrow ______________

flower ______________

star ______________

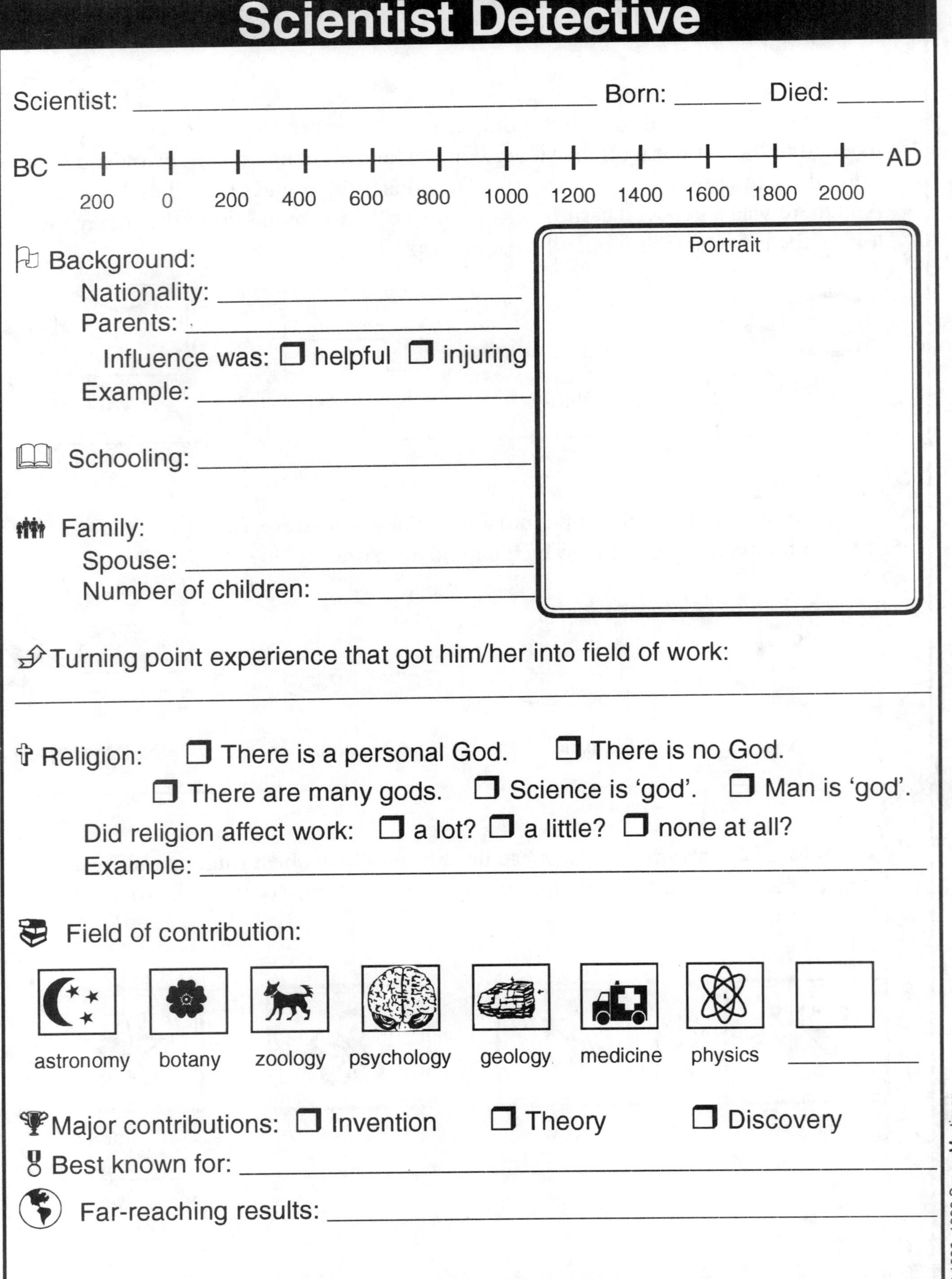

Scientist Detective

Scientist: ______________________ Born: _______ Died: _______

BC —— 200 | 0 | 200 | 400 | 600 | 800 | 1000 | 1200 | 1400 | 1600 | 1800 | 2000 —— AD

Portrait

Background:

Nationality: ______________________

Parents: ______________________

Influence was: ❑ helpful ❑ injuring

Example: ______________________

Schooling: ______________________

Family:

Spouse: ______________________

Number of children: ______________________

Turning point experience that got him/her into field of work:

____

Religion: ❑ There is a personal God. ❑ There is no God.

❑ There are many gods. ❑ Science is 'god'. ❑ Man is 'god'.

Did religion affect work: ❑ a lot? ❑ a little? ❑ none at all?

Example: ______________________

Field of contribution:

astronomy | botany | zoology | psychology | geology | medicine | physics | ___________

Major contributions: ❑ Invention ❑ Theory ❑ Discovery

Best known for: ______________________

Far-reaching results: ______________________

Fingerprint Detective Game (page 2)

a	b	c	d
Name:____________	Name:____________	Name:____________	Name:____________

Directions for Fingerprint Detective Game.

1. Obtain two fingerprints of the left thumb from four different people. Use an ink pad and have each person place his left thumb print first in the box with his name, and another print below it, without his name. (If you do not have an ink pad, an easy way to get a print is by filling in the square below darkly with a # 2 black pencil. Then rub the thumb firmly on the box until blackened. Next, tape a 1 to 1 1/2 inch piece of clear celophane tape over the thumb. The pencil dust will be lifted off the thumb on to the tape. You will have a clear print to attach to the boxes above. Refill the box with the pencil between prints.)

2. Cut boxes apart on dotted lines.

3. One player will place the prints without names on the objects for **Scenario A**. That player will also read the scenario and let the first player to be the detective match the fingerprint with a name to the fingerprint without a name. The second player can be the detective for **Scenario B** and so forth. Save the fingerprints in an envelope taped to the back of the Fingerprint Detective Game page to play again later when you make up your own Detective Game Stories.

Color in darkly
with #2 black pencil

The Inside Story

Bones: Draw in the rest of the skeleton. Draw a line from the name to the correct bone.

Cranium

Mandible

Scapula

Clavicle

Humerus

Sternum

Rib

Vertebrae

Radius

Ulna

Pelvis

Carpals

Metacarpals

Phalanges

Femur

Patella

Tibia

Fibula

Tarsals

Metatarsals

Phalanges

Glue Figure Here

Organs: Draw in the rest of the major blood vessels. Color, cut and glue the organs in the correct places. Kidneys and bladder must be glued first and will be hidden from view. Draw a line from each of the names below to the correct organ.

Brain

Lungs

Heart

Stomach

Liver

Pancreas

Kidneys

Bladder

Small Intestines

Large Intestines

Muscles: Draw in the rest of the muscles.

Scientist Detective

Scientist: ______________________ Born: ______ Died: ______

BC — 200 | 0 | 200 | 400 | 600 | 800 | 1000 | 1200 | 1400 | 1600 | 1800 | 2000 — AD

Background:
Nationality: ______________________
Parents: ______________________
Influence was: ❐ helpful ❐ injuring
Example: ______________________

Schooling: ______________________

Family:
Spouse: ______________________
Number of children: ______________________

Portrait

Turning point experience that got him/her into field of work:

____

Religion: ❐ There is a personal God. ❐ There is no God.
❐ There are many gods. ❐ Science is 'god'. ❐ Man is 'god'.
Did religion affect work: ❐ a lot? ❐ a little? ❐ none at all?
Example: ______________________

Field of contribution:

astronomy | botany | zoology | psychology | geology | medicine | physics | ______

Major contributions: ❐ Invention ❐ Theory ❐ Discovery
Best known for: ______________________
Far-reaching results: ______________________

The Inside Story (page 2)

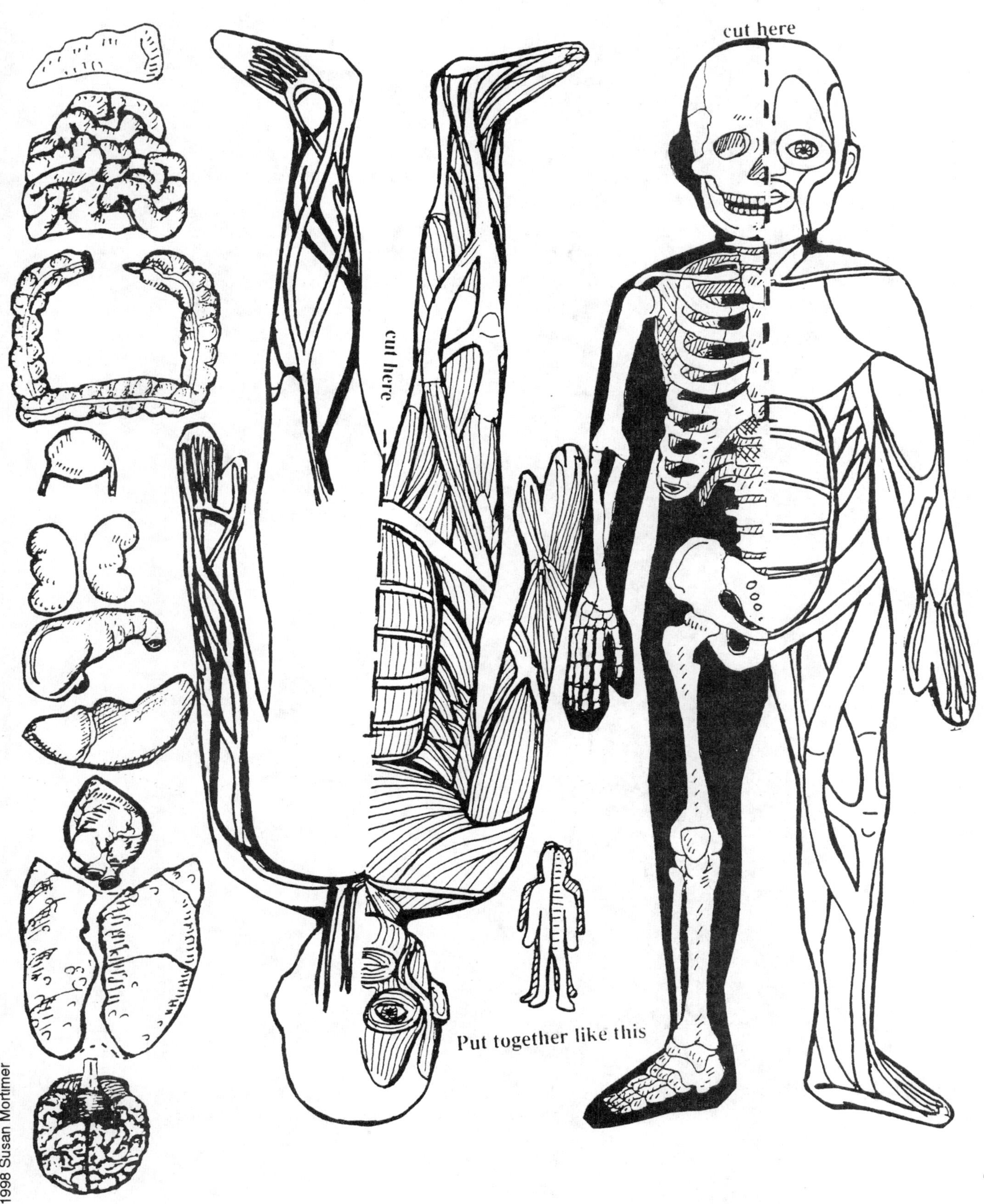
cut here
cut here
Put together like this

Cut and put figures together so that both top sides will be the muscles and both bottom sides will be blank. Glue blank sides on "The Inside Story" page.

Crossword Review 1

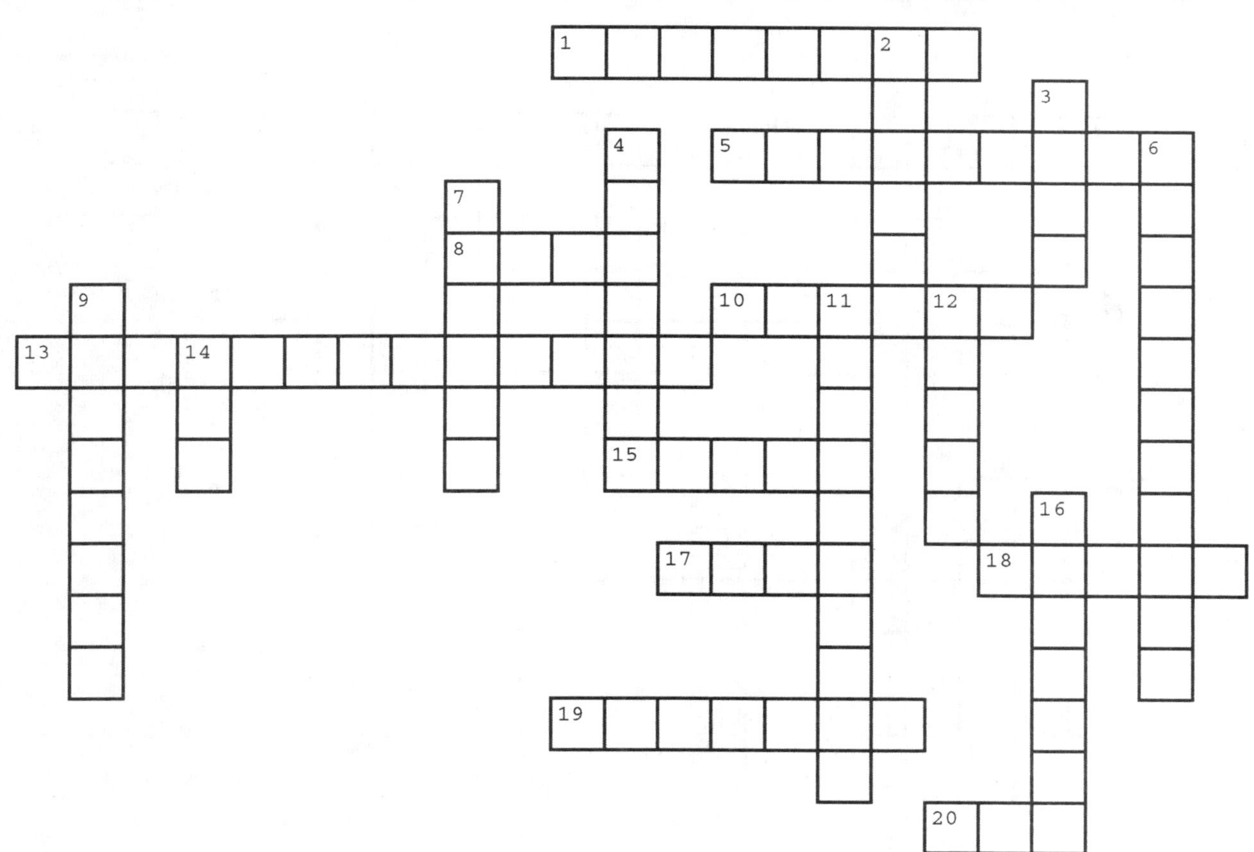
1
2
3
4
5
6
7
8
9
10
11
12
13
14
15
16
17
18
19
20

ACROSS

1) all created things
5) large mass of land
8) an imaginary line passing through the center of the earth from the North pole to the South pole
10) means "to wander in the sky"
13) a fixed group of stars
15) ______ system: the group of planets that revolve around the sun
17) a satellite that reflects the sun's light
18) means "a circle"
19) this planet's distinctive feature is the Great Red Spot
20) the length of time it takes a planet to rotate on its axis

DOWN

2) planet with many colorful rings
3) the length of time it takes a planet to orbit around the sun
4) composed of substances that are neither solid nor liquid
6) earth-like
7) a group or system of stars and other heavenly bodies
9) to turn in a cicular motion on an axis
11) a person who studies heavenly bodies
12) the third planet from the sun
14) a relatively large star at center of the solar system
16) the force that attracts one object to another

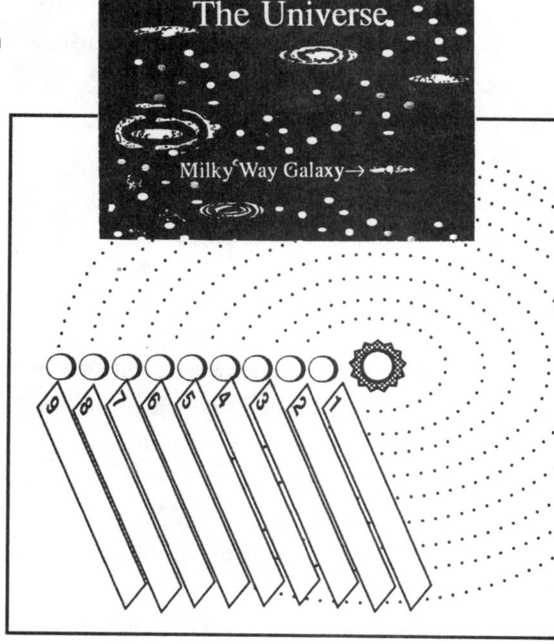
The Universe
Milky Way Galaxy→
9
8
7
6
5
4
3
2
1

Use this crossword for review after Lessons1-4. Then label the planets in order.

Crossword Review 2

1 2 3 4 5 6 7 8 9 10 11 12 13 14 15 16 17 18

ACROSS

5) globe
6) top of tall ocean mountain
7) colorful bent light waves; tell of God's vow to man
9) layer of air closest to the earth's surface
11) upper layer of air with electically charged atoms
13) hard, outer covering of the earth
16) number of continents
18) the outer layer of atmosphere

DOWN

1) movement in the earth's crust
2) condensed oxygen (03)
3) middle layer of the earth
4) blanket of air surrounding a heavenly body
5) second layer of air above the earth's surface
8) cover more than two-thirds of earth's surface
10) gas vital for human life
12) middle layer of air
13) the molten center of the earth
14) circle of life
15) _____ dioxide: gas vital for plant life
17) an opening in the earth through which lava is ejected

inner
outer
lower
upper

29 %
71%

The Earth

 Use this crossword for review after Lesson 5 A, B and C. Fill in labels for the earth.

Crossword Review 3

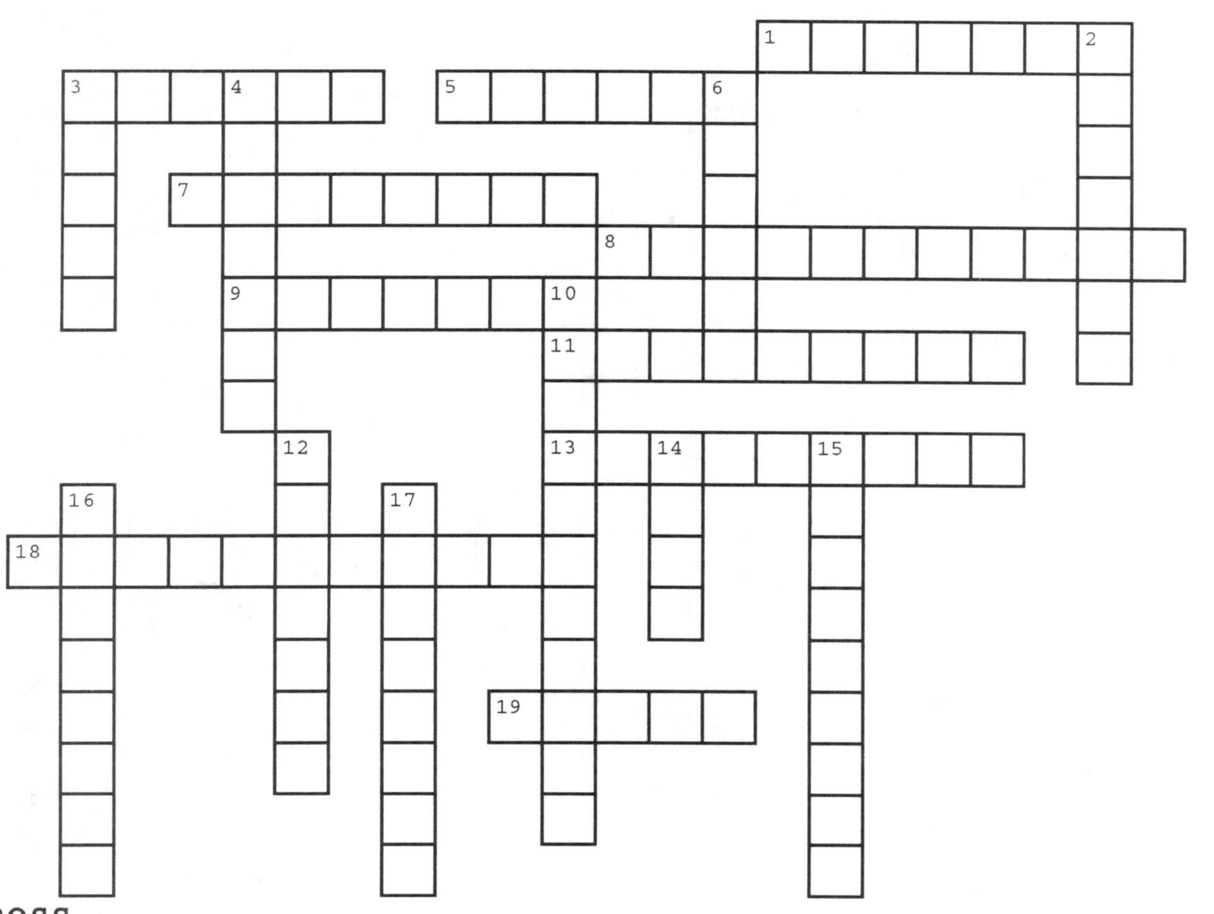
1
2
3
4
5
6
7
8
9
10
11
12
13
14
15
16
17
18
19

ACROSS

1) ____ may be fine, medium or coarse
3) ____ may be extra light, average or extra heavy
5) any evidence of life from the past
7) measured by numbers from 1 to 10
8) rock changed by heat and pressure
9) rock formed as a result of intense heat
11) igneous rock formed by magma cooling above earth's surface
13) igneous rock formed by magma cooling below earth's surface
18) quartz-like
19) molten rock

DOWN

2) to wear away or break down
3) sedimentary rock generally forms in ____
4) example of igneous rock
6) ____ may be no shine, metallic or non-metallic
10) rock made up of layers
12) hardest kind of rock
14) weakest type of rock
15) example of a sedimentary rock
16) metamorphic rock is formed under heat and ____
17) the direction a rock would split or break

________ rocks form from ________ & ________.

________ rocks form from ________ in ________.

________ rocks form from ________ or melted ________.

Non-Living Things

Use this crossword for review after Lesson 6. Then fill in the missing words.

Crossword Review 4

ACROSS

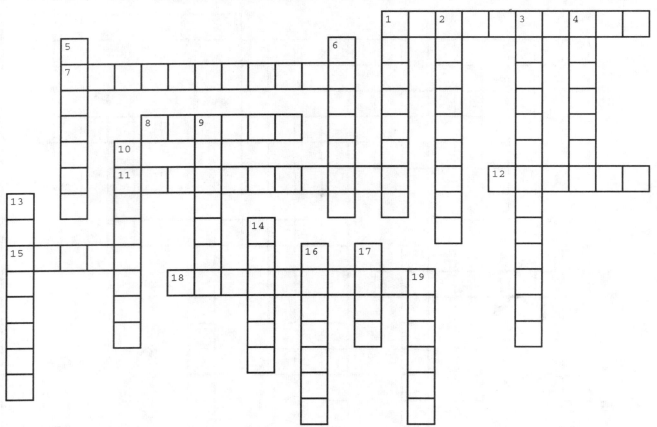

1) half of the earth
7) how hot or cold it is
8) empty space
11) all present
12) high altitude feathery clouds
15) energy that travels in waves from the sun
18) the earth traveling around the sun

DOWN

1) how much moisture in the air
2) have a strong effect on weather; often one side is dryer than the other
3) amount of rain or snow
4) imaginary line dividing the earth
5) low altitude layer of clouds
6) condition of the stmosphere at a given time
9) overall weather pattern of an area
10) the earth turning on its axis
13) smallest piece of a substance
14) made of water vapor
16) mounds or towers of clouds
17) movement of air currents
19) rain or snow cloud

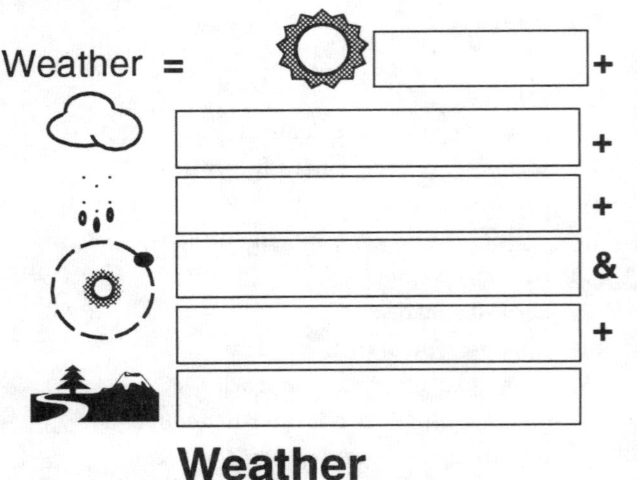

Weather =
+
+
+
&
+
Weather

 Use this crossword for review after Lessons 7-9. Then fill in the missing words.

Crossword Review 5

ACROSS

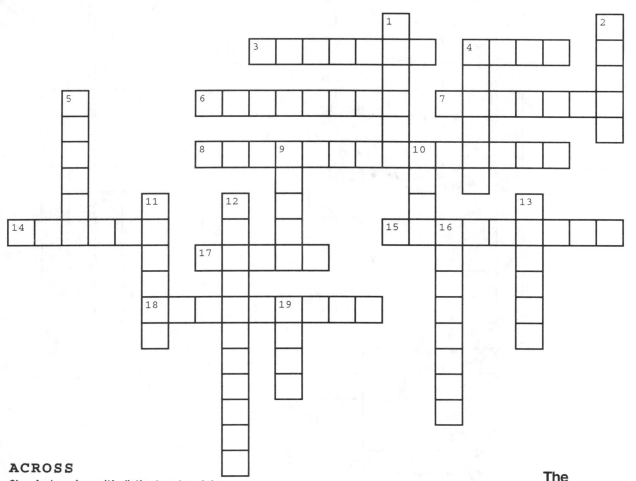

3) hot region with distinct wet and dry seasons
4) stalk of plant
6) ____ trees: broadleaf evergreen trees
7) warm area with wet and dry season and few plants
8) process by which plants create carbohydrates
14) seed-bearing organ of flower
15) ____ trees shed leaves in autumn
17) simple photosynthetic plant found in damp places
18) ____ trees stay green year round

DOWN

1) fertilizing dust in flower
2) refers to the North and South Poles
4) pollen-bearing part of flower
5) simple plant that reproduce by spores
9) coniferous forest below Arctic region
10) plant with woody trunk
11) part of plant that produces seeds
12) green color in plants
13) treeless plains in Arctic Circle
16) sticking together
19) part of plant that seeks nourishment for plant

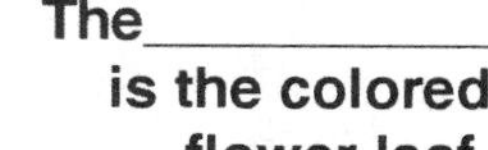

The____________ is the colored flower leaf.

____________ is produced by the ____________.

Pollen travels down the ____________ to fertilize the ____________ and make seeds.

____________ are where photosynthesis takes place as nutrients come up the________ from the ____________.

The Plant Kingdom

Use this crossword for review after Lessons 10-12. Then label the picture correctly.

Crossword Review 6

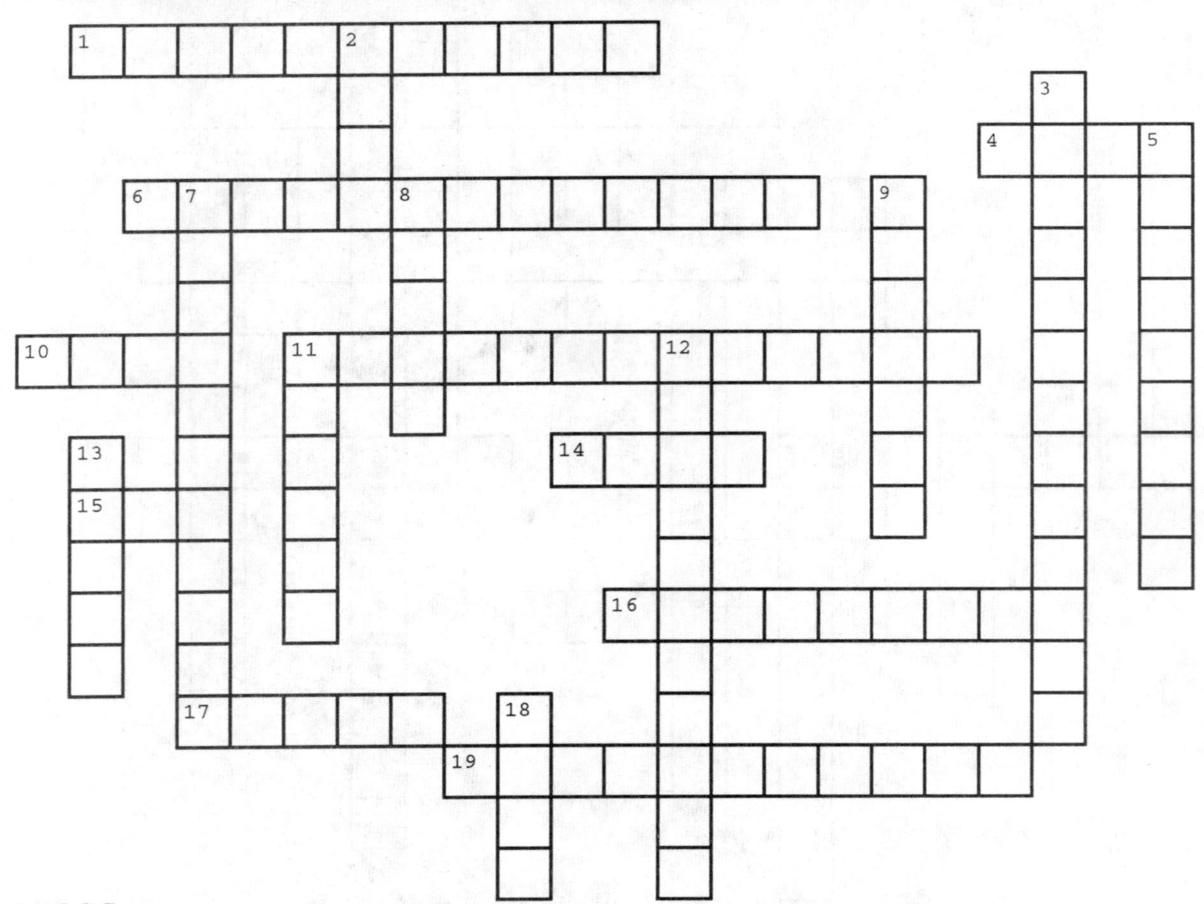

1
2
3
4
5
6
7
8
9
10
11
12
13
14
15
16
17
18
19

ACROSS

1) insects clean up dead plants and animals by ___ them
4) a grasshopper rubs its ___ to make 'music'
6) head united with thorax
10) are examples of industriousness
11) creatures without a backbone
14) flies at night and keeps its wings open when it lands
15) ___ glands keep spiders from sticking to their web
16) animals with 2 main body parts, 4 pairs of legs
17) immature form of insect with incomplete metamorphosis
19) important work of insects

DOWN

2) non-feeding, resting stage in metamorphosis
3) process of change during insects' development
5) breathing holes
7) firm outer skeleton
8) "baby" form in metamorphosis
9) insects are capable of spreading ___
11) invertebrate with 3 body segments, 3 pairs of legs
12) sip nectar through a straw-like mouth
13) an edible delicacy produced by insects
18) ___ lungs are characteristic of arachnids

What makes a spider

_______ antennas
_______ legs
_______ body sections
_______ wings

What makes an insect

_______ antennas
_______ legs
_______ body sections
_______ wings

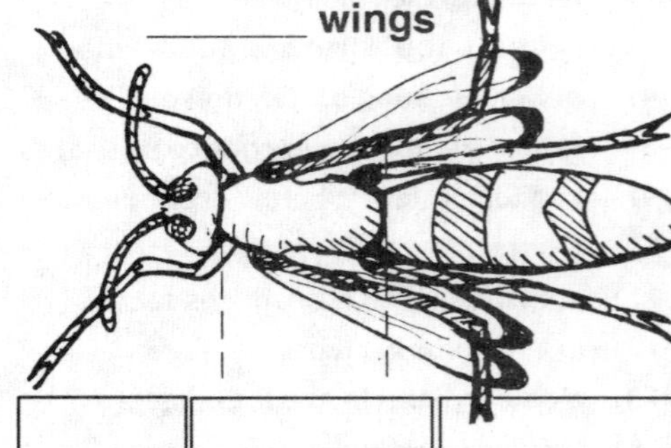

Insects & Spiders

 Use this crossword for review after Lessons 13-14. Then fill in the labels.

Crossword Review 7

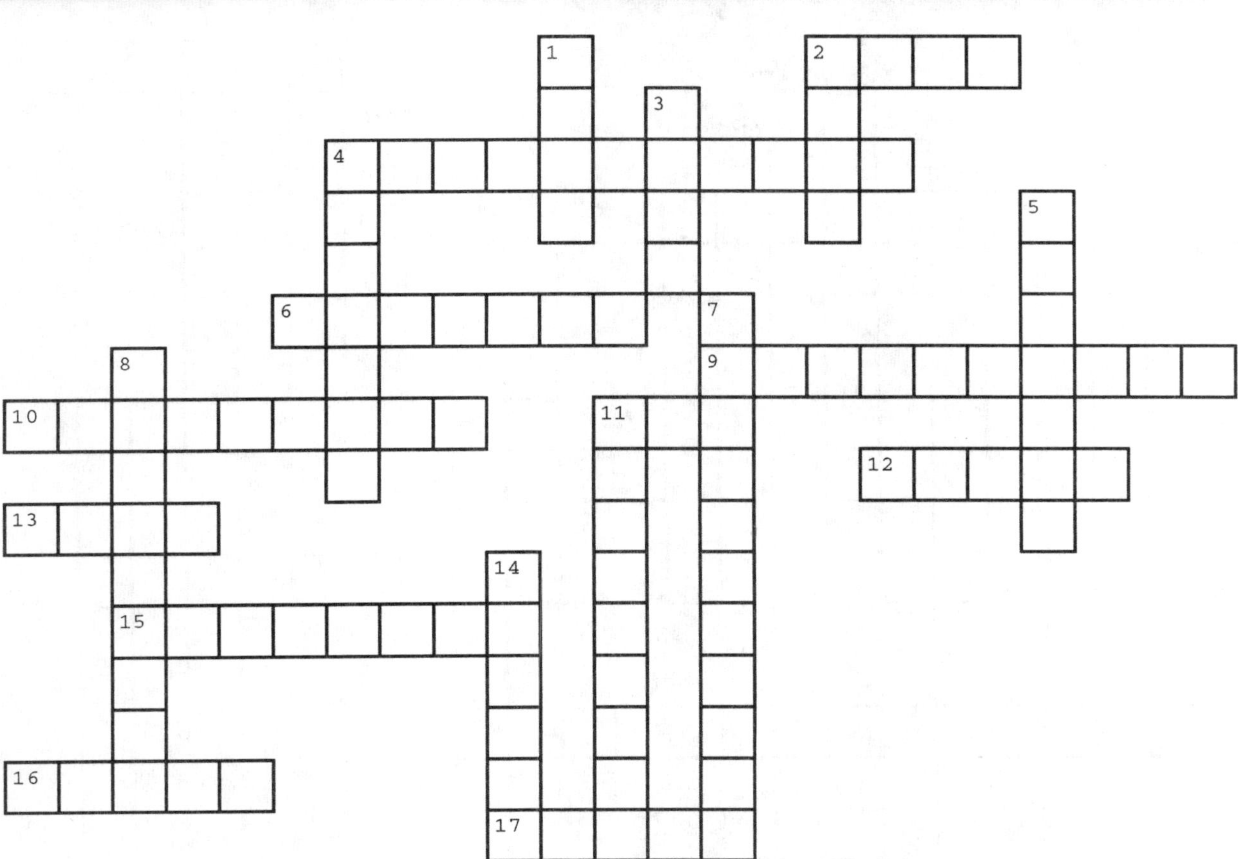

1
2
3
4
5
6
7
8
9
10
11
12
13
14
15
16
17

ACROSS

2) ___ blooded: having a variable body temperature
4) dormant during winter
6) bird's muscular second stomach
9) inactive during dry summer
10) muscles diving the chest cavity from abdominal cavity
11) ___ bladder: enables fish to float
12) water-dwelling mammal
13) cold-blooded water animal with fins, scales, gills
15) organ of blood vessels supplying food and air in womb
16) breahting organ of water animals
17) sponge-like breathing chamber

DOWN

1) warm-blooded vertebrate with feathers, two wings
2) part of bird's food tube, for storing food
3) air ___: air-filled cavities in birds
4) dwelling
5) cold-blooded vertebrate with dry scaly covering
7) creatures with backbones
8) Australian mammals with external pouches for young
11) cold-blooded vertebrate; "double life"
14) warm-blooded vertebrate with hair or fur

Fish are ______ blooded, have __________ & _____, breathe through _______ and lay ____________ eggs.

Reptiles are _____ blooded, have _____, _________ skin, breathe through ________ and lay ____________ eggs.

Birds are ______ blooded, have ___________ & ______, breathe through ________ and lay ____________ eggs.

Mammals are ______ blooded, have _________ or _____, breathe through ________ and have live ________ and _______ for their young.

Amphibians are ______ blooded, eggs hatch in __________ then move to ___________, breathe first through _____ and later through ________.

Fish, Reptiles, Birds, Mammals & Amphibians

Use this crossword for review after Lessons 15-21. Then fill in the missing words.

Crossword Review 8

ACROSS
1) meat-eater
6) balanced relationship between plants and animals
9) produce living individuals
10) strong bands of tissues that hold bones together
12) unable to reproduce
13) born alive
17) plant-eater
18) studies ancient plant and animal life
19) tissues which can produce movement
20) able to reproduce

DOWN
2) bony structure growing on head of male deer
3) nourishment
4) hereditary unit
5) receding influence
7) plant- and animal-eater
8) predominant influence
11) born from an egg
14) framework of the body
15) hard formation growing on head of cows
16) passing characteristic from parent to child

Match the definition to the word:
a. ecosystem ____
b. gene ____
c. omnivore ____
d. reproduce ____
e. recessive ____
f. dominate ____
g. ligaments ____
h. carnivore ____
i. antlers ____
j. nutrient ____
k. sterile ____
l. oviparous ____
m. paleontologist ____
n. muscles ____
o. viviparous ____
p. skeleton ____
q. herbivore ____
r. horns ____
s. heredity ____
t. fertile ____

 Use this crossword for review after Lessons 22-24. Match the definition to the word, then do the crossword.

Crossword Review 9

ACROSS

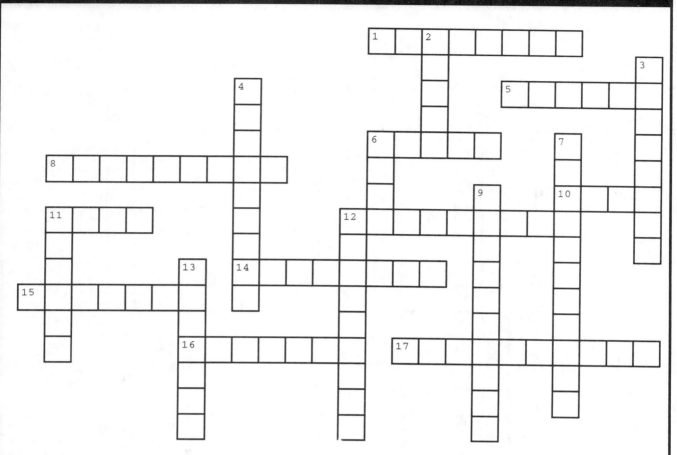

1) brain's center of intelligence
5) pleats of tissue that carry extra blood
6) ___ lobe: center for sight
8) ___ bulb: center for smell
10) the Arctic ___ flies from Arctic to Antarctic
11) ___ whales are the largest creatures on earth
12) ___ pigeons are now extinct in the Americas
14) toothed group of whales
15) lowest portion of brain; controls involuntary functions
16) dead, extinguished
17) smaller portion of brain; controls voluntary muscles

DOWN

2) ___ whales were considered the "right" whale to hunt
3) inborn ability
4) to go from one place to another
6) killer whale
7) insects can detect ___ patterns in flowers
9) threatened with extinction
11) sieve-like bone structure of one group of whales
12) ___ gland: controls growth
13) membrane in cat's eye

Match the definition to the word:

a. olfactory _____
b. migration _____
c. cerebrum _____
d. right _____
e. pecten _____
f. instinct _____
g. optic _____
h. blue _____
i. odontoid _____
j. passenger _____
k. endangered _____
l. ultraviolet _____
m. cerebellum _____
n. pituitary _____
o. extinct _____
p. tapetum _____
q. medulla _____
r. baleen _____
s. tern _____
t. orca _____

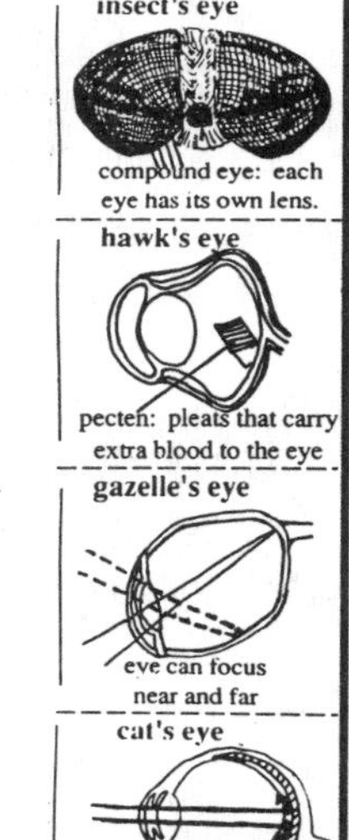

insect's eye
compound eye: each eye has its own lens.
hawk's eye
pecten: pleats that carry extra blood to the eye
gazelle's eye
eye can focus near and far
cat's eye
tapetum: mirror

Use this crossword for review after Lessons 25-26. Match the definition to the word, then do the crossword.

Crossword Review 10

ACROSS

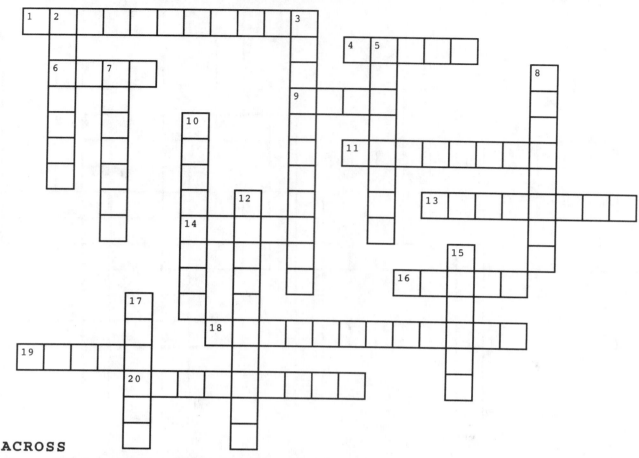

1) ___ reticulum: membrane that provides "transportation"
4) DNA: ___ acids which contain the genetic "master plan"
6) simplest unit of structure of living things
9) female reproductive cell
11) to be with child
13) Your DNA could stretch from the earth to the sun ___ of times.
14) male reproductive cell
16) cell membranes allow ___ and oxygen to enter or leave cell easily
18) "power plant" of cells
19) ___ body: membrane sacs that "package" protein
20) the nucleus ___ and directs all the activities in the cell

DOWN

2) "control center" of cell
3) contain cell's genetic information
5) cell ___ acts like a "guarded wall"
7) "garbage disposal system" of cell
8) lysosomes dispose of invading ___
10) Centrioles work like "magnets" during cell ___
12) rod-shaped structures that function like "magnets"
15) womb: where a baby develops before birth
17) eternal part of man

Draw a line from the word to its location in the cell.

a. cell membrane

b. mitochondria

c. lysosomes

d. DNA

e. nucleus

f. centrioles

g. Golgi bodies

h. chromosomes

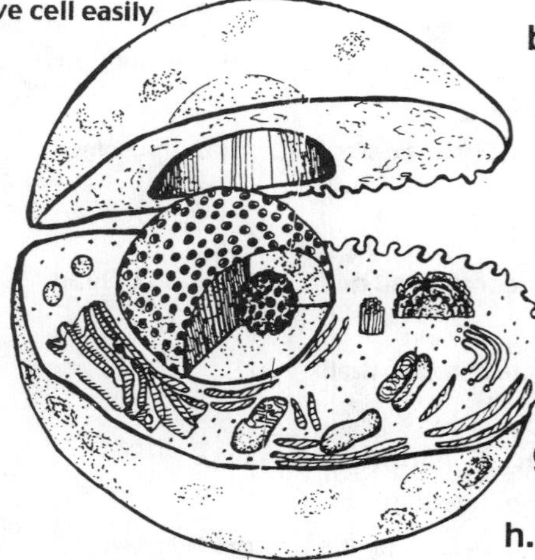

Man: Reproductive System & The Cell

 Use this crossword for review after Lessons 27-28. Then draw a line from the word to its location in the cell.

Crossword Review 11

1 2 3 4 5 6 7 8 9 10 11 12 13 14 15 16 17 18 19 20

ACROSS

4) a pair of organs shapes like kidney beans

7) muscles we can move at will

8) yellow colored liquid wastes

9) gland produces greasy liquid

11) outer layer of skin

13) expel wastes from body

16) fatty tissue

17) protective layer of tissue covering body

19) automatic

20) gland produces perspiration

DOWN

1) controls the "fight or flight" response

2) band of fibrous tissue

3) controls involuntary vital functions

5) muscles that work with conscious effort

6) message lines to the brain

10) a muscular bag that collects urine

12) living layer of skin

14) muscles that extend

15) muscles that flex

18) tubes from kidneys to bladder

Which system is it?

Endocrine = E

Excretory = X

Integumentary = I

Muscular = M

Nervous = N

a. epidermis ____	k. oil gland ____
b. kidneys ____	l. sympathetic ____
c. nerve ____	m. bladder ____
d. thyroid ____	n. involuntary ____
e. extensors ____	o. dermis ____
f. sweat gland ____	p. flexors ____
g. pituitary ____	q. ureter ____
h. autonomic ____	r. medulla oblongata ____
i. adrenal ____	s. cardiac ____
j. cerebrum ____	t. spinal cord ____

Man: Nervous, Integumentary, Endocrine, Excretory & Muscular Systems

Use this crossword for review after Lessons 29-32. Match the system to the word, then do the crossword.

Crossword Review 12

1 2 3 4 5 6 7 8 9 10 11 12 13 14 15 16 17 18 19

ACROSS

2) blood vessels going toward the heart
8) blood vessels going away from the heart
9) prepares food to be absorbed into the blood
11) rippling contractions of intestines
12) tiny air cells
14) tiny blood vessels
16) tube from mouth to stomach
17) liquid part of blood
19) red ones carry oxygen, white ones fight infection

DOWN

1) blood pumping muscles
3) tubing from the stomach
4) chief organ of digestion
5) soft center of bones
6) the gall bladder stores this substance
7) strong fibers that connect bones
10) windpipe
11) seal broken blood vessels
13) red viscous liquid that circulates in man and animals
15) digestive gland behind the stomach
18) secretes bile

Which system is it?

♥ Circulatory = C

Digestive = D

Respiratory = R

Skeletal = S

a. pancreas ____
b. clavicle ____
c. heart ____
d. intestines ____
e. mandible ____
f. corpuscles ____
g. alveoli ____
h. trachea ____
i. stomach ____
j. femur ____
k. plasma ____
l. peristalsis ____
m. marrow ____
n. platelets ____
o. phalanges ____
p. esophagus ____
q. tibia ____
r. veins ____
s. lungs ____
t. patella ____

Man: Skeletal, Digestive, Circulatory & Respiratory Systems

 Use this crossword for review after Lessons 33-36. Match the system to the word then do the crossword.

Appendix

In the beginning was the Word, and the Word was with God, and the Word was God. He was with God in the beginning. Through him all things were made; without him nothing was made that has been made. In him was life, and that life was the light of men. John 1:1-4 (NIV)

Considering God's Creation Songs

And God Was Pleased!

On the first day of creation,
God made the dark and light,
And He called it day and night.
And God was pleased.

On the second day of creation,
God made the water and the air,
And this was the atmosphere.
And God was pleased.

On the third day of creation,
God made the land and sea,
And every plant, flower, grass, and tree.
And God was pleased.

On the fourth day of creation,
God made the stars, the moon, the sun,
Thus the seasons were begun.
And God was pleased.

On the fifth day of creation,
God made the birds and fish,
And any sea creature you could wish.
And God was pleased.

On the sixth day of creation,
God made animals fill the land,
Then He formed man with His hand.
And God was pleased.

On the seventh day of creation,
God looked at what He'd done,
And rested to enjoy each one.
And God was pleased.

Day and Night

God made the sun to rule the day,
God made the moon to rule the night,
And when we go to Heaven one day,
Jesus alone will be our Light.

The Planets

The planets starting from the sun are
Mercury and Venus,
The Earth, then Mars and Jupiter, and
Saturn and Uranus.
The next in line is Neptune and Pluto
after that,
The Lord our God fixed them in space,
And He keeps them all in place.

Rainbows Over You

Rainbows **O**ver **Y**ou, **G**od's **B**lessed **V**ow,
That He will never flood the earth again.
Rainbows **O**ver **Y**ou, **G**od's **B**lessed **V**ow,
And to His Word, our God is always true.
Rainbows **O**ver **Y**ou, **R**ed, **O**range, **Y**ellow,
The colors in the sky tell of God's care.
God's **B**lessed **V**ow, **G**reen, **B**lue, **V**iolet,
They promise that our God is always there.

The Water Cycle

Let's take one little drop of rain
And follow it to the ground again.
It flows to the river and out to the sea,
And evaporates, a cloud to be.
Rain, rain that comes today,
Will come back another way.

Not Just a Weatherman

"Cirrus" is the cloud that floats the highest
in the sky,
It looks like wispy curls of smoke that
scurry by.
Big fluffy cotton candy clouds are known
as "cumulus,"
And "stratus" clouds are layered straight
down close to us.

As weathermen who read the weather we
can read God's signs,
He gives them in His Holy Book,
His Spirit guides our minds.

Then "nimbus" means a cloud is dark and
filled with rain or snow
And "alto" tells us cloud are high and
not down low.
We put these words together and we can
then define
All types of clouds and we can tell what
weather we might find.

Don't just be a weatherman, but learn
to read God's signs,
He gives them in His Holy Book,
His Spirit guides our minds.

God is Light

God says in His Word He is light,
And it's true that He gives us our sight.
For our physical eyes, He shows us
our way,
And our spirit He leads every day.

God says there's no darkness in Him,
He has no hidden shadows within.
He's transparently Holy,
He's wondrously Pure,
And His promise to guard us is sure.

God sees the same if it's night or it's day,
If we're home or we're far away,
He made us and knows us, and
He loves us so,
He wants us His love to know.

Bear Fruit

Behold the sower went out to sow;
And some seeds fell by the road.
The birds came by and ate them up,
And none were left, we're told.
And other seeds fell on the rocks
And quickly grew, then died
Because their roots could not survive
the sun.

So don't let lack of understanding or
shallowness of root,
Or cares or riches of this world keep
you from bearing fruit,
But let the love of Jesus grow down deep
so you can stay alive
And you can bear a hundred fold of fruit
for Him.

Still other seeds fell in the thorns,
And the thorns soon choked them out.
But other seeds fell in good soil,
That's what this song's about.
The good soil yielded forth a crop
Some even a hundred fold,
Some sixty and some thirty times the start.

So don't let lack of understanding
or shallowness of root,
Or cares or riches of this world keep
you from bearing fruit,
But let the love of Jesus grow down deep
so you can stay alive
And you can bear a hundred fold
of fruit for Him.

Clean

My bread is old, it's growing mold,
I'll have to throw it away.
I found mildew in the tennis shoe
I wanted to wear today.

My mother told me she was cold,
A fire would feel real good.
It wouldn't start, the logs fell apart.
A fungus had rotted the wood.

Along came sin; Adam let it in.
It destroyed his walk with God.
God cursed the ground, and Adam found
Thorny weeds taking over the sod.

When Moses heard God's powerful
Word,
He told the people plain,
"If you obey and walk God's way,
You'll be blessed with crops and rain."

But they also heard the warning word,
"If you will not obey,
You are under a curse, it will get
much worse,
There will come mildew and decay."

Now I understand it is by God's hand
That the mold and fungus grow.
It's a lesson on sin: if I let it stay in,
It will ruin my life, I know.

My bread I threw, with the tennis shoe,
On the pile of rotten wood.
I confessed my sin, Jesus Christ came in.
I will walk with Him for good.

Creatures God Made

Fish are cold-blooded creatures God made,
They have scales, fins, and swim
in the deep,
They lay eggs, and they breathe in the
water through gills,
A swim bladder helps them float while
they sleep.

Reptiles are cold-blooded creatures
God made,
They have dry, scaly skin and lay eggs,
Their lungs breathe the air, and their hearts
have three parts,
And they crawl on their bellies or legs.

Birds are warm-blooded creatures
God made,
They have feathers, two feet, and
two wings,
They lay eggs, and their hearts beat the
fastest of all,
And they breathe God's good air as
they sing.

Mammals are warm-blooded creatures
God made,
They have hair, and give milk for
their young,
And whether they live on the land
or the sea,
They all breathe God's air with their lungs.

Amphibians are cold-blooded creatures
God made
They lay eggs and in water are
hatched,
But when they grow up their gills into
lungs change
And damp land then becomes their new
range.

You'll Know Them by Their Footprints
How can you tell there's a rabbit
around,
Just by looking at the ground?
How can you tell that a bird's nearby,
Without ever looking at the sky?

You'll know it by their footprints and
there's more,
By where they walk and what they live for.
You'll know them by their footprints,
You'll know them by their footprints.

How can you tell that a skunk's been
there,
Just by smelling of the air?
How can you tell that a bear was
here,
But that he's long gone and there's no
need to fear?

You'll know it by their footprints and
there's more,
By where they walk and what they live for.
You'll know them by their footprints,
You'll know them by their footprints.

How can they know that a Christian
passed by,
Without a word and without a sigh?
How can they know there's a better
place,
Before they see Jesus face to face?

They'll know us by our footprints and
what's more,
By where we walk and what we live for.
They'll know us by our footprints,
They'll know us by His footprints.

What if the Sun Shut Down?
What if the sun shut down?
What would we all do then?
The plants could not make food
It would be the living end.
There would be no vegetables,
no fruits, no grass, no grains,
no wheat,
And then no cows, no milk,
no chickens, no eggs, no meat.
We need the sunshine. Thank God
for the sunshine.
We need the sunshine. Thank God
for the sunshine.

What if the sea dried up?
What would we all do then?
The plants could not make food.
It would be the living end.
There would be no vegetables,
no fruits, no grass, no grains,
no wheat,
And then no cows, no milk,
no chickens, no eggs, no meat.
We need the water. Thank God for
the water.
We need the water. Thank God for
the water.

What if the air went bad?
What would we all do then?
The plants could not make food.
It would be the living end.
There would be no vegetables,
no fruits, no grass, no grains,
no wheat,
And then no cows, no milk, no
chickens, no eggs, no meat.
We need the atmosphere. Thank God
for the atmosphere.
We need the atmosphere. Thank God
for the atmosphere.

Someday this world will end,
A new one will take its place.
Old things will pass away.
We'll see Jesus face to face.
We won't need no vegetables,
no fruits, no grass, no grains,
no wheat,
Won't need no cows, no milk,
no chickens, no eggs, no meat.
We just need Jesus. Thank you,
God, for Jesus.
We just need Jesus. Thank you,
God, for Jesus.

Wouldn't This World be Crazy?
If a kangaroo could have a kitten,
And a dog could have a calf,
Wouldn't this world be crazy,
Wouldn't your mother laugh?
Because you might be a monkey
And swing from tree to tree
Or you might even be a fishy
And swim in the deep blue sea.

But God made each creature special
Each one makes its own kind
So you'll never see a doggy mooing
And your mother won't lose her mind.
Because she knows you are a human
Though you might swing in a tree,
And you'll never be a real live fishy
Though you might swim in the deep blue
sea.

Psalm 139
(For Sheri, Wendy, and Christopher)
You saw me when I was formed
In the womb all alone.
You knit me together there
Your workmanship shows
so much care.

You recorded in Your Book
Before a breath I ever took,
Every minute of each day
And every word that I would say.

And how precious it is, Lord,
And with joy my heart has soared,
For I can't count the times each day
That Your thoughts have turned
my way.

If I go to a distant star
Or beneath the ground so far,
I could still hear Your call
For it was You who made it all.

The morning winds I could ride
To the world's other side.
For even there Your hand will guide,
In Your arms I'd still abide.

Even in the darkest night
I can not hide from Your sight
Because darkness is as light
For Your love is shining bright.

In the past, as You have lead,
You laid Your hand upon my head.
Chart my path, for You know best
Where to walk and when to rest.

Test every thought I ever had.
Point out what has made You sad.
Cleanse my heart and make me true
And lead me home to be with You.

And how precious it is, Lord,
And with joy my heart has soared,
For I can't count the times each day
That Your thoughts have turned
my way.

A Man of God
(Adam's Song)
I don't care if you play football
or play in the band,
I don't care if you're a doctor
or a garbage man,
It doesn't matter if you're
good in school or great at art,
There's just one thing I care
with all my heart;

That you grow up to be a man of God,
That you use His Word as a
measuring rod,
That you love your neighbor
as yourself,
That you do not trust in this
world's wealth,
That you grow up to be a man of God.

I don't care if you're a loner
or have lots of friends,
I don't care if your clothes are new
or they have lots of mends,
It doesn't matter if you're tall and thin, or
short and round,
There's just one important thing
that I have found;

That you grow up to be a man of God,
That you use His Word as a
measuring rod,
That you love your neighbor
as yourself,
That you do not trust in this
world's wealth,
That you grow up to be a man of God.

The Skeletal System
The bones are where we start with
the skeletal system.
They are the frame that gives your shape
And some are big and some are little.
Bones are alive and they will mend if
broken parts are kept together.
Some bones have joints so they can bend,
And some make red blood cells in
the marrow.
So drink your milk and keep strong bones
for your skeletal system.

The Digestive System
The mouth is where we start
with the digestive system.
The teeth chew up the food
And it goes down the esophagus
Into the stomach where it's churned
and fats and proteins are digested.
Then in the small intestines nutrients get
right into the blood
And the large intestines pass wastes out
of the digestive system.

The Circulatory System
The heart is where we start
with the circulatory system.

The heart pumps blood around.
Through arteries the blood will pound
Taking food and air to cells in every
square inch of your body.
Then veins take wastes away through
lungs and kidneys
when you're healthy
Taking blood back to the heart
in the circulatory system.

The Respiratory System

The nose is where we start
with the respiratory system.
The air comes in and then goes down
the trachea into the lungs
Where oxygen is then released
into the circulatory system.
Carbon dioxide is returned into the air
and then breathed out
Back through the nose and through the
mouth in the respiratory system.

The Nervous System

The brain is where we start with
the central nervous system.
The nerves are hooked up to the skin
And send the message to the brain
Telling if it's hot or cold and if it hurts
or if it feels good.
The brain then sends a message back And
gives a warning if there's danger,
Keeping skin and body safe with
the nervous system.

The brain is where we start with
the autonomic nervous system.
The nerves send messages along,
So heart and lungs will function strong.
And all the vital organs work without
a conscious thought or effort.
The nerves say slow it down or speed it
up, be ready if there's danger,
So you stay healthy and alive with
the autonomic nervous system

The Muscular System

The muscles are where we start with
the muscular system,
The muscles are attached to bones,
So that the bones can move around.
And ligaments and tendons help to keep
the muscle movements stable.
So exercise and make them strong and
eat good meals at the table,
Then you can move and get around
with your muscular system.

It's Not What You're Eating

You're restless and weary,
you can't sleep at night.
Your ulcer is hurting,
your weight isn't right.
You eat brown bread and veggies,
and a soft drink or two
Well, it's not what you're eating,
it's what's eating on you.

It's not what you're eating,
it's what's eating on you.
It's the thoughts that you're thinking
that make you feel blue.
It's the sinning and heartache,
a bottled feeling or two.
Well, it's not what you're eating,
it's what's eating on you.

Friend, things could be different
if you're willing to start,
Just erase the feelings
and clean up your heart.
By looking above you
and letting Jesus take hold,
He'll change what's eating on you,
and He'll carry your load.

It's not what you're eating,
it's what's eating on you.
It's the thoughts that you're thinking
that make you feel blue.
It's the sinning and heartache,
a bottled feeling or two.
Well, it's not what you're eating,
it's what's eating on you.

Fill Our Hearts

(Andrew's Song)

Lord, let me love with open hand,
This child you gave to me,
May he learn of your love through mine,
And seek your child to be.
Lord, guide me step by step to know,
The way to show my son,
That you and you alone, dear Lord,
Are everything in one.

Lord, may I show him day by day,
To put you first in line.
So by example, he can learn,
To have a Friend like mine.
As we rise up and walk together,
As we go to sleep,
May you, Lord Jesus fill our hearts,
For they are yours to keep.

If Everybody Does it, We Don't
Mom, my friend has a new toy
that I want.
Dad, the guys are all goin' to camp.
Grandma, nobody now
can believe that!
You're not cool and neither is Gramp.

Well, son, the Lord has called us
to be different,
We can't just go along with the crowd,
So the best guidelines that
we can think of,
Is to not do what most are allowed. So—

If everybody does it, we don't,
If everybody has it, we won't,
If everybody's goin',
we'll go the other way,
If everybody does it, we don't.

Skin Deep
(Abby's Song)
If you see a pretty face walking down
the street
Remember, it's just skin deep,
If you think someone's good looking
from their head to their feet
Remember, it's just skin deep.
But if someone does a good deed
and their words are true
What they're like inside is really
coming through

So let your outside in
Be like your inside out
And let God's love shine through
in all you do.
Don't let your focus stray
To things that fade away
And let God's love shine through
in all you do.

If you spend a lot of hours to fix your
outside up
Remember, it's just skin deep,
If you look into a mirror and want to
cover up
Remember, it's just skin deep,
But if you can do a good deed and your
words are true
What you're like inside is really coming
through.

So let your outside in
Be like your inside out
And let God's love shine through
in all you do.
Don't let your focus stray
To things that fade away
And let God's love shine through
in all you do.

Jesus Says So Lovingly
Her life was far from innocent, but
when it came to change,
They still accused and threw their
stones, now don't you think
that's strange?
For Jesus to the woman said,
"Child, go and sin no more,
"Your sins were blotted out to me,
when you came in my door."
And Jesus said, so lovingly,
"Go and sin no more."

He lived his life just as he pleased,
he lived it for himself,
But when the master called, he came,
and found a heavenly wealth.
And Jesus to the man did say,
"Come unto me and live,
"Die to yourself and follow me,
a brand new start I'll give."
And Jesus said, so lovingly,
"A brand new start I'll give."

We all have ups, we all have downs,
a war inside you'll find,
But grace abounds where Christ resides,
let Him renew your mind.
And Jesus says to all who hear,
"Love God and neighbor too,
"And show My love to everyone, in
everything you do."
And Jesus says, so lovingly,
"Show love in all you do."

Speak up for the Lord
(Amos' Song)
Speak up for the Lord,
Lift your voice and speak up
for the Lord.
Every chance you get, tell of His love
and grace,
To everyone everywhere.
Tell of His death, how He rose again,
And that He's coming back.
Speak up, yes, speak up for the Lord.

Speak out for the Lord,
Lift your voice and speak out
for the Lord.
Tell the world what's wrong and
what's right,

And that they need God's love and
God's light.
Say, "Humble yourselves before
the Lord,
Turn from your wicked ways."
And speak out, yes, speak out
for the Lord.

Speak in to the Lord,
In your heart, just speak in to the Lord.
Say a prayer with each breath
that you take,
All day and each moment that
you're awake.
Speak in to the Lord,
In your heart, just speak in to the Lord.
Live your life to speak in, yes,
speak in to the Lord.

Try, Try Again

Did you tie up your shoes with the first
bow that you tied?
'Course not, you tried, tried again.
Did you learn to read and write with the
first word that you spied?
'Course not, you tried, tried again.

So let's try, try again, yes, let's try,
try again,
They say that practice makes perfect
if you'll only try again.
Come on and try, try again.

Did you climb up the mountain with the
first step that you took?
'Course not, you tried, tried again.
Did you make Thanksgiving dinner for
the first meal that you cooked?
'Course not, you tried, tried again.

So let's try, try again, yes, let's try,
try again,
They say that practice makes perfect
if you'll only try again.
Come on and try, try again.

Have you learned to love the Lord your
God and neighbor as yourself?
Not yet, but try, try again.
Have you realized that money doesn't
count for heavenly wealth?
Not yet, but try, try again.

So let's try, try again, yes, let's try,
try again,
They say that practice makes perfect
if you'll only try again.
Come on and try, try again.

"Psalm 139", words by Susan Mortimer, music by Susan Mortimer and Betty Smith.
"Clean", words by Linda Hubel, music by Betty Smith.
All other songs by Betty Smith.

GLOSSARY

adipose tissue: fatty tissue [L. *adeps*, soft fat]

air bladder (swim bladder): a thin-walled "sack" found in most fish which is used to enable fish to float at varying depths

air sacs: air-filled cavities that reach into almost every part of a bird's body, with connections to the lungs

algae: very simple photosynthetic plants found in water or damp places, containing chlorophyll and other pigments (colorings), and having no true roots, stems, leaves or seeds (L. *alga*, seaweed]

alto-: "higher" [L. *altus*, high]

alveoli: tiny air cells in the lungs [L. *alveolus*, a small cavity]

amphibian: a cold-blooded vertebrate that hatches and develops in the water, breathing with gills, and changes to a land, air-breathing animal as an adult [Gk. *amphi*, on both sides + *bios*, life]

antlers: a bony structure growing on the head of male deer [L. *ante*, before + *oculus*, the eye]

arachnids: a family of animals which have two main body parts, four pairs of legs, and which breathe with book lungs [Gk. *arachne*, a spider]

arteries: blood vessels going away from the heart [Gk. *arteria*, an artery]

atmosphere: the blanket of air surrounding a heavenly body [Gk. *atmos*, vapor]

AU (astronomical unit): the distance from the sun to earth (approximately 93,000,000 miles)

autonomic: self-governing [Gk. *autos*, self + *nomos*, a law]

axis: an imaginary line passing through the center of the earth from the North pole to the South pole [L. *axis*, an axle]

baleen: a sieve-like bone structure in the mouth of one group of whales that allows the whale to strain out the tiny shrimp, plankton, and krill from the ocean water [L. *balaena*, a whale]

biosphere: layer of earth that supports life, including land, sea, and air [Gk. *bios*, life + *sphaira*, a globe, circle. Biosphere = circle of life.]

bird: a warm-blooded vertebrate animal, having feathers, two wings (most can fly), two legs, scaly feet, and a four-chambered heart with the fastest heartbeat of all animals. Its lungs breathe air into air sacs and hollow bones. It has no teeth, but a beak, crop, and gizzard, filled with sand. It reproduces by laying hard-shelled eggs. [O.E. *brid*, bird]

bladder: a muscular bag in the pelvis that collects the urine [O.E. *blaedre*, a blister]

blood: the red, slightly thick (viscous) liquid that circulates in man and animals [O.E. *blod*, blood]

book lungs: the lungs characteristic of arachnids, which have tiny compartments, like the pages of a book

capillaries: network of tiny blood vessels connecting arteries and veins [L. *capillus*, hair]

carnivore: meat-eater [L. *carnis*, flesh + *vorare*, to devour]

cell membrane: the covering of the cell, which acts like a "guarded wall", controlling what enters or leaves the cell [L. *membrana*, parchment]

cell: the simplest unit of structure of living things [L. *cella*, a small room]

centrioles: rod-shaped structures that function like "magnets" during cell division

cephalothorax: the head united with the thorax which form one part of the spider's body [Gk. *kephalē* , the head + *thorax*, chest cavity]

cerebellum: the smaller, back portion of brain; controls voluntary muscles and balance [L. *cerebrum*, the brain]

cerebrum: largest part of brain, center of intelligence, movement [L. *cerebrum*, the brain]

chlorophyll: the green color in plants which traps sunlight and makes photosynthesis possible [Gk. *chlŏ ros*, green + *phyllon*, leaf]

chromosomes: contain the cell's genetic information [Gk. *chroma*, color + *soma*, a body]

cirrus or cirro-: "wispy" (delicate, fleecy, feathery clouds made up of ice crystals, "mares' tails," high altitude) [L. *cirrus*, a curl of hair]

climate: the overall weather pattern of an area [Gk. *klima*, slope]

cohesion: sticking together [L. *cohaerere*, to stick together]

cold-blooded: having a variable body temperature and activity level that changes according to the temperature of the surroundings

consider: To ponder, contemplate with awe, think about deeply [L. *considerare*, observe]

constellation: a fixed group of stars [L. *cum*, together + *stella*, a star]

continent: large mass of land [L. *cum*, together + *tenere*, to hold]

core: the center of the earth, consisting of molten ore [L. *cor*, the heart]

creation: All that which is created [L. *craere*, to make out of nothing]

crop: a sac-like enlargement in a bird's food tube, where it stores food before digesting it

crust : hard, outer covering of the earth—19 to 22 miles thick [L. *crusta*, covering]

crystalline: mineral body (like quartz) with regular geometric shapes [Gk. *kruos*, frost]

cumulus or cumulo-: "puffed up" (dense puffs, mounds or towers of clouds with flat bases) [L. *cumulus*, a heap]

day: the length of time it takes a planet to rotate on its axis [O.E.*daeg*, day]

deciduous trees: hardwood broadleaf trees that generally shed their leaves in autumn [L. *decidere*, to fall down]

dermis : living layer of skin below epidermis [Gk. *derma*, the skin]

desert: an area, either cold or hot which lacks moisture most of the year [L. *deserere*, to abandon]

diaphragm: the muscles dividing the chest cavity from the abdominal cavity [Gk. *dia*, through + *phragma*, fence]

digestion: to prepare food to be absorbed into the blood [L. *digerere*, to arrange]

DNA: (deoxyribonucleic acid) an arrangement of amino acids that contain the genetic "master plan"

dominant: the predominant influence [L. *dominari,* to be master]

earthquake: movement in the earth's crust [O.E. *erothe*, earth + *cwacian*, to shake]

ecosystem: balanced relationship between the plants and animals in a given area [Gk. *eklogē* , a house + L. *systema,* organized whole]

endangered: threatened with extinction [*en*-in, with + M.E. *danger*, power]

endocrine: tissues and organs that produce internal secretions [Gk. *endon*, within + *krinein*, to separate]

endoplasmic reticulum: sheets of membrane that provide "transportation" for protein within the cell

epidermis: outer layer of skin, made up of dead cells [Gk. *epi*, upon + *derma*, the skin]

equator: an imaginary line dividing the earth into the northern and southern hemispheres [L. *aequus*, equal]

erosion: to wear away or break down into small pieces [Gk. *erodere*, to wear away]

esophagus: the tube from the mouth to the stomach [L. *oesophagus*, esophagus]

estivation: a state of inactivity, especially during dry summer [l. *aestus*, summer]

evergreen trees: trees with narrow leaves that stay green the year round

excretory system: the parts that expel wastes the body [L. *excernere*, to sift out]

exoskeleton: firm outer skeleton [Gk. *exo-*, outside + *skeletos*, dried up]

exosphere: the outer-most layer of atmosphere [Gk. *exo*, outside]

extensors: muscles that extend or stretch out [l. *extendere*, to stretch out]

extinct: no living specimens or survivors [L.*extinctus*, dead, extinguished]

extrusive: refers to igneous rock formed when magma cools above the surface of the earth [L. *ex*, out; *trudere*, to thrust]

fertile: able to reproduce [L. *fertilis*, fruitful]

fertilize: to make fruitful or able to reproduce [L. *fertilis*, fruitful]

fish: cold-blooded water animal with a backbone, fins, scales, and gills [O.E. *fisc*, a fish]

flexors: muscles that flex or bend up [l. *flexus*, bent]

flower: the part of the plant that produces seeds [L. *flox*, flower]

fossil: any evidence of life from the past [L. *fossum,* to dig]

fungus: very simple plants that do not produce food by photosynthesis, but feed on living or dead plants or animals; they do not have true roots, stems, leaves, seeds or chlorophyll, and reproduce by means of spores; **fungi** is the plural word [L. *fungus*, mushroom or fungus]

galaxy: a group or system of stars and other heavenly bodies [Gk. *galac*, milk; galaxy = milky circle, hence, Milky Way Galaxy]

gall bladder: the small sac which stores bile produced by liver [O.E. *gealla*, gall + *blaedre*, a blister]

gaseous: composed of sub-stances that are neither solid nor liquid [Gk. *chaos*, chaos]

gene: the hereditary unit that passes hereditary characteristics from parent to child [Gk. *genos*, origin]
generally grows underground [O.E. *wyrt*, root]

genetics: the study of heredity [Gk. *gignesthai*, to be born]

gills: the breathing organ of water animals which take oxygen out of the water

gizzard: a bird's muscular second stomach, where food is ground after being partially digested in the first stomach

Golgi body: a group of flattened membrane sacs that "package" protein

gravity: the force that attracts one object to another [L. *gravitas*, heavy]

habitat: dwelling, home [L. *habitare*, to dwell]

hair follicle: gland which produces thread like growth [O.E. *haer*, hair + L. *folliculus*, a little bag]

heart: a special muscle that pumps blood to all parts of the body [O.E. *heorte*, heart]

hemisphere: half of the earth [Gk. *hemi*, half + *sphaira*, a globe]

herbivore: plant-eater [L. *herva*, grass + *vorare*, to devour]

heredity: passing on characteristics from parents to child [L. *heres*, an heir]

hibernation: dormant or inactive state, especially as in winter [L. *hibernare*, fr. *hiems*, winter]

horns: a hard formation growing on the head of goats, cows, and other animals [O.E., *horn*, horn]

humidity: how much moisture there is in the air [L. *humidus*, moist]

igneous rock: rock formed as a result of intense heat [L. *ignis*, fire]

insect: a large group of invertebrate animals which, in the adult stage, have three body segments, including a head, thorax, and abdomen, three pairs of legs and may have two pairs of wings [L. *in*, in + *secare*, to cut]

instinct: inborn ability to do certain actions without being taught

integumentary: protective layer of tissue covering body [L. *integere*, to cover]

intestines: the bowels, the tubing from the stomach to the anus [L. *intestinus*, intestines]

intrusive: refers to igneous rock formed when magma cools below the surface of the earth [L. *in*, within + *trudere*, to thrust]

invertebrates: creatures without a backbone (vertebrae) [L. *in-*, not + *vertebra*, spine]

involuntary muscles: muscles which work without conscious thought

kidneys: a pair of organs that excrete urine

larva: the immature "baby" form of animals that change structurally to become adults, through complete metamorphoses [L. *larva*, ghost]

ligaments: strong fibers that connect the bones [L. *ligare*, to bind]

light: energy that travels in waves, mostly from the sun, and travels very fast (186,200 miles per second) [O.E. *leoht,* light]

liver: the organ which secretes bile [O.E. *lifer*, liver]

lungs: internal, sponge-like breathing chamber of vertebrate land creatures [O.E. *lungen*, lung]

lysosomes: the "garbage disposal system" of the cell, which dispose of invading materials and bacteria

magma: hot, molten (melted) rock [Gk. *magma*, to knead]

mammal: a warm-blooded vertebrate covered with fur or hair, breathing air with lungs and a diaphragm, having a four-chambered heart, and the largest and most developed brains. The female has gland that produces milk to feed her young, and most give birth to live young (viviparous). [L. *mamma*, mother, breast]

mantle: the middle layer of the earth, [L. *mantellum*, a cloak, covering]

marrow: the soft center of bones [O.E. *meary*, marrow]

marsupial: a group of mammals in Australia which give birth to incompletely developed young, and then care for them several months in an external pouch [Gk. *marsypion*, pouch, bag]

medulla: lowest portion of brain; controls involuntary breathing and heartbeat [L. *medulla*, marrow]

mesosphere: the middle layer of air [Gk. *mesos*, middle]

metamorphic rock: rock which has been changed by heat and pressure [Gk. *meta*, over + *morphe*, shape]

metamorphosis: the process of change during the growth and development of insects [Gk. *meta*, over +*morphē* shape]

migration: to go from one place to another (in search of warmer climates for breeding and food) [L. *migrare*, to go]

mitochondria: are the cells "power plants" and produce the cell's energy

molecules: the smallest piece of any substance that can be identified as that substance [L. *moles*, a mass]

monsoon region: a hot region with distinct wet and dry seasons

mountain regions: the 25% of earth's land surface over 3,300 feet above sea level, with plant and animal life varying according to altitude

muscle: a band of fibrous tissue that can produce movement [L. *musculus*, a muscle]

nerve: fiber which sends or receives messages from the brain [L. *nervus*, sinew]

nimbus or nimbo-: "dark rain" (dense rain or snow cloud) [L. *numbus*, a cloud]

nucleus: the "control center" of the cell which control and directs all the cell's activities [L. *nucleus*, kernel]

nutrient: something that nourishes [L. *nutrire*, to nourish]

nymph: the immature form of an insect with incomplete metamorphosis [Gk. *nymphē* , bride]

oil gland: cells which produce a greasy liquid [L. *oleum*, oil]

olfactory bulb: center for smell [L. *olere*, to smell + *facere*, to make]

omnipresent: present in all places at the same time [L. *omnis*, all + *praesens*, being present]

omnivore: plant- and animal-eater [L. *omnis*, all + *vorare*, to devour]
optic lobes: center for sight [Gk. *optikos*, vision]
orbit: the path of a heavenly body as it rotates around another body [L. *orbis*, a circle]
oviparous: hatched, born from an egg [L. *ovum*, an egg + *parere*, to give birth]
ovum: the female reproductive cell [L.*ovum*, an egg]
ozone layer: a protective layer of condensed oxygen, O_3 (which has a peculiar smell) in the stratosphere [Gk. *ozein*, to smell]
paleontologist: someone who studies plant and animal life of ancient times (the fossil record) [Gk. *palaios*, ancient + *logos*, discourse, word]
pancreas: the digestive gland behind the stomach [Gk. *pan*, all + *kreas*, flesh]
parasympathetic: a part of the nervous system that control involuntary vital functions in an energy conserving way [Gk. *para*, beside + *sun*, together + *pathos*, feeling]
pecten: pleats of tissue that carry extra blood (as to eye of hawk)
peristalsis: rippling contractions of the muscles in the intestines
petal: the colored flower-leaf [Gk. *petalon*, a thin plate]
photosynthesis: the process by which a plant creates carbohydrates [Gk. *photo*, light + *sun*, together + *thesis*, a placing]
pistil: the seed-bearing organ of a flower [L. *pistillum*, a pestle]
pituitary gland: gland which controls growth and other functions
placenta: an organ of blood vessels that supply food and air exchange for the babies developing inside female mammals [Gk. *plakounta*, a flat cake]
planet: a heavenly body that revolves around the sun [Gk. *plane*, to wander; planet = to wander in the sky]
plasma: the liquid part of your blood that carries the food to each cell [Gk. *plasma* from *plassein*, to form or mold]
platelets: plate shaped cells that help to seal off broken blood vessels [Gk. *platus*, broad, flat]
polar: refers to the North (Arctic) and South (Antarctic) Poles [Gk. *polos*, a pivot]
pollen: the fertilizing dust in a flower [L.*pollen*, fine flour]
precipitation: amount of rain or snow [L. *praeceps*, headlong]
pregnant: to be with child [L. *praegnans*, to be with child]
pupa: an insect in the non-feeding, resting stage between the larval and adult forms [L. *pupa*, girl, doll]
recessive: the receding influence [L. *recessus*, to recede]
rectum: lower portion of large intestines [L. *rectus*, straight]
red corpuscles: red blood cells, the part of the blood that carries oxygen to the cells and carbon dioxide away from the cells [L. *corpusculum*, a small body]
reproduce: to multiply or produce living individuals [L. *re-*, again + *pro-*, forward + *ducere*, to lead]
reptile: a cold-blooded vertebrate, with lungs for breathing air, dry, scaly covering for body, and a three chambered heart (except for alligator and crocodile which have four chambered hearts). Most live on the land and lay eggs with a tough, leathery shell. They crawl on their bellies or short legs. [L. *reptilis*, creeping]
root: the part of the plant that seeks nourishment for the plant
rotation: to turn in a circular motion on an axis [L. *rota*, a wheel]
savanna: a warm area with wet and dry seasons, scrub type plants and only scattered trees
sedimentary rock: rock made up of layers of materials settled underwater [L. *sedere*, to settle]
skeleton: the framework of the body [Gk. *skeletos*, dried up] [L. *musculus*, a muscle]
solar system: the group of planets, their satellites (moons), comets, meteors, asteroids, and so forth, that revolve around the sun [L. *sol*, sun]
sperm: the male reproductive cell [Gk. *sperma*, seed]
sphere: globe [Gk. *sphaira*, a globe]
spiracles: breathing holes in the abdomen of spiders and insects, and another name for the blow hole of whales [L. *spirare*, to breathe]
spirit: the eternal part of man [L. *spirare*, to breathe]
spores: cells sent out by bacteria, fungi, algae, mosses, ferns and so forth, capable of developing into new adult plants [Gk. *spora*, a sowing]
stamen: the pollen-bearing part of a flower [L. *stamen*, fiber, thread]
star: any celestial body that gives off light [L. *stella*, a star]
stem: the stalk of a plant [O.E. *stefn*, stem]
sterile: unable to reproduce [L. *sterilis*, barren]
stomach: the chief organ of digestion [Gk. *stomachos*, the gullet]

stratosphere: the second layer of air above the earth's surface [L. *stratum*, layer]

stratus or strato-: "layer" (straight layers of low altitude fog-like clouds) [L. *sternere*, to spread out]

sweat gland: cells which produce perspiration or moisture from skin [O.E. *swat*, sweat + L. *glans*, an acorn]

sympathetic: a portion of the nervous system that controls involuntary vital functions and the "fight or flight" response [Gk. *sun*, together + *pathos*, feeling]

taiga: coniferous (cone-bearing) forest below the Arctic region [Russ. *taiga*, coniferous forest]

tapetum: membrane in cat's eye that reflects light like a mirror [L. *pituita*, mucus]

temperate forest: a deciduous forest in a region that has four seasons

temperate grassland: a plain of grasses where not enough rain falls to sustain a forest, but which has more rain than a desert.

temperature: how hot or cold it is [L. *temperare*, to moderate]

terrestrial: earth-like [L. *terra*, the earth]

thermosphere: the very cold upper layer of air which contains many electrically charged atoms [Gk. *thermos*, heat]

toothed (odontoid): the second group of whales which have teeth, and eat fish and other sea creatures.

trachea: the windpipe or tube in the throat which connects the mouth and nose to the lungs [Gk. *tracheia*, windpipe]

tree: a plant with a woody trunk [O.E. *treow*, a tree]

tropical rain forest: a hot area with heavy (59–78 inches) rainfall, teeming with plant and animal life

tropical trees: broadleaf evergreen trees

troposphere: the layer of air closest to the earth's surface [Gk. *tropos*, a turn]

tundra: treeless plains in the Arctic Circle [Russ. *tundra*, a marsh]

universe: all created things [L. *unus,* one + *versum,* to turn]

ureter: the tubes from the kidneys to the bladder [Gk. *ouron*, urine]

urine: the yellow colored liquid that contains water soluble wastes from the body [Gk. *ouron*, urine]

uterus: the womb; the female organ where a baby develops before birth [L. *uterus*, womb]

vacuum: vacant or empty space [L. *vacuus*, empty]

veins: blood vessels going toward the heart [L. *vene*, vein]

vertebrates: creatures with backbones [L. *vertebra*, spine]

viviparous: born alive [L. *vivus*, living + *parere*, to give birth]

volcano: an opening in the earth through which gases, ash, and lava are ejected [L. *Vulcanus*, the god of fire]

voluntary muscles: muscles we can move at will [L. *voluntas*, free will]

weather: the condition of the atmosphere at any given time or place [O.E. *weder*, weather]

white corpuscles: white blood cells which serve to fight infection [L. *corpusculum*, a small body]

year: the length of time it takes a planet to orbit around the sun [O.E. *gear*, year]

My Glossary

____

____

____

____

____

____

____

____

____

____

____

____

____

____

____

____

____

____

____

____

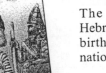